The Heredity Factor

The Heredity Factor
Genes, Chromosomes, and You

By William L. Nyhan, M.D., Ph.D.
with
Edward Edelson

Grosset & Dunlap · Publishers
A Filmways Company
New York

Illustration Credits

The authors gratefully acknowledge permission to include the following illustrations in *The Heredity Factor:*

Fig. 13 (Right): Courtesy of H. Lehmann, M.D., St. Bartholomew's Hospital, London. Reproduced with permission from *Biochemical Frontiers in Medicine,* edited by H. Busch (Boston: Little, Brown and Company, 1963), p. 118.

Fig. 13 (Left): Courtesy of Dr. Faith H. Kung, University of California, San Diego.

Fig. 14: Reproduced with permission from the publication by J. Leisti in the *Annales Academiae Scienturum Fennicae 179:*6, 1971.

Figs. 22, 23, and 29: Courtesy of Dr. Uta Francke, University of California, San Diego.

Figs. 24 and 25: Courtesy of Dr. O. W. Jones, University of California, San Diego.

Published simultaneously in Canada
Library of Congress catalog card number: 75–27908
ISBN 0–448–12239–1
First printing
Printed in the United States of America

To my patients—
They and their families provided the reasons for this book.

Note: This book has been written in collaboration between a physician/geneticist and a layman. The occasional use of the first person singular reflects the highly personal and sensitive interaction between the doctor and his patients.

Acknowledgments

I am indebted to many people who have helped make this book a reality. The most important was Eileen O'Farrell Borgwardt, who typed the entire manuscript, much of it from longhand. She also drew all the illustrations. My secretary, Mrs. Dorothy MacElhose, helped with some of the typing. She and Mrs. Ruth Brown made many arrangements for the successful prosecution of this project. Special thanks go to Mrs. Ruth Y. Berini, Director of the National Genetics Foundation. She saw the need for a book of this kind some years ago and helped in its initiation. Mrs. Berini was a constant stimulus and provided valuable counsel all along the way. She and her associates, Mrs. Gay Sachs and Mrs. Elinor Frank, provided important information from their files. I have had a long association with the National Foundation—March of Dimes. This organization has constantly supported my research. The Foundation has a major commitment to human genetics. Many patients, parents, and colleagues have enthusiastically endorsed the idea of this book and have freely discussed genetic problems that have become the fabric of the book. Among my colleagues at the University of California at San Diego, I am indebted to Drs. Nadia Sakati, O. W. Jones, Uta Francke, J. E. Seegmiller, Jerry Schneider, and Lawrence Schneiderman. I am particularly indebted to Dr. John O'Brien, who has done so much for human genetics and whose experience has graced many of these pages. Dr. Roger Rosenberg, formerly of UCSD and now at the University of Texas—Southwestern Medical School at Dallas, has collaborated with me on a number of projects in the genetics of neurologic disease. His scholarship has made an important contribution to the book and to my thinking about neurologic disease. My editor, David Frost, has been patient, understanding, and supportive.

I am indebted to Robert J. Benowicz who deserves major credit for bringing *The Heredity Factor* to its present form. In his masterful editing he took a manuscript that was often rough—and sometimes overly complex—and polished it with care. This required a considerable amount of rewriting and a complete understanding of the purposes of the book. I expect to see his name on the cover of the next book on which he works.—W.L.N.

Contents

Preface

From where do we come? What are we? Where are we going?

—Paul Gauguin

We wrote this book because so many people asked us for it. In the practice of genetic counseling, we see many people—parents, grandparents, and children—with all sorts of problems. In order to help them understand where they are, how they got that way, and what will help them best plan for the future, we have to give them a mini-course in genetics. It is often not enough, especially in one sitting. Many families have asked, "Where can we read about these things?" Where, indeed? There is an enormous literature in genetics. Most of it is written for geneticists. No one else can understand it. Some is written for physicians or medical students. We cannot send patients to these sources and hope that they will be helped. There appears to be a need for a book about the fundamentals of modern genetics, one that emphasizes inherited human disease. This book is written for you.

Human genetics is the science of human variation or the differences from one individual to the next. Among the more pleasant ways to convince yourself of this business of human variation is to amble up the main street of any American city on a sunny afternoon in May.

Some variations among individuals may result from differences in the environment each lives in, but a major reason for variation among human populations is genetic. The shape of a nose, the color of an eye, the tilt of a smile are characteristics we inherit from one or more of our ancestors. We take this for granted and it is reassuring. Less comforting is the fact that a major number of human illnesses is also inherited. Knowledge of how this works is important because it is increasingly possible to do something about these diseases either through treatment or through prevention.

The names of many patients and their families have been changed, not to protect the innocent, but to preserve the confidential nature of the doctor-patient relationship. Some families have already permitted a discussion of their problems and identification by name in nationwide news media. In these instances we have used the patients' real names. They have recognized that publicity is important in generating funds for research and in reaching those with similar problems who might be unaware of where to go for help or who are reluctant to seek it. They also know that every man, woman, and child is directly or potentially confronted by the possibility of genetic disease.

We hope this book will be useful to those already confronted with a genetic disease. Not all these diseases are hopeless or necessarily tragic. Many parents and affected children have overcome the handicaps of genetic disorders, recognizing their inheritance as a challenge to be met rather than a defeat to be suffered. What better example can be provided than the educated foot of Tom Dempsey, field goal kicker for the Los Angeles Rams? Although Tom's kicking foot and right hand have been malformed since birth, he literally booted his team into the 1975 NFL playoffs. He is one of the best in the business. He is one of many who have overcome handicaps and gone on to achieve personal and public triumphs.

For those with an immediate need for genetic counseling we have included specific information about all the common conditions and about many of the others. In the final chapter of the book we have described the process of counseling and have indicated sources of help. We have also compiled a series of questions and their appropriate answers. These are questions frequently asked by people seeking genetic counsel.

Some may consider their involvement with inherited disease to be remote. Most of those who are faced with potential genetic difficulties have no idea of their vulnerability. We envision a kind of preventive genetic medicine and counseling for all. If people read about patterns of inheritance and genetic disease, they can begin to think about prevention before they have problems. Some very simple information can help. If mothers had their children before they got to be thirty-five, one of the major causes of mental retardation would disappear. It would be advisable for men to observe the same rule and reproduce only when young. Members of some ethnic groups are prone to specific genetic disorders. Through comparatively simple testing, it is possible to identify people who carry the genes that determine many of these disorders. A little knowledge and intelligent planning can go a long way toward the prevention of problems in future generations. Students in high schools would be better off learning about this kind of biology as well as the molecular biology they are now taught. Only a tiny number will end up as scientists. Most will end up having children.

Along with practical knowledge and information we hope to convey the content and excitement of genetic research. An unprecedented number of

Nobel prizes has been awarded for fundamental work in the field. The pace of discovery continues to quicken. In no other scientific discipline is there a quicker application of the fruits of research to the solution of everyday human problems. The beginnings of this science were only yesterday. The future is already upon us.

1.
A Look at Genetics Today

Man has always been interested in his origins. He had an intuitive feel for inheritance and its effects long before the science of genetics was born. People have made family trees for ages, especially those who could claim a famous or infamous ancestor. Implicit in the preparation of such a record is the possibility that subsequent generations might possess some of the desirable or undesirable characteristics of an ancestor. Of course, they might, but the science that tells us what and how is in its infancy.

Physicians recognized that certain diseases were inherited well before the classic discoveries of Mendel during the last century. The effective collaboration between practicing clinicians and theoreticians has led to the understanding that genetics impinges on every branch of medicine. Knowledge developed through the coordination of theory and practice now influences the diagnosis and treatment of many diseases. Genetic counseling can help prevent the transmission of some diseases to future generations. It can help families understand and live with their problems. It is for these reasons that almost everyone wants to know more about human inheritance.

The science of genetics has been moving forward at an astonishing rate. Since 1900 an enormous amount has been learned. In the past twenty-five years there has been an acceleration in progress that has produced an explosive increase of scientific knowledge in the field. The tools and disciplines of genetic research cut across many branches of science. They range from molecular biology and biophysics to behavioral science. The excitement of this field has had a certain amount of public recognition. Ten Nobel prizes have been awarded to scientists working in genetics, five of them during the period between 1958 and 1968. Three were awarded in 1975. The first, in 1933, was given to Thomas Hunt Morgan for work on the nature of the gene. This basic unit of heredity is now understood to be the deoxyribonucleic acid (DNA) molecule. The structure of DNA was elucidated by James Watson, Francis Crick, and Maurice Wilkins, who shared the Nobel Prize in 1961. The 1968 prize was jointly awarded to Marshall Nirenberg, H. G. Khorana, and Robert Holley, who cracked the code of the DNA molecule and explained the mechanism by which the information contained in a gene ultimately determines the structure of a protein. No other branch of science has so illuminated our knowledge of life so quickly.

Exciting new developments will continue to appear. There is no sign that the pace is slowing. More investigators are working on genetic problems. Genetic centers are springing up around the globe. With the advance of basic science, we are concurrently seeing the prompt application of the discoveries of research to man and his problems. The skills of the genetic enzymologist and the cell biologist are already being used in clinical medicine. This translation of research into human service will accelerate.

Much of what goes on in the office of a practicing geneticist is little different from what might go on in any doctor's office. Not long ago a woman placed an urgent call to my office. My secretary, who was new, did not know the woman by name, but because the call was long distance, she was properly concerned and asked to take a message. The woman said, "Just tell him I'm pregnant." My secretary was upset to think that she had gotten involved in an unwelcome slice of my personal life.

I had first seen this woman caller, Mrs. Eliot, and her family some years earlier on a visit to the Fairview State Hospital in Costa Mesa, California. Fairview is an institution for the mentally retarded. The state of California allocates its two thousand beds there to the most severely handicapped, very many of them bedridden because they are unable to walk. At the time of my visit the first child of the Eliots was just being admitted to Fairview after two years of heartache and disappointment. He was severely retarded. Not only was he unable to walk, he could not sit unassisted. Worse than that, he would never be able to do these things. When his teeth came in, he had begun to bite himself. It was this behavior that led to institutionalization. Understandably, parents find self-mutilation strange, painful to watch, and very difficult to manage. I was quickly able to diagnose his disease as the Lesch-Nyhan syndrome, an unusual condition, then recently discovered. Its effects on the nervous system are devastating, and research has not yielded knowledge that alleviates these neurological symptoms of the disease. The boy is still at Fairview.

I next heard of the Eliots when their pediatrician called to report that they had just had another baby, a boy whom he had examined. He found no apparent abnormalities but knew that the first child had also appeared perfectly normal at birth. By that time, understanding of the disease had progressed. It is caused by a defective enzyme, one of many molecules that in its usual form is essential to life. I asked the pediatrician to send me a sample of unclotted blood. Within an hour of the sample's arrival I knew the new baby had the disease.

By this time some approaches to treatment had been developed. These were initiated within days of birth. We now know that this treatment controls certain chemical aspects of the disease: its effects on the kidneys and other organs. It does not alter the devastating neurological symptoms of the disorder. This baby is also at Fairview. He is retarded and has begun to bite his lip.

A few months ago I saw Mrs. Eliot at Fairview. She said she was trying to become pregnant. She wanted another baby and was willing to risk having another like her first two. Mr. and Mrs. Eliot did not exactly see eye to eye on this issue, but she seemed to control their ultimate decision. I asked why she wanted to try again after all the suffering she, her husband, and their children had experienced. Her answer was simple: "I want to have a normal baby."

Research into the Eliots' genetic problem had come a long way since I had seen their first child. By then I knew it might be possible for Mrs. Eliot to bear a healthy, normal baby. I explained that I would like to help but that to avoid having a third defective child would involve close medical supervision, careful attention to the progress of her pregnancy, and possibly some painful decisions. Mrs. Eliot's acceptance of my offer was gratifying. At worst I would hope to prevent the birth of another hopelessly ill individual and at best could anticipate the delivery of a normal, healthy baby.

The defective enzyme that produced the tragic condition in Mrs. Eliot's first two children can now be detected in fetal cells grown in the laboratory. These cells are obtained from the pregnant woman by a technique known as amniocentesis. The amniotic or watery fluid that surrounds the developing fetus always contains some cells that naturally wash off the skin of the fetus. In amniocentesis some of the fluid is extracted, without damage to either mother or child. Through careful handling the extracted cells can be encouraged to grow and divide in the laboratory. The resulting mass of cells, a tissue culture, provides the opportunity to analyze and evaluate the genetic well-being of a developing fetus. The presence of any trace of the defective enzyme in the fetal cells or amniotic fluid of Mrs. Eliot's third pregnancy would have unquestionably indicated the tragedy of another affected child.

This brings us back to Mrs. Eliot's telephone message, which delighted me and bewildered my secretary. I was pleased because the apparently cryptic call affirmed Mrs. Eliot's commitment to a genetically monitored or evaluated pregnancy. When her amniocentesis was performed during the fourteenth week of pregnancy, analysis of the amniotic fluid and fetal cells revealed no trace of the insidious defective enzyme. A normal, healthy baby was predicted. Tommy Eliot was born on April 4, 1974. He is a happy, bouncing, alert little boy, free from the crippling symptoms that affect his older brothers.

The kinds of assistance provided to the Eliots with their third child represent a new form of clinical genetics. Its practice raises new questions and new problems. Most important, it raises new hope.

Andrea was born four years ago. She was the first child of Dr. and Mrs. Gold, a healthy, attractive, and intelligent young couple. Mrs. Gold's pregnancy was uneventful. Andrea's birth weight was normal. She was a beautiful and alert baby who made excellent progress during her first three months. She was a joy to her new parents. At six months her father detected an abnormal tendency toward physical weakness in Andrea. At first her condition was noticeable only to a physician, but it shortly became evident even to a casual observer. This was followed by a kind of listlessness. By ten months she could no longer sit without support, although she had previously passed this developmental milestone. She had been a cheerful baby; she readily recognized her parents, slept well, ate normally, and did not cry much. Now she was so weak that she had difficulty controlling the movements of her head. A new problem was an increasing irritability to sound. Her father felt she did not focus her eyes as well as before. Infants who see normally, even in the earliest days of life, will look an examiner in the eye when that person's face is brought into close, head-on contact with theirs. If the examiner moves his head in an arc, the normal baby will follow this movement with its eyes. This capacity is called "fixing and following." It is used as a standard pediatrician's test of visual and cerebral function. When Andrea's ability to fix and focus began to decline, Dr. Gold asked a neurologist to see her. On examination the neurologist found two disturbing red spots in the most important group of nerve cells in her eyes. This confirmed a sad diagnosis. Andrea suffered from Tay-Sachs disease.

After her first birthday Andrea's physical condition steadily declined. By fourteen months she began having convulsive seizures. She was so weak that she no longer showed any really purposeful, spontaneous movements. Vision continued to diminish. Her muscles were spastic and her deep reflexes were hyperactive. She had positive Babinski responses—her great toes curled up instead of down when the soles of her feet were stroked. By eighteen months she had difficulty swallowing and had to be fed by tube. At two she was blind and completely paralyzed. She lay limp and frog-legged. Her head had begun to enlarge. Her only real response to stimuli was a characteristic hypersensitivity to noise. Even the slightest sound in her vicinity would startle her, and she would appear to jump all over. At two she had the first of many episodes of pneumonia. She died of pneumonia at four.

Andrea's disease was first described in the nineteenth century by Warren Tay, a British ophthalmologist, and Bernard Sachs, an American neurologist. Tay-Sachs disease is, formally, a member of a family of degenerative diseases known as sphingolipidoses. That imposing name comes from fatty substances called sphingolipids that accumulate in the brain cells of patients with the disease. This accumulation causes a steady deterioration of the nervous system that starts in the first years of life. It accounts for the enlargement of the head as the disease progresses. It kills most patients before their fourth birthday.

It was Dr. Sachs who noticed one of the most important genetic features of Tay-Sachs disease. Most of its victims are children of Jews from eastern Europe—Ashkenazim, as they are called. The gene for Tay-Sachs disease is transmitted as an autosomal recessive or "hidden" gene. People can carry this insidious gene but manifest none of the symptoms of sphingolipidoses because they also possess another, normal gene that dominates or covers the effect of the autosomal recessive. Approximately one in every thirty Ashkenazim carries the gene for Tay-Sachs disease. Using classical calculations for determining the incidence of such a condition, the odds that two carriers of the recessive gene will marry is one in nine hundred; that is, once in every nine hundred marriages among Ashkenazim, two people carrying this recessive gene will come together. In marriages in which both parents are carriers, each possessing one of the lethal autosomal recessive genes, every child has a one-in-four chance of inheriting two of these dread genes and of developing the disease. The disease manifests itself, as it did with Andrea, only when two of the hidden autosomal recessive genes are united. Both Dr. and Mrs. Gold are unwitting carriers of one recessive gene for Tay-Sachs disease.

Every year some one hundred to two hundred children with Tay-Sachs disease are born in the United States. Most are the children of Jewish couples. The Tay-Sachs gene is also found, but at a much lower frequency, in other ethnic groups; 15 percent of children with Tay-Sachs disease are not Jewish.

At present nothing can be done to reverse the inexorable pattern of the disease. Medical care is no more than custodial, and it is both psychologically and monetarily expensive. Kingsbrook Jewish Medical Center in Brooklyn maintains a sixteen-bed Tay-Sachs ward as part of its Birth Defects Center for Sphingolipidoses. Authorities there estimate that it costs forty thousand dollars a year per bed—not to treat the condition, for it is untreatable, but simply to provide what comfort is possible during the slow, relentless neurological degeneration that causes death.

Until 1969 the situation was simply that hopeless. But during that year Drs. John O'Brien and Shintaro Okada of the University of California, San Diego, found the molecular defect that underlies Tay-Sachs disease. In the August 15 issue of *Science* they reported that patients with Tay-Sachs disease demonstrated a total absence of an essential enzyme known as hexosaminidase A (or hex A for short), which ordinarily breaks down sphingolipid molecules. This enzyme is essential in preventing the accumulation of GM_2-ganglioside, a specific sphingolipid molecule, in brain and other neural tissue. In the absence of hex A the concentration of GM_2-ganglioside becomes progressively greater, interfering with normal neurological functioning and ultimately resulting in death. For the proper breakdown of the GM_2-ganglioside molecule to occur, one of its end portions, called a hexosamine, must be split off. The enzyme controlling this specific process is, of course, hexosaminidase, or hex A. This fact had been known for some time. What proved puzzling was the observation that hexosaminidase levels in the blood, brain, and other tissues of patients with Tay-Sachs disease seemed perfectly normal. O'Brien and Okada developed a technique for analyzing hexosaminidase that revealed there were two distinct components of the molecule. They designated them A and B. In patients with Tay-Sachs disease the A enzyme was missing. This accounted for the faulty breakdown of GM_2-ganglioside. It is one of the more assuring aspects of science among men that the riddle of this Jewish disease was solved by an Irishman and a Japanese.

In the absence of hex A, fatty substances pile up in the brain and cause Tay-Sachs disease. Building on the initial discovery, Dr. O'Brien and his colleagues soon found that they could detect the presence or absence of hex A with a simple blood test. Normal individuals have a high level of the enzyme. Tay-Sachs children have none. Carriers of the recessive gene have levels between these two extremes. That finding proved to be of major importance.

Andrea's parents were both Ashkenazic Jews. Their ancestors came to the United States from Poland and Germany. One of Dr. Gold's first cousins had had Tay-Sachs disease and had died in 1943 at three years of age. There was no history of the disease on Mrs. Gold's side. The couple wanted to have a family and adopted a second child. However, they really wanted to have children of their own. They heard about amniocentesis and contacted Dr. O'Brien.

Hex A is an important enzyme that is widely distributed throughout the body. O'Brien and his colleagues have found that it is normally present, freely floating, in the amniotic fluid surrounding the fetus. It is also present in a sufficiently large amount to be detected directly by analysis, or assay, of amniotic fluid cells on the day they are obtained. It is present in highest concentration in amniotic fluid cells that have been grown in tissue culture. In cells obtained from the fluid bathing a fetus with Tay-Sachs disease, hex A is present in very low, almost negligible concentration.

Chemical analysis or assay of amniotic fluid and fetal cells is essential for an accurate intrauterine diagnosis of the disease. It is most convincing when done with cultured cells, cell masses grown in the laboratory from an original fetal cell and bearing a sample of the genetic material from the unborn child. In O'Brien's laboratory each sample of amniotic fluid and uncultured cells is immediately assayed for the presence of the hex A enzyme. This immediacy is particularly important for pregnancies *at risk*, pregnancies in which there is a known probability of disease. A culture is then prepared and the definitive diagnosis is made based on results obtained from assaying the cultured cells. The confirmation provided by the tissue culture technique ordinarily takes a number of weeks. Sometimes the cells do not grow, and there may not be time to perform another amniocentesis and prepare another culture. In this case a decision can be based on the results obtained from assays of the fluid and the uncultured cells. In O'Brien's hands the three types of analysis—amniotic fluid, uncultured cell, and cultured cell assays—have never failed to agree. The actual genetic condition of the fetus or child has always confirmed the prenatal prediction.

The Golds considered all this information and undertook a monitored pregnancy. Amniocentesis was performed at eighteen weeks. The activity of hex A was found to be extremely low in the amniotic fluid and in the uncultured amniotic cells. When the cultures matured, the concentration of hex A remained minimal. The three assays provided convincing evidence for a prenatal diagnosis of Tay-Sachs disease. This was heartbreaking. The wheels of statistical fortune that apply to inheritance as well as the gaming table seemed to be grinding both slow and fine. With each pregnancy the chances for bearing a diseased child is one in four if both parents are carriers of the autosomal recessive trait. This in no way prevents people from having two or more affected children in a row. The second pregnancy was terminated at twenty weeks. The fetus was chemically evaluated and the diagnosis was confirmed. Not only was hex A absent, but the lethal GM_2-ganglioside molecule was already being stored in large quantities within the fetal tissue.

Shortly thereafter the Golds tried again. Amniocentesis was performed at eighteen weeks. This time the fluid and uncultured cell assays were normal. When the tissue culture was ready for analysis, it contained large amounts of the essential hex A enzyme. A chromosomal study of these cultured cells revealed two X chromosomes in each, indicating that the child would be a female. The prenatal prediction was that the baby would be a normal girl. She was. Labor and delivery came at the usual time, and at birth Emily Gold looked great. Her hex A enzyme concentration was normal. Her parents were overjoyed. She has, of course, been frequently examined since birth, with particular attention paid to her eyes and her nervous system. Everything is perfectly normal. Emily is what we were after. A normal baby.

The happy and successful births of Tommy Eliot and Emily Gold are gratifying, yet no sensitive human being can forget the pain and suffering that preceded them. One cannot obliterate the memories of Tommy's older brothers at Fairview or the agonies of Andrea. As elated as both the Eliots and the Golds have been about their normal children, they have not failed to raise difficult and penetrating questions. They have asked why practical genetics has been excluded from formal education and, more generally, why society remains ignorant or aloof of the genetic tools available to prospective parents through genetic counseling. As Dorothy Gold observed, "It is my desire that our experience with Andrea might prevent the same suffering and sorrow from happening to other people." Her generous wish proved prophetic and was fulfilled sooner than anyone could have expected.

The Hunts were contemporaries of the Golds. Both couples lived in the same city and knew each other slightly. They were of approximately the same age, economic status, educational background, and social heritage. Like the Golds, the Hunts were descended from Ashkenazim. A major difference between the two families was the Hunts' son, David, a normal, healthy lad of four. About the time Andrea's condition began to deteriorate seriously, Joan Hunt heard about the Golds and Tay-Sachs disease through a local community center. She was already pregnant for a second time and felt reassured by David's obvious robustness. As a cautious woman she did not fail to discuss her knowledge of Tay-Sachs disease and amniocentesis with her husband. To her surprise he did not immediately dismiss her information and concern. He remembered his grandmother's story of an unfortunate sister left behind in the old country. His great aunt's misfortune had centered around her two infant children. They had died quite young. He recalled that mention of this relative and her children was both rare and subdued and wondered if the taboo had been imposed because the infants had been somehow physically handicapped or mentally retarded.

The Hunts agreed to consult a genetic counselor, who arranged for Joan to have a precautionary amniocentesis during the eighteenth week of her pregnancy. The results of an immediate assay of amniotic fluid and uncultured cells revealed the presence of very little hex A. A diagnosis of Tay-Sachs disease was confirmed when analysis of cultured fetal cells revealed a similar absence of the essential enzyme. The Hunts were naturally distressed to learn they were both carriers of a lethal recessive gene and their anticipated baby was destined to suffer the effects of an insidious disease. However, the knowledge provided by genetic counseling helped cushion the shock. With little hesitation they agreed to a therapeutic abortion. Examination of the fetus revealed a marked absence of the hex A enzyme and definite signs of neurological degeneration typical of Tay-Sachs disease. Since that time the Hunts have borne two perfectly healthy, unimpaired children. They are now a family of five normal and happy people. Through a clear understanding of genetic principles and willingness to employ the tools of preventive genetic medicine, they avoided the heartache and suffering of a handicapped child. They were fortunate and Dorothy Gold had her wish.

Practical genetics at its best is beginning to take the guesswork out of family planning. The job for the future is to extend greatly the number of inherited conditions that can be handled in this or some other equally definitive, positive way. The job for the present is to bring the highly specialized services that are available today to all who can use them.

2.
The Language of Genetics: Its Classical Origins

It probably started with Darwin.

In 1859 Charles Darwin, the English naturalist, proposed a theory that explains both the essential unity and the bewildering diversity of living things. The theory suggests that the immense varieties of living things in the world today have evolved from common or shared ancestors under the pressures of a process he called natural selection.

Observing species in their wild state provides convincing evidence for evolution and its continuing function. Plants and animals reproduce at a tremendous rate, yet the population of a species tends to remain constant from generation to generation. Survival or demise is determined by selective factors imposed by the environment. These may include the presence or absence of competing species and such limiting factors as the availability of space, heat, light, and food. Because the offspring of a species possess many variations, some are better adapted than their fellows to compete for the finite resources of their environment. These adaptative variations may be a more efficient beak or a more protective color or greater speed or a preference for food that other individuals would not consume. Whatever their competitive edge, the groups of individuals with the fittest variations tend to produce more offspring that survive. Because most variations are transmitted from generation to generation, the progeny of successful competitors tend to populate the earth.

Environments do change. Favorable variations in one set of circumstances may become unfit in another, with the extinction of whole species as the result. Previously less fit variations may become highly favorable in an altered environment, and populations may emerge with dramatically different characteristics from their predecessors. In time populations of a single species may become so isolated from one another through different environmental selection factors that they can no longer interbreed and produce fertile offspring. In this fashion, two species may evolve from one.

Darwin's theory of evolution rapidly supplanted older attempts to explain the origin of the species. However, it left one major question unanswered. How were characteristics transmitted from parents to their offspring? Evolution assumed that subsequent generations could be slightly different from prior generations and that a selectively advantageous characteristic would be inherited by future generations. The theory contained no explanation for how variations arose or how, despite differences, we could account for basic similarities between parents and their children.

Darwin himself summarized the problem: "The laws governing inheritance are for the most part unknown. No one can say why the same peculiarity in different individuals of the same species, or in different species, is sometimes inherited and sometimes not so; why the child often reverts in certain characteristics to its grandfather or grandmother or more remote ancestor." These two sentences provided the central issue for a science that was not to get a name for nearly half a century.

The science of genetics tries to explain how characteristics are transmitted from generation to generation, how similarities are preserved, and how differences arise. Increased knowledge about the laws of inheritance allows physicians to understand better the diseases that are genetic and how they are transmitted.

During the second half of the nineteenth century, answers to some basic questions became available. An obscure scientist named Gregor Mendel had been at work in an improbable and out-of-the-way laboratory—a monastery garden. He had published experiments in 1866 that outlined most of the basic principles of classical genetics. At the time Mendel wrote, the world was not ready to pay heed. His work did not receive recognition until well after his death.

Mendel, an Austrian monk, was born in 1822 of peasant parents. As a young man he entered the Augustinian monastery at Brunn, Austria. This freed him from the hardships of an impoverished youth and gave him the opportunity to conduct experiments in natural history, a subject that had always fascinated him. It was in the monastery, unnoticed by the world, that Mendel's genius bloomed.

He set out to study how characteristics are transmitted from one generation to another. Others had attempted to study the problem, but with variable, confusing results. The patterns of inheritance that emerged from such studies were never clear. Unlike earlier experimenters, Mendel picked a simple organism and studied only one of its characteristics at a time.

The organism he selected was the ordinary pea plant, which was highly suitable for his experiments. The plant ordinarily fertilizes itself with its own pollen. By removing the pollen and using pollen from another plant with different characteristics or variations, Mendel exercised precise control over the reproductive patterns of the plant. He used pea plants with many sharply different variations. One variety had round seeds; another had wrinkled seeds. Some were yellow; some were green. Some were tall plants and some short. Mendel singled out seven different specific characteristics for study.

In a typical experiment, Mendel began with a few dozen plants with wrinkled seeds and about the same number with round seeds. He fertilized each kind of plant with pollen from the other; the "wrinkled" plants were fertilized with "round" pollen and vice versa. The resultant plants, called hybrids, predictably should have exhibited characteristics of both parents. Mendel waited until the plants had grown and ripened. He opened the pods and examined the peas.

He found that they were all round. There were no wrinkled seeds at all. This characteristic seemed to have vanished without a trace. The same was true in every other experiment. When tall plants were crossed with short plants, all the hybrid plants were tall. When yellow peas were hybridized with green peas, all the offspring were yellow.

Mendel then studied what occurred when two of the first-generation hybrids were crossed with each other. The results were surprising. When he crossed the round hybrids that had come from round and wrinkled parent plants, the missing characteristic magically reappeared in some peas of the second generation. From the hybrid tall plants he got both tall and short plants, and from the hybrid yellow peas he got both yellow and green peas. He had uncovered a general principle of inheritance.

Mendel then took a most important step. He counted the different kinds of plants. Simple as that seems today, the application of mathematics to biology was a major scientific advance. By counting the different kinds of offspring, Mendel discovered a ratio of major importance, a mathematical relationship that remains one of the fundamental formulas of genetics. Counting the peas in the round/wrinkled experiment, he found 5,474 round peas and 1,850 wrinkled peas, a ratio of about 3 to 1. That 3-to-1 ratio showed up with regularity in every experiment in which hybrid plants were mated.

Mendel considered his results and evolved a theory, one predicting that a physical reality underlies the mathematical ratio. He reasoned that each characteristic must be governed by a single factor (now called a gene) within the plant. He did not know what that factor was, but he knew that it had to be an independent unit that was transmitted from generation to generation without being changed. The apparent constancy of the factor had been demonstrated by the green pea characteristic that reappeared when two first-generation hybrids were crossed with each other. Mendel found evidence for two kinds of factors (a gene and its allele). One kind was able to prevail over the other when both were present in a hybrid plant. The factor for round peas was able to dominate or hide the factor for wrinkled peas, and the factor for tall plants dominated that for short plants. Mendel called the prevailing characteristics *dominant* factors. The other kind, which vanished in one generation only to reappear in the next, he called *recessive* factors, or characteristics. Here was a second major principle of genetics.

By analyzing the mathematics of his experiments, Mendel was able to explain that there are probably two factors, a gene and its allele, which determine each trait. He reasoned that one factor came from each parent. In order to illustrate how this works, he represented the dominant factor with a capital letter, for instance, A. He represented the recessive factor by a small letter, a. The resulting two-factor description for a trait (AA, Aa, or aa) is referred to as the *genotype*. Alternative factors, or genes, for the same trait are known as alleles.

Using this shorthand, we may reconsider the first experiment performed by Mendel. He crossed plants with two purely dominant factors (AA) with plants containing two purely recessive factors (aa). Each offspring received one factor from each parent. Every plant in the hybrid generation possessed a genotype with one dominant and one recessive factor. The genotype for all these plants was Aa. In chart form, the first hybridization looks like this:

		aa parent	
		a	a
AA parent	A	Aa	Aa
	A	Aa	Aa

All offspring have the Aa genotype and express the characteristic of the dominant allele.

When the hybrids were crossed with each other, all the parent plants were Aa, as the following chart shows:

		Aa parent	
		A	a
Aa parent	A	AA	Aa
	a	Aa	aa

The genotype ratio for the offspring is 1AA:2Aa:1aa. Three express the characteristic of the dominant allele (1AA and 2Aa), and one shows the characteristic of the recessive allele (1aa).

Looking carefully at the chart, we see that one of the four combinations contains the recessive factor alone (aa). Each of the other three has at least one dominant factor and will therefore express only the dominant trait. This is a 3-to-1 ratio—the very ratio that Mendel found in his experiments.

This is an important ratio, one that is often of great importance in medical genetics. It is clear from the chart that only one of the four combinations contains the dominant (AA) constitution. The other two of the four are hybrids (Aa) like the parents. We would call these (Aa) individuals heterozygotes or heterozygous carriers of the recessive factor. A zygote is the new organism that results from the fusion of two sex cells or gametes at the time of fertilization. A heterozygote is so called because it contains one factor for each of two alternative alleles. Such an individual is said to be a carrier of the recessive allele, which does not visibly express itself. A homozygote bears two factors for the same allele (AA or aa). Its *phenotype* or appearance will be that of the one characteristic of its genotype—dominant or recessive. A seed may be phenotypically round with a homozygous dominant (AA) genotype or a heterozygous (Aa) genotype. A phenotypically wrinkled seed must have the homozygous recessive genotype (aa). If (a) were a recessive gene that determined a disease, one of the four possible crosses of heterozygous (Aa) parents would lead to an (aa) child with the disease.

Mendel's discovery that the factors governing inheritance are quite tangible is of enormous importance. They are transmitted in units from parent to offspring. Today Mendel's factors are called genes. The science of inheritance is called genetics.

Mendel's experiments showed that each of the single plant traits he studied was determined by two genes. One gene comes from each parent. We have noted that different forms of the gene governing a given trait are called alleles. A species may possess more than two alternative alleles for a particular trait. The A, B, and O alleles for blood type provide an example in humans. However, no more than two alleles for the same trait are typically found in the same individual. For reasons that are not fully understood even today, one allele of a pair tends to dominate the other if they occur in the same organism, plant or animal, as a heterozygote. What Mendel found to be true for peas is just as true for people.

A plant inheriting the allele for a wrinkled seed from one parent and the allele for a round seed from the other parent would have only round seeds. A plant would have wrinkled seeds only if it inherited two wrinkled-seed alleles, one from each parent. In the language of genetics, the allele for the round seed is dominant, while the allele for the wrinkled seed is recessive.

In these simple experiments with plants, Mendel had discovered answers to questions that had puzzled scientists for centuries. Now he knew why traits persisted in families. The genes for those traits were passed on from generation to generation. He also knew why some traits disappeared, sometimes only to reappear generations later. Traits caused by recessive genes could remain hidden until chance introduced the same recessive gene from another parent.

In later experiments Mendel obtained a result that at first seemed to be an unwelcome surprise. When he crossed bean plants containing white flowers with plants having reddish-purple flowers, the next generation of plants had an amazing spectrum of colors, all the way from pure white through different shades of red to purple. This sort of result was at first very confusing, but Mendel was able to understand what was occurring. The flower's color was governed not by a single gene but by two or more genes working in conjunction. Whereas only three varieties or genotypes are possible when one gene and two alleles control a trait, nine varieties result from two-gene and multiple-allele control and twenty-seven varieties from three-gene control—enough to create an apparently endless range of colors.

In 1866 Mendel published his essential findings in a scientific paper that gave the rules still regarded as basic to genetics:

1. Each inherited trait is governed by factors that today we call genes. Genes can exist in different forms that we now call alleles.
2. There are two sets of genes, one set inherited from each parent.
3. The genes are ordinarily transmitted unaltered from parent to child. A recessive gene may seem to vanish, yet it is present, unimpaired, and will reemerge when the opportunity presents itself. The traits of each generation are produced by a reshuffling of the gene combinations of past generations. This explains both the similarities and the differences between generations.

The experiments of Mendel and his interpretations of them were brilliant. With them he explained many of the mechanisms of inheritance. When he published his paper, nothing happened. Nothing at all. The scientists of his time simply ignored what he had done. Mendel became abbot of his monastery, a post that forced him to give up his experiments. He died in 1884, unknown in the world of science.

It was not until 1900 that Mendel's work was understood and appreciated. In that year three scientists who had independently rediscovered Mendel's rules found his paper. To their credit, each of these three men, Hugo De Vries of the Netherlands, Karl Correns of Germany, and Erich Tschermak of Austria, immediately gave Mendel full credit for the discovery of the laws of inheritance. Today Mendel is honored as the father of genetics.

Many questions were left unanswered by Mendel's work. Did the genes actually exist, or were they just mathematical concepts that had no basis in reality? If genes did exist as real physical units, what was their composition, where were they located, and how were they transmitted from generation to generation?

An important question was in the nature of a paradox. Darwin's theory of evolution postulated that new species arose because of differences from generation to generation. But Mendel's genes seemed to be permanent, unchanging factors. The changes required by evolution would have to come from a permanent alteration in a gene, not from a simple reshuffling of the same genes. That permanent inheritable alteration in a gene is called a mutation.

Other questions had to be resolved. Some of the answers were being found even while Mendel's paper gathered dust on library shelves. In 1879 a German biologist, Walther Flemming, discovered that he could study processes in living cells by using dyes that were absorbed by some parts of the cell but not by others. In particular, Flemming studied the nucleus of the cell, the small, membrane-enclosed portion of the cell often found near the center. Flemming found that the dyes he used were absorbed by a material in the nucleus that he called chromatin, from the Greek word for "color." By using his dyes in cells at different stages of their life cycles, Flemming found himself observing an unusual sequence of events.

The chromatin would first gather itself into threadlike bodies. Then the membrane surrounding the cell nucleus would dissolve. A new object, which Flemming called the aster because of its starlike shape, next appeared, divided in two, and sent its two parts to opposite ends of the cell. The strands radiating from the two parts of the aster attached themselves to the threads of chromatin and slowly pulled the chromatin apart. These threads, which are now called chromosomes, were soon at opposite ends of the cell. Then the cell divided in two, forming a wall between the two parts, and new nuclei formed in each new cell around the chromosomes. At the end of the process there were two cells, each with a full complement of chromosomes.

Flemming's finding was duly noted but not really understood. In 1902 Walter S. Sutton, an American scientist, pointed out that Mendel's factors, or genes, and Flemming's chromosomes seemed to have a lot in common. Both are transmitted from generation to generation. Study of the sex cells showed that while eggs from the female are considerably larger than sperm from the male, both have nuclei of the same size, and each nucleus contains a half set of chromosomes. The sperm and the egg, when united, form a new being that has a full set of chromosomes. There was a remarkable resemblance between this observable physical fact—one set of chromosomes from each parent—and Mendel's law—one set of genes from each parent.

There was a major difficulty that prevented an absolute conclusion that chromosomes and genes were identical. There did not seem to be enough chromosomes. The fruit fly, for example, has only eight chromosomes (in four pairs). Yet it has hundreds of different characteristics, each requiring its own gene or genes.

There was a possible solution. Each chromosome could contain many genes. The credit for proving this belongs to Thomas Hunt Morgan, an American scientist who worked at Columbia University in the early part of this century.

Morgan began his experiments because he had doubts about Mendel's findings. Had he been a lesser man, he might have gained brief fame by using one of his discoveries to cast doubt on Mendel. But Morgan was one of the century's great geneticists, and he showed his ability in many different ways, including his willingness to try explanations that were truly inventive.

Morgan worked with the ordinary fruit fly. Its Latin name is *Drosophila*. This fly has many advantages as an experimental subject. It is easy to take care of. It breeds quickly and multiplies rapidly. A new generation is produced every few days.

Morgan's fruit flies all had red eyes. One day a fly with white eyes appeared in the laboratory. Morgan bred this white-eyed fly, a male, with a normal red-eyed female. Soon there were many red-eyed descendants but no white-eyed descendants. This indicated that the gene for white eyes was recessive. Following Mendel's lead, Morgan bred the red-eyed descendants with each other and got a major surprise.

That surprise was not with the ratio of red-eyed flies to white-eyed flies in the third generation. That was 3 to 1, as expected from the Mendelian rules. The surprise was that all the females had red eyes and all the white-eyed flies were males. This was something that Mendel's rules did not explain.

Morgan provided an answer that both preserved and broadened the laws of genetics. He had discovered sex-linked inheritance. He proposed that the gene for red eyes and the gene that determined female sex were on the same chromosome. Looking closely at the chromosomes through the microscope, Morgan found what some others had noticed before him. Only three of the four sets were perfectly matched. The fourth set was perfectly matched in females, but in males one of the chromosomes of the set was noticeably smaller than the other. Apparently this set of chromosomes determined the sex of flies; a short chromosome and a full-sized chromosome in the set produced a male, while two full-sized chromosomes produced a female.

Today it is known that what is true of the fruit fly is true of all sexually dimorphic animal species. Sexually dimorphic species are those in which male and female organs are found on different individuals. No matter how many sets of chromosomes are found in the species (in man there are 23 pairs, or 46 chromosomes), the genes for sex are located on a specific one of those pairs. The male usually has one smaller sex chromosome, while the female typically has two full-sized sex chromosomes. Because of their shapes, the full-sized sex chromosome has come to be called the X chromosome, while the smaller one, found only in males, is called the Y chromosome.

It seemed logical to Morgan that if a chromosome were visibly smaller than the other one of its pair, the smaller chromosome would have fewer genes on it. That explained why only males in the third generation had white eyes. There was probably no room on the small Y chromosome for the gene for eye color. The story of Morgan's flies is illustrated in Figure 1. When the gene for white eyes was present on a female X chromosome, the gene for red eyes on the other X chromosome was dominant. Therefore all the females had red eyes, whether they were homozygous (X^RX^R) or heterozygous (X^RX^r). In the parentheses the capital (R) represents the dominant red-eye gene and the small (r) the recessive white-eye gene. For a female to have white eyes, she would have to be homozygous (X^rX^r) for the X-linked recessive gene. In the original cross all of the males in the F_1 (first filial) generation had red eyes because they were X^RY. All of the females were heterozygous (X^RX^r). When these F_1 males and females were crossed with each other, the possible females were X^RX^R and X^RX^r, both of which would have red eyes. Half the males would have red eyes (X^RY). When the gene for white eyes showed up on the male's one X chromosome (X^rY), there was never an allele for eye color on the short Y chromosome. Any male with a gene for white eyes had white eyes. His genotype is said to be hemizygous.

Morgan had discovered the first sex-linked trait. Today many sex-linked or

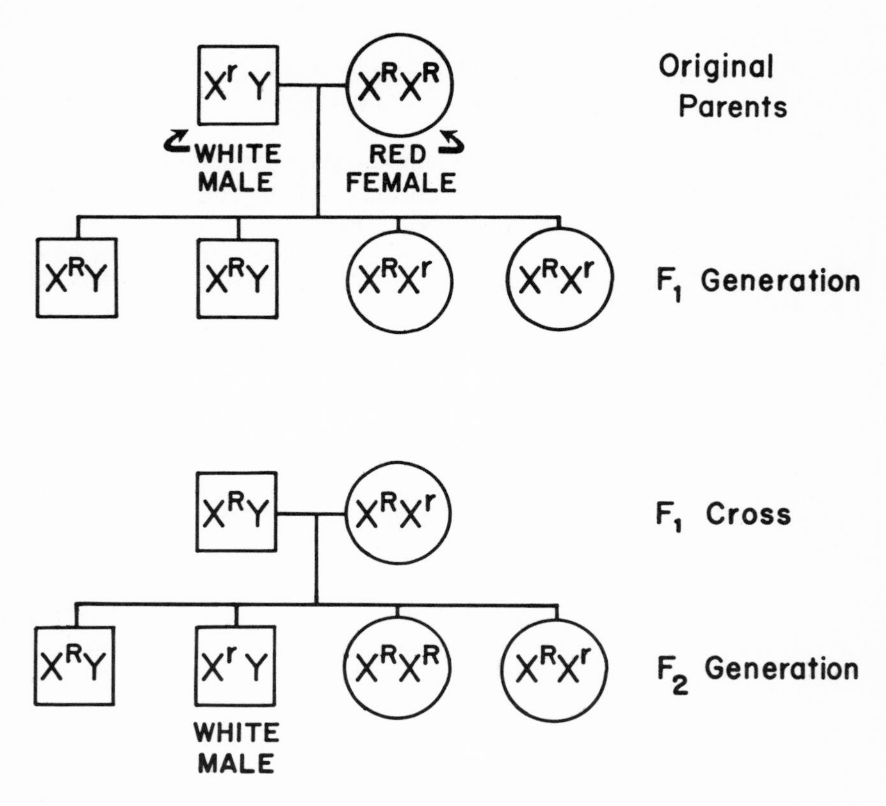

FIGURE 1. *The experiment of Dr. Thomas Hunt Morgan in which he discovered sex-linked inheritance. In the diagrammatic representation, the original male fly is shown in the box at the top with his X and Y chromosomes, while the female to which he was mated is shown in the circle with two X chromosomes. R indicates the dominant gene that determined red color; r the recessive gene that determined the absence of red, or white. The children in F_1 were all red. F_1 and F_2 are used to describe the first- and second-generation mating following the original parental cross. A cross between two members of the F_1 generation led to the reappearance of white offspring, and they were always male. This is the way an X-linked or sex-linked recessive works.*

X-linked traits are important in medical genetics. Some conditions, such as hemophilia, are caused by recessive genes that are located on the X chromosome. Females can carry the abnormal gene, but their other X chromosome usually has the normal dominant allele that prevents the hemophilia gene from expressing itself. The sons of such women are not so fortunate because they have no room on their Y chromosome for the normal gene. Because the gene for hemophilia is recessive, a woman would have to inherit two such alleles (X^hX^h) in order to suffer from the disease. As a nonhemophiliac heterozygous carrier (X^HX^h), a female may transmit the recessive allele to her sons, who will automatically suffer from the disease (X^hY). This explains why hemophilia occurs almost exclusively in males. It can occur in a female, but her mother would have to be heterozygous (X^HX^h) and her father would have to have hemophilia (X^hY).

While he was studying the chromosomes, Morgan made another logical proposal. Since there are only four sets of chromosomes in the fruit fly, all the fly's traits can be linked in four distinct groups. Each of these corresponds to the genes joined together on one chromosome. But Morgan found that these groups are not unchangeable. As the chromosomes are dragged apart during cell division, they can become entangled. Bits of chromosomes "cross over." Crossing over is illustrated in Fig. 2.

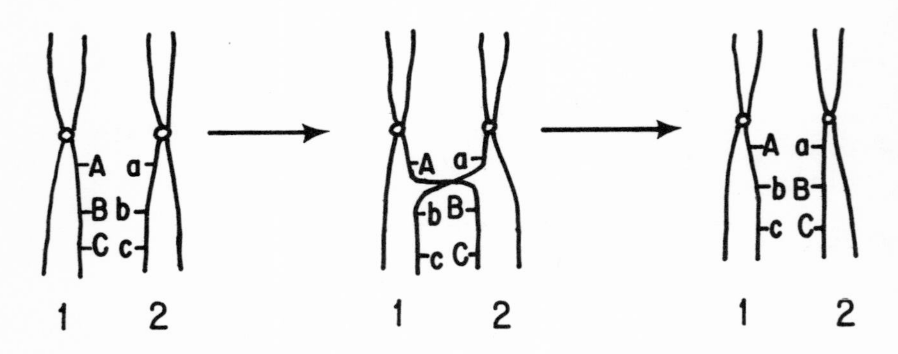

FIGURE 2. *Crossing over. In the diagram a section of chromosome 1 carrying dominant genes* (A, B, C) *is exchanged or "crosses over" with a section of chromosome 2 carrying the recessive alleles* (*a*, *b*, *c*).

On the basis of his discovery of chromosomal crossing over, Morgan began a major study. He mapped the location of genes on chromosomes by studying crossing over during matings. The theory was simple. If the genes for two traits were close to the center of a chromosome, they would almost never cross over. If they were far from the center, they would cross over often. By studying the frequency of crossing over in millions of flies, Morgan eventually was able to make a fairly precise map showing the sites of an enormous number of traits on each chromosome.

Morgan had started out doubting the existence or concept of the gene. Now not only had he determined the genes' existence and their location within the cell, but he had also mapped them with precision. For this work Morgan received the Nobel Prize in 1933.

Other scientists were simultaneously tackling another question about the gene and evolution: the nature of change in genes. Morgan's white-eyed fly cast some light on the subject. The alteration in eye color initially had been caused by an unexplained change in the nature of a gene, a change called a mutation.

It was assumed, and still is, that all genetically determined variations in living things are first caused by such mutations. Attempts to study mutations and their effects were hampered by the fact that very few mutations occur spontaneously. Attempts at inducing mutations by exposing genes to all sorts of influences—extreme cold, heat, alcohol, lead, and poisons, for example—accomplished little. The gene seemed to be a tough and independent unit. This, of course, is a useful evolutionary characteristic because the viability of each living organism depends on the integrity of its genes.

Then, in 1927, H. J. Müller, a graduate of Morgan's chromosome mapping team, exposed the chromosomal genes to X rays. He exposed fruit flies to X rays and then bred them. The results were striking. There were an unprecedented number and variety of mutations. It was significant that the mutations were made by man and open to scientific study. As Müller said later, "The roots of life, the genes, had indeed been struck and they had yielded." The ability to produce mutations for scientific study was so valuable that Müller was awarded the Nobel Prize. His technique provided a basis for exploring the nature of a gene—an exploration that continues in earnest today.

There were other important questions to be answered; for example, how did a gene control the characteristics of a living organism? Biologists knew that the work of the living cell is carried out by a family of chemicals known as enzymes. Enzymes are protein molecules composed of long chains of smaller amino acid molecules. Enzymes exist in many different varieties. Their differences are based on the number and arrangement of the various constituent amino acids. Many enzymes contain a coenzyme portion that is typically composed of a vitamin or mineral. We require specific vitamins and minerals in our diet in order to provide these essential coenzymes.

For each vital function in a cell there is an enzyme that helps carry out the requisite chemical reaction. If a substance A must be converted to substance *C*, passing through an intermediary stage, substance *B*, the cell must contain specific enzymes A and *B* for these transitions to occur. Should either enzyme A or *B* be missing or be present in inadequate amounts, the required chemical conversion will not occur. The result will be the absence of essential substance *C* and the buildup of potentially toxic quantities of substances A or *B*.

$$\text{Substance A} \xrightarrow[\quad]{\text{Enzyme A}} \text{Substance } B \xrightarrow[\quad]{\text{Enzyme } B} \text{Substance } C$$

Since such enzyme mechanisms control all cellular processes, it was tempting to speculate whether the production and activity of enzymes are controlled by genes.

In a series of brilliant experiments two American scientists, George W. Beadle and Edward L. Tatum, established that this is indeed the case. Beadle and Tatum worked with a pink bread mold called *Neurospora crassa*. This organism demands very little for life. Given sugar, water, minerals, and one B vitamin, *Neurospora* will make all the things that are essential to its existence. Beadle and Tatum set out to make life more complicated for *Neurospora*. They exposed samples of the mold to radiation and produced mutations. Some of the mutant molds lost their ability to synthesize one or more essential substances. As a result, they needed more than the basic sugar, water, minerals, and one B vitamin that satisfied the normal mold. Sometimes only one additional vitamin or amino acid was needed, sometimes many. The mutant molds, if properly supplied with the missing nutrients, would retain their new property, the *in*ability to synthesize certain nutrients, for generations. There had clearly been a change in the genes.

As Beadle and Tatum interpreted their experiments, the mutations they produced had altered the cell by depriving it of the ability to make certain enzymes. Sometimes only one enzyme was absent because the X rays altered only one gene. The lack of this enzyme destroyed the cell's ability to synthesize an essential nutrient, which now had to be added to the organism's diet for survival. Beadle and Tatum knew that the mutations that prevented enzyme formation and activity were caused by damage to the genes. They concluded that the genes determined the production of enzymes. The rule that they proposed was simple and direct: the one-gene/one-enzyme hypothesis. It says that a single gene does its work by directing the synthesis or formation of a single enzyme protein.

The work by Beadle and Tatum clearly demonstrated how a single gene, in controlling the formation of a single enzyme, ultimately controls all cellular processes. The diagram for the conversion of substance A to substance C can be expanded as follows:

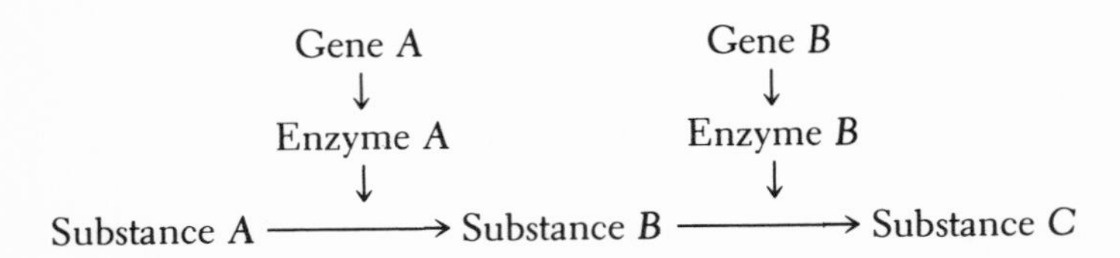

The one-gene/one-enzyme rule still stands, although its form has been modified and expanded. It is recognized that all proteins are not necessarily enzymes. Genes work by controlling the synthesis of all proteins. Some proteins are made up of individual polypeptide chains. Like proteins, polypeptide chains are composed of chemically bonded amino acid molecules. They are distinguished from proteins because they contain fewer linked amino acids and because each polypeptide may be determined by a separate gene. A more general reading of the basic rule becomes one gene/one polypeptide. The rule is important in medical genetics because many inherited diseases in man are known to be caused by the lack of a single enzyme. Failure to provide the necessary enzyme can basically be traced to a single faulty gene. What Beadle and Tatum showed with the simple bread mold has now been demonstrated many times in the more complex human organism.

In the dread Tay-Sachs disease the recessive allele fails to direct the proper synthesis of the enzyme that is called hex A. This enzyme is essential in converting a portion of a sphingolipid molecule, GM_2-ganglioside, to a waste product that can be eliminated from the body. GM_2-ganglioside is ordinarily produced in nerve cells. An individual inheriting the homozygous recessive genotype (aa) fails to produce the essential hex A enzyme, with the result that GM_2-ganglioside builds up to concentrations that ultimately prove fatal.

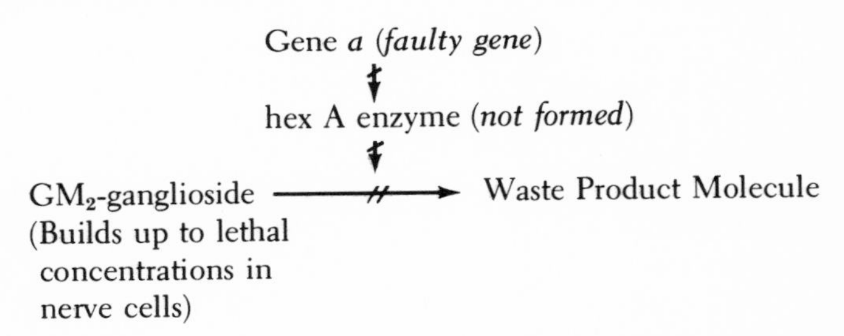

With each new discovery, new questions arise. So it was with the gene. Knowing how a gene exerts its control over a cell did not explain its molecular composition and function. Until the chemical nature of the gene was known, the way in which it determined the synthesis of enzyme proteins would also remain obscure.

The first major step in determining the chemical composition of the gene was taken during World War II by a team of scientists headed by Oswald T. Avery at the Rockefeller Institute. Avery's team began with a problem of infectious disease. They worked with pneumococcus, the microorganism that causes pneumonia. They knew of two different forms of this microbe. One has a smooth coat and the other a rough-looking coat. The smooth-coated microbe is encased in a sugar capsule that evidently protects it from attack by a host's chemical defense mechanisms. It is virulent and causes disease. The rough-coated microbe, lacking a sugar capsule, is not so protected and is normally rendered innocuous by a host's chemical defenses. It had been discovered that if dead bacteria of the smooth-coated, virulent kind and living innocuous bacteria were together injected into an animal, living smooth-coated microbes could later be found in the animal. Avery and his colleagues reasoned that unless the smooth-coated, virulent pneumococci had risen from the dead, something had penetrated the rough-coated organisms and transformed them into the smooth, virulent type. It was logical that this transforming factor must have originated in the smooth-coated, virulent microbes. Avery set out to determine the nature of the transforming factor. His work was made easier because this transformation could also be demonstrated in cultures of pneumococci grown *in vitro*, that is, grown in the laboratory outside an animal host.

After lengthy and brilliant chemical and biological studies, Avery found that the transforming factor indeed passed from the dead to the living pneumococci. The factor was DNA, deoxyribonucleic acid. DNA was a molecule that no one had really been paying much attention to, although it had been discovered in 1869 by a Swiss chemist named Friedrich Miescher. Because the molecule is mildly acidic and is found almost entirely in the nuclei of cells, it had been called nucleic acid. Some biologists had studied nucleic acid and found that its molecules are very large, very long, threadlike structures. When isolated in quantity from living tissues, fresh DNA aggregates into what looks like ordinary thread. Nucleic acid had been studied, classified, and forgotten. Its function was unknown.

The implications of Avery's work were clear and dramatic. If foreign DNA from the smooth-coated pneumococcus could invade another cell, the rough-coated pneumococcus, and cause transformations in the host cell's physical features and characteristics, the foreign DNA must be acting as a dominant gene. This dominating activity involves evident control over the synthesis of enzyme proteins. In the case of rough-coated pneumococci, the invading smooth-coated DNA dictated the formation of enzymes that led to the production of the sugar capsules that made smooth coats. Following the implication of Avery's discovery, scientists have provided overwhelming evidence that the genetic material is in fact DNA.

These findings had tremendous significance. They demonstrated not only that the gene is finite, as Mendel predicted, but also that it is contained in chromosomes, as suggested by Sutton. Analysis of a typical chromosome reveals a series of DNA molecules linked together by protein segments.

Avery's identification of DNA as the primary genetic molecule led to intensive study and analysis of the previously forgotten nucleic acids. It was evident from the outset that DNA must have at least two very impressive molecular functions. The first was a capacity to duplicate itself in precise fashion, as genes and chromosomes were known to do during reproduction. The second was to direct the formation of enzymatic proteins. How DNA might control protein synthesis seemed particularly problematic since the vast majority of DNA molecules are concentrated in the cell nucleus while the formation of protein was known to take place in the cytoplasm, that part of the cell outside the nucleus.

The answer to the problem was suggested by a careful review and analysis of nucleic acid chemistry. Two distinct kinds of nucleic acid molecules were identified: deoxyribonucleic acid (DNA) and ribonucleic acid (RNA). Both molecular types are found to contain smaller three-molecule units called nucleotides. Every nucleotide, whether of DNA or RNA, is composed of a chemically bonded phosphate, a sugar, and one of four nitrogen-containing base molecules. The differences between DNA and RNA nucleotides are principally two. The sugar molecule in an RNA nucleotide is ribose, a molecule containing five carbon atoms. The sugar molecule in DNA is deoxyribose, which, as its name suggests, is a ribose sugar with an oxygen atom removed. The four possible nitrogen base molecules in an RNA nucleotide are adenine, guanine, cytosine, and uracil. The four possible nitrogen base molecules in a DNA nucleotide are adenine, guanine, cytosine, and thymine. Uracil replaces thymine in one form of the RNA nucleotide. We might diagrammatically represent a pair of nucleotides as follows:

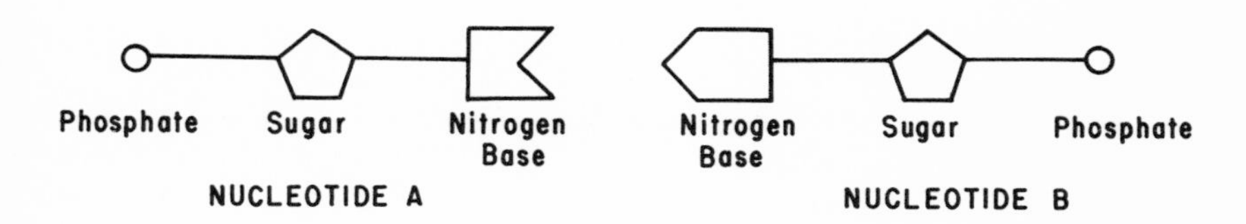

A number of curious facts were uncovered about the various nitrogen bases found in nucleic acids. Cytosine, thymine, and uracil are physically and chemically similar. They are classified together as molecules called pyrimidines, represented in nucleotide A above. Adenine and guanine similarly share many physical and chemical properties. They are classified as molecules called purines, represented in nucleotide B above. Analysis of the concentrations of nitrogen bases from the DNA of many different species invariably reveals that concentrations of adenine (A), a purine, are the same as those of thymine (T), a pyrimidine, and that concentrations of guanine (G) are equal to those of cytosine (C).

Taken together, this knowledge of nucleotide chemistry and nitrogen-base concentration provided a compendium of interesting facts. A coherent ordering of these bits of information to explain both DNA replication and protein synthesis required the work of genius.

The requisite intelligence was provided by an American, James D. Watson, and a Briton, Francis H. C. Crick. Working together at the Cavendish Laboratory at Cambridge University in England, they brilliantly synthesized the known facts of nucleic acid chemistry to explain the physical structure of DNA. The observed equivalency of adenine/thymine (A-T) and guanine/cytosine (G-C) concentrations suggested a pairing of the nucleotides:

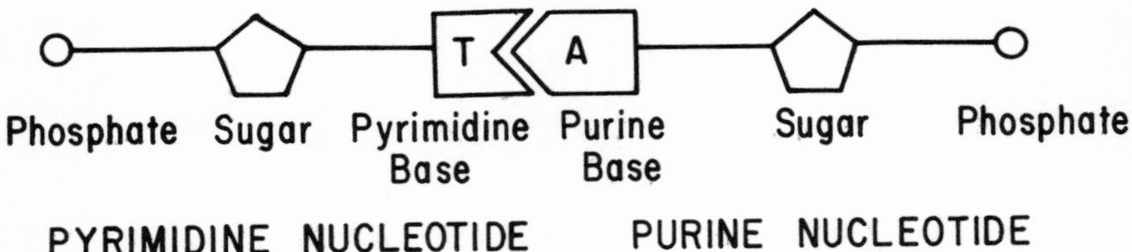

From what is known of the physical and chemical properties of the various nucleotide components, it was possible to conceive of their linkage in such a fashion that the phosphate of one nucleotide could be chemically bonded to the sugar of another.

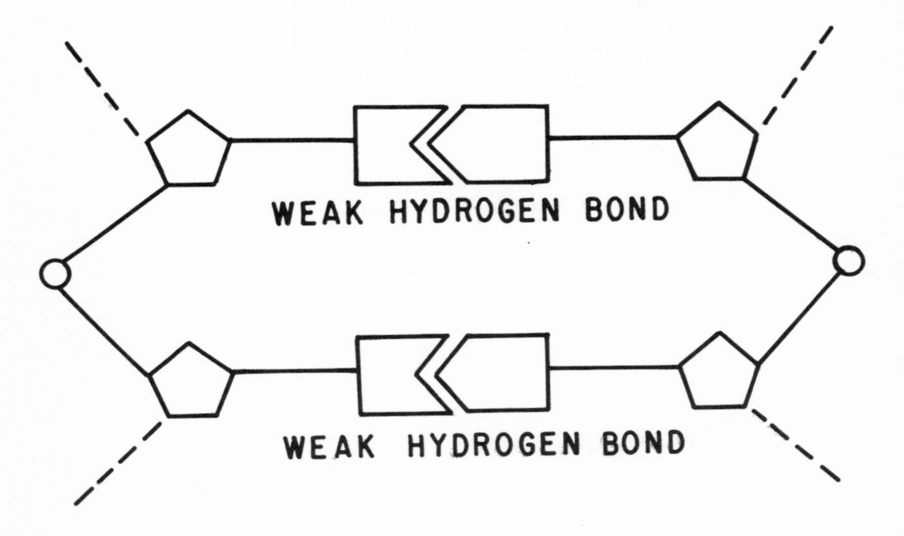

It was known that purines might be chemically bonded to pyrimidines by relatively weak hydrogen linkages. The model that emerged for the DNA molecule suggested a ladder whose vertical supports are composed of alternating phosphate and sugar molecules (Figure 3). The rungs of this hypothetical ladder are composed of various purine and pyrimidine base pairs.

A knowledge of the three-dimensional geometry that would be dictated by the angles at which the various nucleotides would have to be chemically linked suggested that the ladder was coiled into a kind of braid or helix. The ultimate molecular structure can be imagined as the result of two complementary chains of DNA nucleotides coiled around a common axis with the appropriately paired bases joined by hydrogen bonds. The bases, which are physically flat, are thus piled one on top of another like a stack of pennies. This concept of a helical structure was confirmed through X-ray crystallography of pure DNA.

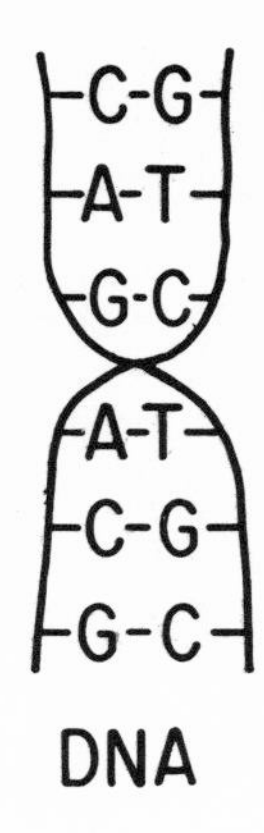

FIGURE 3. *DNA. A section of a gene is illustrated.*

Watson and Crick's structural model provided a mechanism for explaining DNA replication, which is essential for the molecule to function in the self-reproduction of the genetic material. A specific enzyme breaks the weak hydrogen bonds linking the various purine and pyrimidine pairs. The resulting separation of the two complementary DNA strands causes the helix to uncoil and allows free nucleotides in the nucleus to bond with appropriate unpaired nitrogen bases on either of the two complementary strands (Figure 4). Under

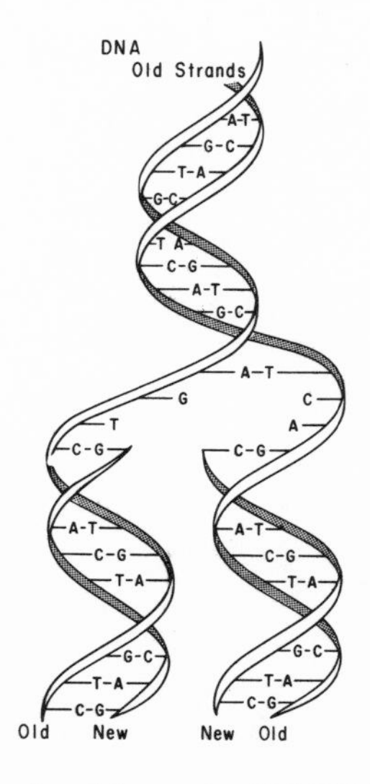

FIGURE 4. *Diagrammatic representation of the way in which DNA replicates or copies itself. Thus in the mechanisms of genetics a cell receives an exact copy of the DNA of the cell that made it.*

the influence of specific enzymes, the previously free nucleotides are chemically bonded, and two exact copies of the original DNA molecule are formed. Watson and Crick were awarded the Nobel Prize for their important work on the molecular basis of genetics.

The explanation for how DNA in the nucleus of the cell controls and directs the synthesis of proteins in the cytoplasm was provided by Marshall Nirenberg of the National Institutes of Health. The discovery of RNA throughout both the nucleus and the cytoplasm suggested that it might play an intermediary role in conveying instructions from the DNA master molecules of nuclear chromosomes to the ribosomes, the sites of protein synthesis in the cytoplasm. Nirenberg demonstrated that DNA directs the synthesis of a form of RNA that acts as this predicted messenger. RNA nucleotides, freely available in the nucleus, are paired with the purines and pyrimidines of the master DNA in the following fashion (Figure 5):

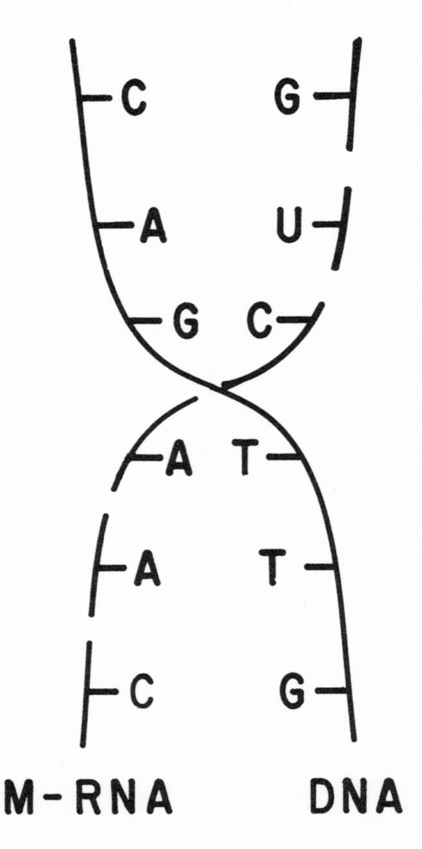

FIGURE 5. *The formation of messenger RNA (M-RNA) from DNA.*

The DNA thus produces a mirror image of its own purines and pyrimidines in number and sequence, except that uracil is everywhere substituted for thymine. The resulting molecule is called messenger RNA (M-RNA). It is separated from its DNA parent through the action of an enzyme. The coded M-RNA migrates into the cytoplasm through channels connecting the nucleus with the cell membranes (Figure 6). The M-RNA passes through the mem-

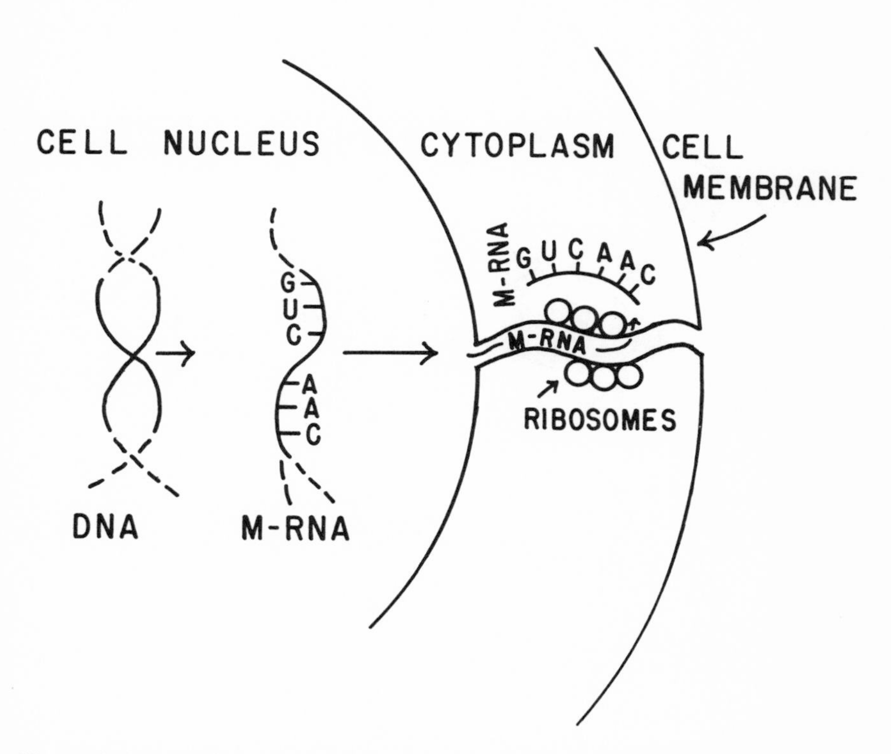

FIGURE 6. *Passage of genetic messages, coded from the DNA to the messenger RNA, to the cytoplasmic ribosomes where they direct the synthesis of proteins.*

brane and attaches itself to the ribosomes in such fashion that its unpaired purines and pyrimidines project into the cytoplasm.

At least twenty varieties of a smaller form of the RNA molecule are found in the cytoplasm of all cells. Each of these is chemically specific for a single kind of amino acid. This specificity is a function of a triplet code of unpaired nucleotides at the end of each molecule. The function of this RNA, called transfer RNA (T-RNA), is to transfer amino acids to the ribosome, where they are chemically bonded to one another to form polypeptides or proteins. Their arrangement is determined by the master pattern provided by the nuclear DNA through its M-RNA intermediary. For example, the transfer RNA that specifically carries the amino acid valine to a ribosome has three unpaired nucleotides (C, A, G, in sequence) and the T-RNA specific for the amino acid asparagine has three unpaired nucleotides (U, U, G, in sequence). The nucleotide sequence of these molecules will align the two amino acid molecules in such a fashion that they may link up, thus forming a peptide. As other amino acids are added, the peptide becomes a polypeptide. The whole process is shown in Figure 7.

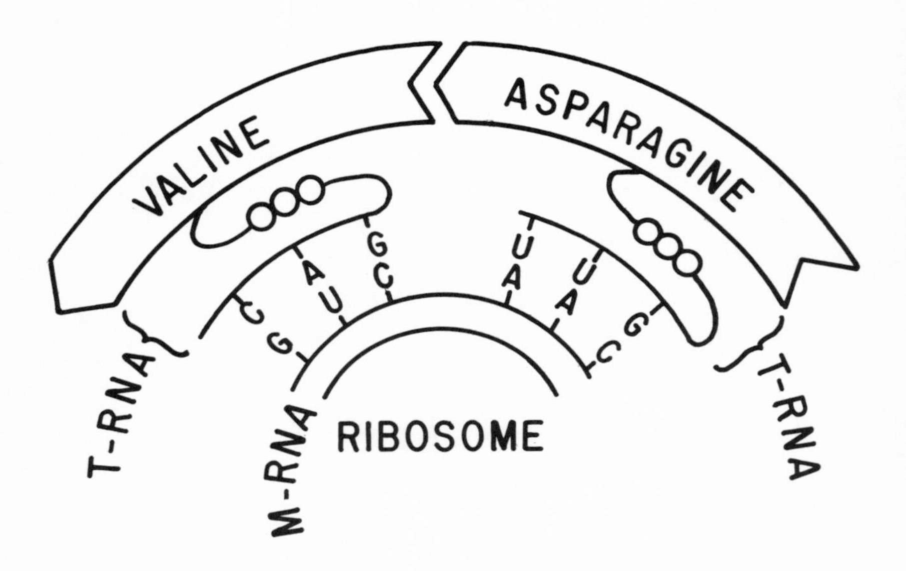

FIGURE 7. *Protein synthesis. The way in which transfer RNA molecules bring the amino acid (that the code calls for) to just the right spot on the M-RNA.*

In this fashion different amino acids are chemically linked to one another to form the immense variety of structural and enzymatic proteins required by a cell. Nirenberg was awarded the Nobel Prize in 1968 for his explanation of how the genetic DNA of chromosomes controls the cytoplasmic synthesis of proteins.

The implications of this extraordinary research into nucleic acid chemistry are of considerable importance. Differences among genes in one cell and between the cells of different species are accounted for by variations in the number and sequences of the purines and pyrimidines found in the master DNA molecules. The many kinds and varieties of proteins unique to a given organism are also a function of this coding mechanism. Mutations are now easy

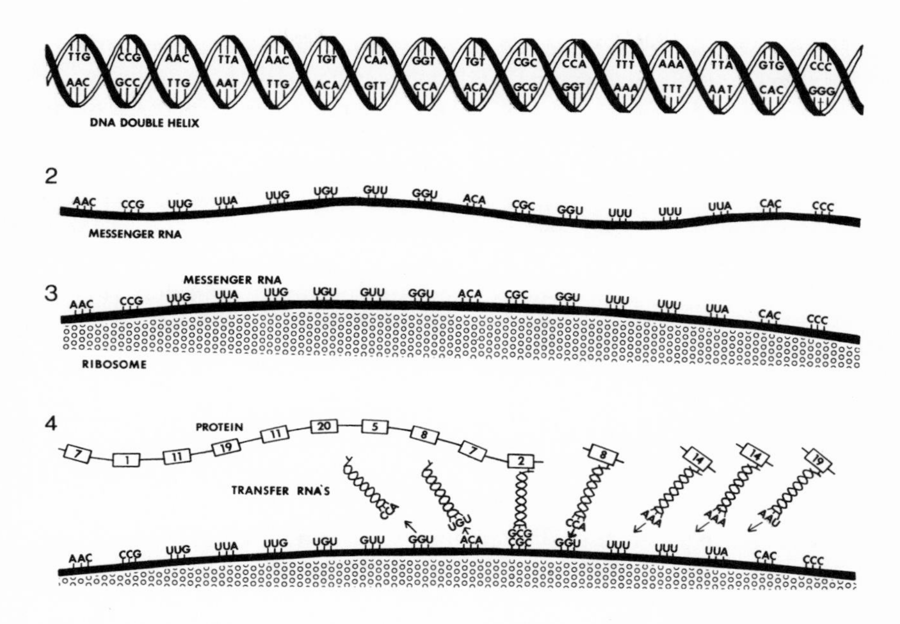

FIGURE 8. *The molecular nature of genetics. The DNA is shown at the top (1) in a helical or coiled structure. The code is shown in the triplet structure in which the purine and pyrimidine bases are represented by their first letters, A for adenine, T for thymine, G for guanine, and C for cytosine. A is always opposite T, and G is always opposite C. M-RNA synthesized according to the DNA instructions leaves the nucleus (2) and migrates into the cytoplasm where it becomes attached to ribosomes (3). Transfer RNAs (T-RNA) align appropriate amino acids for protein synthesis (4) according to the M-RNA nucleotide sequence.*

From "The Genetic Code: II," by Marshall W. Nirenberg, from Scientific American, *208:80, No. 3, March 1963. Copyright © 1963 by Scientific American, Inc. All rights reserved.*

to comprehend. They represent alterations in the number, sequence, or identity of the nitrogen bases in the DNA molecule. DNA is resistant to change. This is important in determining the constancy of genetic transmission generation after generation. It is not completely immune to change. Some chemicals, X rays, and some viruses can alter a DNA linkage. A change in one base—for instance, a switch from a guanine to an adenine—would be translated very differently into messenger RNA and would change the amino acid ultimately added to the protein at that point. This might markedly alter the protein it produced. The result could well be a genetic disease. Several inherited human disorders are known in which the cause is a substitution of a single amino acid in an otherwise normal protein. Sickle cell anemia is an example. The substitution that causes this disease results from a mutation in just one unit of a DNA molecule that is in itself thousands of units long.

Much is known about the nature of the gene and the nature of inheritance.

To scientists, this knowledge is in a sense behind them. They are working to discover the endless sequence of events in the living cells whose details are now unknown. As the border of scientific knowledge advances, so does the frontier of medical practice. This is particularly the case in genetic disease.

The language adopted by Mendel, who spoke of dominant and recessive factors, is used today in genetic diseases of man. The arithmetic of inheritance of dominant and recessive traits, worked out so laboriously by Mendel in his experiments with pea plants, is used today by genetic counselors to explain to prospective parents their chances of bearing healthy or unhealthy children. The language and the mathematics are the same. For a disease caused by a single recessive gene carried by both parents, the 3-to-1 ratio described by Mendel still applies. The chances are one in four in such a marriage that an affected child will be born or conversely three in four that a normal child will be born.

Work on the chemical nature of the gene and the way in which DNA directs the synthesis of proteins has made many of the current exciting advances in clinical genetics possible. They are the foundation for future advances.

3. The History and Development of Medical Genetics

We have seen how the science of genetics has unfolded in a mathematically elegant and logical progression. One discovery neatly followed another over a century of brilliant research. The history of medical genetics is less clearly delineated. There is now an explosive burst of activity after a long period in which the science of genetics had little impact on the work of physicians or on the lives of their patients. The past two decades have launched a concerted application of genetic science to the solution of people's problems.

Future historians will credit the birth of medical genetics to our era. A parallel may be drawn between this period and that time when Pasteur described the germ theory of disease. Major discoveries were made virtually every month. In the same way the application of research in genetics to medical practice is occurring and will continue to occur at an unprecedented rate. Creativity in this field has not reached its peak.

The birth of genetic medicine cannot be traced to a single event. Its development reflects the generally explosive growth of genetic science and molecular biology. A new approach to treatment or management captures the imagination of physicians and the public and inevitably leads to greater efforts in research and in diagnosis. The event that probably launched the current wave of activity in genetic medicine was the development of amniocentesis. This technique gives a prospective parent information about an unborn child. Amniocentesis provides specific, precise information on which a decision to continue or terminate a pregnancy can be made. It brings to genetic counseling, which previously had been exclusively dependent on probability statistics, the possibility of a specific diagnosis and a specific decision concerning the management of a particular genetic condition. The medical, social, and moral implications of that development are resounding through our society. Amniocentesis can now provide an answer to a small number of problems. Its importance in the history of medical genetics is that it teaches us that something practical and effective can be done in facing potential genetic disorders.

The real beginnings of genetic medicine occurred many years ago. Physicians have known for centuries that some malformations occur in a predictable percentage of births. Many of these conditions had been described in detail by the ancients. Achondroplastic dwarfism, a genetic condition in which the trunk is of normal size but the arms and legs are abnormally short, was pictured in Egyptian sculpture in 3000 B.C. Harelip was recorded in pre-Columbian Peruvian pottery.

Among the earliest studies in human genetics were those of Sir Francis Galton, who was a first cousin of Charles Darwin. Galton did some extremely valuable work. By studying identical twins, who inherit identical genetic constitutions, he was able in part to determine the influences of the environment on individuals. Galton was a master of statistics and a student of human differences. He was largely responsible for introducing statistical methods into the genetic study of human populations.

In Stuttgart, Germany, in the early years of the twentieth century, an obstetrician began to apply practically the laws of Mendel to human inheritance. This physician, Wilhelm Weinberg, began to make a most important distinction between a person's appearance, or phenotype, and his inherited characteristics, or genotype. What Weinberg did was to apply Mendel's statistical laws to matings between people. Many of the mathematical techniques that Weinberg introduced are still actively employed by geneticists today.

At virtually the same time, one of the giants of human genetics, Sir Archibald E. Garrod, was working in England. Garrod was a physician who made important discoveries that are fundamental to science. He deduced them from clinical practice rather than laboratory research.

Garrod began his studies on a condition called alkaptonuria. This disorder has one striking attribute. A patient's urine turns black on exposure to air. This in itself is harmless. However, similar changes occur in the joints. Patients with this problem develop severe arthritis in early middle age. Garrod found that the black pigment in the urine resulted from a chemical called homogentisic acid.

In working with patients who suffered from this condition, Garrod discovered another striking fact. In three out of four families in which alkaptonuria occurred, the parents of patients were first cousins. This was a far higher percentage than could be explained by chance. It was an index of Garrod's genius that he arrived at the explanation for this statistical fact. His explanation reveals a general genetic principle. He reasoned that the condition is caused by a recessive gene inherited according to Mendelian laws. The reason it occurs with the intermarriage of first cousins is that the gene is rare and will express itself infrequently in the homozygous recessive condition if mating is entirely random throughout a population.

Recent work has established the molecular nature of the defect in alkaptonuria. The mutant gene determines an abnormality in the activity of the liver enzyme, homogentisic acid oxidase. The defect is rare, and it is recessive.

The principle Garrod revealed has proved to be of major importance in medical genetics. It is quite simple. An individual receives one-half of his or her genes from one parent and the other half from the other parent. Any parent and child have half their genes in common. When that child has a child, he transmits half his genes to his offspring. Therefore, a grandchild and grandparent have one-quarter of their genes in common.

When first cousins marry, they have a fairly large chance of sharing the same harmful recessive gene. In any marriage where two persons have the same recessive gene, the familiar Mendelian ratio applies. Every child of that marriage has one chance in four of inheriting a recessive gene from each parent (aa) and also of inheriting the condition caused by that recessive gene.

The same mathematics that governed the inheritance of traits in Mendel's pea plants governs the inheritance of recessive traits in man. If each parent has one normal gene (call it A) and one abnormal gene, the recessive (call it a), each child of the marriage inherits one gene for the trait from each parent. By Mendelian law, each child has one chance in four of inheriting two normal genes (AA), one chance in four of inheriting two abnormal genes (aa), and two chances in four of inheriting one normal gene and one abnormal gene (Aa).

The recessive trait will phenotypically express itself only when the two recessive genes (aa) are present. This happens in only one in four cases. There is a predictable 3-to-1 ratio of normal offspring to abnormal offspring. Two of the three normal individuals are heterozygous (Aa). They carry the recessive gene and can pass it on to the next generation.

Detecting this pattern of inheritance is easier in pea plants than it is in people. There are many fewer humans to study, and most families have very small numbers of offspring. The picture is also clouded because the effects of the environment are more prominent in people. Through careful observation and scrupulous record keeping, Garrod was able to detect the pattern in alkaptonuria. He published his findings in 1902.

More important than detection of this inheritance pattern was the theory Garrod developed concerning the cause of the condition and the manner of its inheritance. He suggested that urine of people with alkaptonuria turns black because something is wrong with the normal process by which homogentisic acid is metabolized in the body. He in effect said the flaw is due to the lack of an enzyme that splits the molecule of homogentisic acid. He proposed that the enzyme was missing because the gene controlling the enzyme was defective. This was the first statement of the one-gene/one-enzyme hypothesis.

In the last chapter we saw how Garrod's theory has been amplified into our current molecular understanding of genetics. Beadle and Tatum won the Nobel Prize for their work on the one-gene/one-enzyme theory. It is impressive that Garrod expressed these ideas based on clinical observations. His work was amazingly advanced. He did all this at a time when little was known about inheritance. The concept of the gene had yet to be proposed. Enzymes, then called "ferments," were poorly understood.

Garrod named alkaptonuria and other conditions like it "inborn errors of metabolism." In later years he identified several other such errors of metabolism. In each instance his observation could be explained by the concept of a missing or faulty enzyme resulting from a defective gene. His little book, *The Inborn Errors of Metabolism,* is a medical classic. His work was of immense significance. It showed that a practicing physician could contribute in important, fundamental ways to the advancement of basic science. Like Mendel, he was generally unappreciated by contemporaries.

During the years following Garrod's work, a foundation of useful knowledge was gradually acquired. Several other conditions were identified as inborn errors of metabolism. They were observed to be transmitted according to the classic Mendelian recessive pattern. James V. Neel, working at the University of Rochester after World War I, found that sickle cell anemia followed the recessive inheritance pattern. This disease occurs almost exclusively among blacks, for whom it is a rather common problem.

A Norwegian doctor, Ivar Asbjørn Følling, discovered phenylketonuria (PKU) in 1934. His close attention to the observations of a young mother paid off handsomely. The woman who came to see Følling had two severely retarded children. She noticed their urine had an odd odor. When Følling added a simple chemical reagent, ferric chloride, to the urine, it turned a rich green. This provided the key to the disorder, which is caused by the lack of activity of a liver enzyme. PKU is transmitted as a recessive genetic disease. Følling's work led to the first large-scale program for the early detection of an inherited genetic disease.

A real burst of activity in the history of medical genetics began after the end of World War II and shows no sign of abating. In a pattern established then and continuing today, laboratory research and clinical genetics are closely linked. Pure research has often ended with important advances rapidly applied to the practice of medicine. The transfer of information from the laboratory to the bedside and the doctor's office has never been so fast, and it is accelerating.

This modern era of molecular medical genetics was ushered in by the important discovery of S. Jonathan Singer, Linus Pauling, Harvey Itano, and Ibert C. Wells. It involved sickle cell anemia, a genetic disease that is caused by a recessive gene common in black populations. In this disease the red blood cells tend to lose their normal rounded shape and become deformed. They take on an elongated appearance resembling sickles, the feature that gives the disease its name. The sickle cells aggregate in blood vessels and cause clots and blockages. These cells are destroyed more easily than their normal counterparts. The disease kills approximately half of all patients before their thirtieth birthdays.

Pauling threw himself into the work of finding the cause of this disease. Soon he was able to demonstrate a flaw in the hemoglobin molecule. The alteration in the molecule changed its electric charge so that it behaved differently from normal hemoglobin when placed in an electric field. This was a historic discovery. For the first time the actual molecule that caused a genetic disease could be readily identified and clearly distinguished from the corresponding, normal molecule. The presence of the abnormal hemoglobin could be detected in heterozygous carriers of the disease. Thus, the parents of patients with sickle cell anemia could be shown to have both the normal and the sickle hemoglobin.

Another important advance in medical genetics occurred in 1952. Until that year the study of chromosomes in human cells had been frustrating and imprecise. Because the chromosomes are intertwined throughout the nucleus, it is difficult to count them and virtually impossible to study them accurately.

One day in 1952 Dr. T. C. Hsu of the University of Texas in Galveston encountered one of those happy accidents that often make for significant progress in research. He noticed a cell preparation in which the chromosomes were spread out, and each could be easily distinguished from the others. Looking for the reason, he found that a laboratory technician mistakenly had added a salt solution that did not contain the usual amount of salt, or sodium chloride. The solution was hypotonic; that is, its concentration of sodium and chlorine ions was less than that of the cells. This caused the cells to absorb water. As they swelled, their chromosomes spread apart. This stroke of good fortune suddenly made the precise study of chromosomes a realistic possibility.

The importance of the discovery was made evident just a few years later by two scientists working at the University of Lund in Sweden. Dr. Joe Hin Tjio, a native of Indonesia and a citizen of the Netherlands, and Dr. Albert Levan used Hsu's method to make a systematic count of the number of chromosomes in human cells. Every textbook agreed that human cells contained 48 chromosomes, but Tjio and Levan never found more than 46 chromosomes in human cells. It turned out that the textbooks were wrong. Earlier methods had never been accurate enough to provide a precise answer to such an apparently simple question. It is sobering to realize that something so fundamental as the chromosome number in man has been known for less than twenty years.

The chromosomes exist in pairs. Of the 23 pairs found in humans, one pair determines gender and is known as the sex chromosomes. The remaining 22 pairs are called autosomes. A female results from the presence of two X chromosomes; a male results from an X sex chromosome and a Y sex chromosome.

Dr. Murray L. Barr, working at the same time as Tjio and Levan, made a discovery that has had considerable practical as well as fundamental importance. He was examining cells under the microscope, as thousands of scientists had before him. He observed something that everyone else had missed. Some of the cells had a dark spot in the nucleus. The spot was often but not always situated at the edge of the nucleus. He realized that the dark spot was never seen in cells from males. It could only be found in female cells. Barr studied cells from males and females of many species and found the same thing. In all mammals cells from females had the same spot. This structure is now known as the Barr body. It is the second X chromosome typically found in females.

This was truly a significant discovery. For the first time a method was available for distinguishing a male from a female cell by simple microscopic examination. This is much easier than standard methods for identifying X and Y chromosomes that require a laboratory where cells can be grown in tissue culture. The Barr body method of sex determination is used to distinguish whether babies are male or female. It can also be used to tell if an unborn fetus whose cells have been obtained by amniocentesis is a boy or a girl.

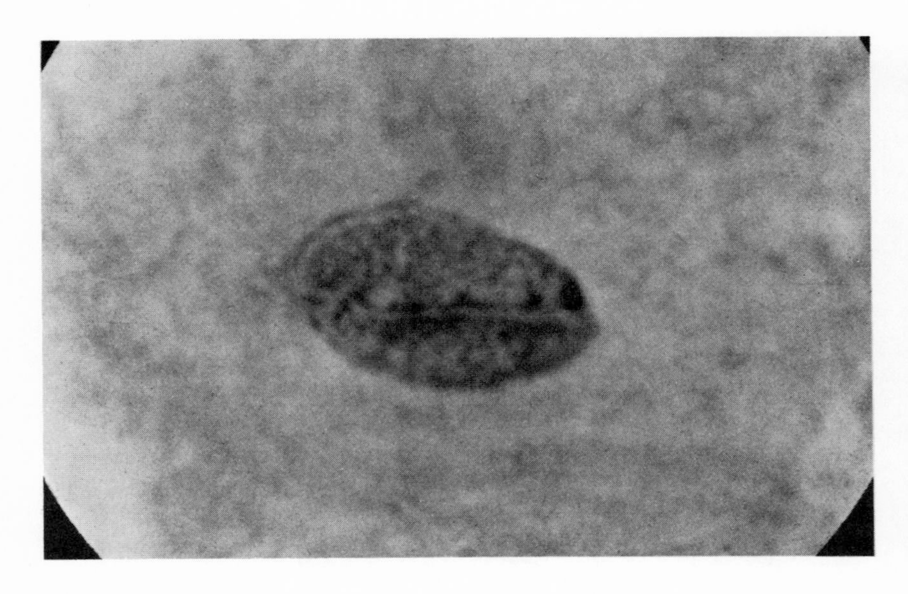

FIGURE 9. *Sex chromatin or Barr body. The cell was obtained from the mucous membrane of the mouth of a normal human female. It was stained with Giemsa stain. The dark structure in the center is the nucleus of the cell. If the nucleus were the face of a clock, the Barr body (darker structure) would be at almost three o'clock.*

Other investigators were simultaneously studying the chromosomes of human cells. They found more abnormalities than they had expected. At first these abnormalities involved the sex chromosomes. The usual complement, XX for females and XY for males, was not always evident. In some cases cell division was imperfect. So was the complement of sex chromosomes. Females with only one X chromosome are relatively common. They have a disorder known as the Turner syndrome. They are typically very short and have underdeveloped ovaries. Their cells contain no Barr body. Females with three, four, or even five X chromosomes were also discovered. These women always have one less Barr body than their number of X chromosomes. A woman with an XXX genotype has cells with two Barr bodies. Males have been detected with two Y chromosomes (XYY). Other males have been found with two or more X chromosomes (XXY).

In 1961 another critical cytogenetic discovery was made. Cytogenetics is the study of chromosomes. Dr. Jerome Lejeune, a French geneticist, was studying the chromosomes of children suffering from a form of mental retardation known as the Down syndrome, sometimes referred to as mongolism. Lejeune found that the children he studied had an extra chromosome. They had 47 chromosomes instead of the usual 46. The extra chromosome was an autosome. This was the first time that a disease had been linked to an abnormality of an autosomal chromosome. A new mechanism for the causation of genetic disease had been uncovered.

Cytogeneticists have carefully classified the chromosomes. Their method is a logical one. Pairs have been ranked by size and numbered, from the largest pair (number 1) to the smallest (number 22). In the Down syndrome the extra autosome is from chromosome pair number 21. The Down syndrome may now be subclassified as trisomy 21 because there are three of these chromosomes rather than the usual two.

While these discoveries were being made, there was progress in bringing genetic knowledge to the patient and his family. By 1955 a score of medical centers in the United States had medical genetic facilities. Today virtually every medical center, at least every university medical center, has a genetic counseling program in which patients and families can get advice. Genetic counselors are professionals who may come from a variety of disciplines. Their stock in trade is informed advice. Many early genetic counselors were people with Ph.D.s in genetics. Today most are physicians with special knowledge in genetics. Most are pediatricians or internists. Some are neurologists or obstetricians. In addition, some schools have begun training paraprofessional personnel, counselors with bachelor's or master's degrees in a specialized area of counseling who work with physicians.

All kinds of people come to see a genetic counselor. Most are parents or prospective parents who are concerned about the possibility of having a child with an inherited abnormality. In most cases the parents have already had one child with an abnormality. In others a couple is worried about having children because of a family history of abnormal births.

The genetic counselor, armed with knowledge about conditions that are inherited genetic diseases and with an understanding of Mendelian patterns of inheritance, must first establish a diagnosis in the patient. Once the condition has been identified and determined to be inherited, the genetic counselor is in a position to provide some very practical advice.

In coming to his conclusions, the genetic counselor may study family records available on either side of a marriage. This study often has its mysterious aspects. A trek to an old churchyard to study inscriptions on tombstones or a careful reading of an old family Bible may prove very rewarding. American families have been traced back to their origins in Europe, where records of families are often remarkably well kept. Once all the information is gathered, the genetic counselor sits down with the couple seeking guidance. The counselor explains the operation of Mendelian laws and then lays out the odds for having a normal or an abnormal child.

In some instances these odds are familiar ones. Often a couple who has had a child with phenylketonuria (PKU) seeks genetic counseling, and the wife is already pregnant for a second time. There is one chance in four that the fetus has PKU. More often the couple is still considering whether to have more children. The genetic counselor spells out the odds and gives advice. The decision concerning additional children is up to the couple. It is now an enlightened decision, structured by their past experience and by a precise understanding of the odds.

Counseling can be a very important factor in alleviating suffering. Through knowledge and family planning, heartache can be prevented. At the same time it should be recognized that the role of the counselor is a relatively passive one. The counselor can make a diagnosis and explain its implications for further children, but not much else. For this reason, in the recent past there have been very few genetic counselors. What has revolutionized the profession has been the development of new ways to treat genetic disease. The most dramatic of these so far is amniocentesis. This method of genetic management may seem a bit negative, since the only treatment available for positive diagnosis is therapeutic abortion. Families at risk undertake a monitored pregnancy with the idea of having normal children. They risk the possibility of an abortion along the way to this goal. Their odds are the familiar Mendelian ones of 3 to 1 for a normal child.

The possibility of doing something about genetic disease has brought many more doctors into counseling. It is now beginning to bring them more patients and families. This is only the beginning. There will soon be more effective methods of treatment and more effective methods of management. They will be applicable to an infinitely larger number of problems. The future for genetic treatment is very bright. At present many people could be helped through genetic counseling.

4. Dominant Inheritance Patterns and Autosomal Dominant Diseases

It takes a worried man to sing a worried song,
It takes a worried man to sing a worried song,
It takes a worried man to sing a worried song,
I'm worried now, but I won't be worried long . . .

Woody Guthrie was one of this country's most talented folk singers. He wrote and sang many songs as he traveled throughout the United States. None was sadder or truer than his ballad of a worried man. In his early forties, when he should have been entering the prime of life, Woody went into a long decline caused by a slow but relentless degeneration of brain tissues. In his last years he was bedridden and immobile, able to communicate only by opening and closing his eyes. He died in 1967 at the age of fifty-five. His had been a gallant but hopeless struggle.

Woody Guthrie was the victim of Huntington's disease, or Huntington's chorea. This genetic disorder is probably the best-known member of a family of diseases caused by a single autosomal dominant gene.

The patterns of inheritance for Huntington's chorea superbly but tragically illustrate Mendel's principles for the transmission of dominant traits. In a genotype where one or both of a pair of alleles is dominant (Aa or AA), the expression of the particular trait is determined by the dominant gene(s). The presence of a recessive allele, in most cases, does not significantly affect the phenotype. Eye color in humans may be determined by two alternative genes, a dominant allele (B) for brown and a recessive allele (b) for blue. The brown-eyed phenotype expresses itself with either the homozygous dominant or heterozygous genotype (BB) or (Bb). Blue eyes appear only with the homozygous genotype (bb). This familiar pattern of inheritance is both typical and normal. (However, it is now known that the inheritance of eye color may be more complex; it is possible for two blue-eyed parents to have brown-eyed children.)

Problems arise if either a dominant or recessive allele is functionally abnormal. In Tay-Sachs disease the faulty gene is recessive. Its failure to direct the synthesis of an essential enzyme is manifested only in the presence of the recessive genotype (aa). The affected individual must necessarily have received a defective gene from each parent. In Huntington's chorea and similar genetic disorders, the abnormal gene is dominant. Its phenotypic expression is guaranteed by the inheritance of a single defective gene from one parent.

Not all abnormal dominant genes produce crippling, lethal diseases. Their effects are generally much less severe than those expressed in Huntington's chorea or in the autosomal recessive diseases. One typical abnormal dominant gene expresses itself in very short fingers. The condition is known as hereditary brachydactyly and cannot be considered a disease. An affected individual survives virtually uninfluenced by his genotypic condition. Having short fingers in no way alters the ability or inclination to reproduce and bear viable offspring.

There is a simple evolutionary reason for the typically mild phenotypic expression of an abnormal dominant gene. A recessive disease that is quickly fatal can persist in the population because carriers of the defective gene are not usually affected by the disease. The gene can be conveyed from generation to generation without causing damage. It is eliminated only when it is mated with an identical recessive allele. A carrier of a dominant disease gene cannot usually escape the disorder. Any dominant disease that kills its victims quickly cannot be transmitted to future generations. There are several autosomal dominant diseases that produce death, disability, or grotesque malformations. They tend to be caused by a dominant gene that is produced by spontaneous mutation rather than inheritance.

Huntington's disease provides a compelling exception to these general principles. Its persistence generation after generation results from the late appearance or onset of its symptoms. First signs of the insidious destruction of nerve cells usually occur when patients are in their thirties or forties. Sometimes the disease does not make itself known until its victim has lived for fifty years or more. Once the disease becomes phenotypically evident, its course is relentless. Before its onset, most of its victims have already had children.

Arlo Guthrie is Woody's son. He has inherited many of his father's gifts. If you've heard or seen *Alice's Restaurant*, you know his talent is enormous. No one knows what besides genius he has inherited from his father. In the Russian roulette of Huntington's chorea, his chances are exactly even.

A genetic counselor might use the following diagram to explain these statistical odds to Arlo or any other individual at risk. The horizontal columns represent the possible genotypes of his father's reproductive cells. Fifty percent bore the dominant, disease-producing allele, (A). Fifty percent bore the normal recessive allele, (a). The vertical columns represent the single possible genotype present in his mother's reproductive cells. Since Marjorie Guthrie does not have Huntington's disease, her genotype for this trait is the normal recessive, (a).

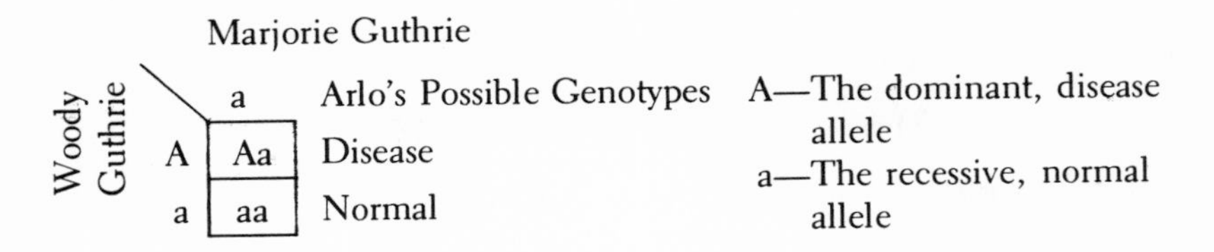

If Arlo has inherited his father's dominant allele, his genotype would be (Aa) and he would have the disease.

A single gene on one chromosome is enough to cause this disease. The corresponding gene on the other matched chromosome is normal, but its effect is so much less powerful that it might as well not be there. At reproduction half the sperm cells in an affected man, such as Woody Guthrie, or half the ova in an affected woman will contain the abnormal gene. The other 50 percent of the sperm or ova will bear the normal gene. Whether the child of such a person inherits the abnormal gene is a matter of chance. Chance decides which ovum will be fertilized and with which sperm. When a person with a dominant gene for the disease marries a normal person, such as Marjorie Guthrie, each child they produce has exactly a 50 percent chance of inheriting the abnormal gene. Each time a couple like the Guthries bears a child, that child has an even chance of having the disease. If the child inherits the dominant gene, each of his children has a fifty-fifty chance of inheriting it. So it goes, generation after generation. If fortune has been kind and the child does not inherit the lethal gene, he will be normal and the dread gene will disappear from his immediate family. Arlo's genetic fate hangs in the balance.

Such a person is faced with a number of immediate and critical choices. If he chooses to marry, he must decide whether or not to have children. If there were a method for identifying the abnormal gene for Huntington's chorea prior to the onset of disease and before the usual time for reproduction, both these decisions could be made with greater certainty. Without such a test, which is possible only in theory but has not yet been developed, the individual must consider his alternatives carefully. The choices are intensely personal and must be made by him alone.

In many cases of Huntington's chorea no choice is made. Children are often unaware that a parent has had the disorder. Since there is no specific test for the disease, it is often misdiagnosed. Many people feel a social stigma attached to a degenerative disease of the nervous system. Families often try to hide the truth from themselves, from their neighbors, and from their children. The importance of a clear-cut diagnosis in any degenerative disease cannot be overemphasized. Children should know the truth. What they don't know can hurt, and hurt for generations.

An individual who has inherited Huntington's chorea is often unaware of his or her unique genetic dilemma. The initial onset of debilitating symptoms after thirty, forty, or even fifty years of a normal, healthy, and productive life often prove poignantly baffling to the affected individual, the family, and the physician.

Larry Jackson was thirty-eight years old. He owned a small but thriving construction business in a small midwestern city. During the spring just before his thirty-ninth birthday, he was arrested on three separate occasions for drunken driving. The first time he had had a few beers. He wondered whether or not he had lost his tolerance for alcohol. The next time he had not had anything to drink. He was worried but did nothing. On the third occasion the police asked him to walk a straight line. He could not. When Larry faced the judge, his speech was, in spite of a tremendous effort at self-control, slurred and thickened. A verdict of guilty outraged his sense of justice. This anger was compounded by overhearing a clerk refer to him as "a common drunk." He justifiably wondered whether he was losing his mind.

Until his day in court Larry had done his best to conceal his bewildering symptoms from both his wife, Laura, and their two teen-age children. His efforts had not been entirely successful. Increasingly, he could detect signs of dismay, indulgence, or anger in their eyes. He saw these reactions following an awkward movement, an irritated remark, or similar abnormal behavior on his part. The responses of his colleagues and clients were more pointed, ranging from avoidance to disgust to amused tolerance. One night at dinner Larry found he could not swallow his food properly. A predictable family storm ensued. In a painful confrontation Larry learned that his family as well as friends and associates suspected the worst—acute alcoholism, drug addiction, business failure, or mental illness. Overcoming his indignation, Larry at last confessed his confusion and anxiety about his evident symptoms. His obvious sincerity allayed some of Laura's and the children's fears. At last the question had surfaced and medical assistance was sought.

Larry's physician faced a difficult diagnosis. The symptoms of different degenerative diseases of the nervous system mimic one another. Outward manifestations of Huntington's chorea are frequently confused with those of Parkinson's disease, epilepsy, multiple sclerosis, schizophrenia, and other diseases. Larry's disorder was originally recognized and identified as hereditary in 1872 by Dr. George Huntington who called the condition "hereditary chorea" after a kind of dance or choreography, because of the uncontrollable movements of the extremities it typically produced. By the time Larry sought medical attention, these abnormal movements were becoming apparent. His physical symptoms were compounded by signs of mental deterioration. He experienced periods of dullness, irritability, memory loss, and poor judgment.

Although his doctor properly recognized that Larry's signs of mental and physical deterioration were symptomatic of a neural degenerative disease, he was not able to make an absolute diagnosis of Huntington's chorea. He had no knowledge of the family history. Larry had been raised by a maiden aunt. His parents were divorced when he was a child. He went to live with his mother's sister when he was ten. He knew his mother had been committed to a hospital and died there when he was twelve. Because she was so debilitated and incomprehensible when he visited her, he had asked very few questions. His aunt had been relieved by his reticence. Although she had been aware that her sister's disease might have been hereditary, she was loath to discuss the possibilities and implications with Larry. He was such a fine, healthy boy.

When the diagnosis of Huntington's chorea was finally made, based on close physical examination and a review of genetic history, Larry slipped into a state of deep depression. He found himself at the mercy of a disease that was insidiously causing him to lose control over his mind and body. This progressive deterioration inevitably ends with death. There is no known treatment.

Larry, Laura, and the children found the diagnosis difficult to accept but agreed that its certainty was preferable to prior ignorance. The family now works at keeping Larry as comfortable as possible. The two children, Linda and George, are faced with serious questions about their future plans. Laura has joined Marjorie Guthrie's Committee to Combat Huntington's Disease. (The CCHD address is Room 2016, 250 West 57th Street, New York, N.Y. 10019.) Their aim is to bring public attention to the disease and to promote research into its cause, identification, and potential alleviation.

The Jacksons know that Huntington's chorea may affect as many as one hundred thousand people in the United States, many of whom are unaware of their condition. About 2 percent of these individuals show symptoms in childhood. Another 5 percent are not affected until after the age of sixty. In most, onset occurs between thirty and forty-five years of age. There is just enough variability in the time of onset to keep a family member who is at risk uncertain for most of his life.

Research into Huntington's chorea is in its infancy. The targets are obvious. Because a treatment of the disease seems sufficiently remote, efforts at prevention are more realistic. A way is needed to detect the causative dominant gene before it expresses itself in disease symptoms. A genetic marker like the concentration of the hex A enzyme in Tay-Sachs disease would be most useful. If it could be used to identify the abnormal gene before the age of reproduction, affected individuals might be less apt to have children. In this way some control could be exerted over the incidence of new cases. If this hypothetical marker could be used to detect the faulty gene during pregnancy, definitive control could be exerted. Affected individuals could undertake monitored pregnancies, and the critical fetal genotype could be determined before birth. They could decide to bear only normal children.

Because any individual who carries the gene for Huntington's chorea is eventually affected by the disease, the genetic counselor can ultimately determine whether or not the defective gene has been transmitted to descendant generations. This fact is useful in constructing diagnostic genealogies and in counseling offspring at risk. Such useful genetic information is not always available when dealing with other autosomal dominant diseases.

In some abnormal dominant conditions both parents of an affected child may appear phenotypically normal although the disease trait was clearly expressed in a grandparent, great-grandparent, or other forebear. The skipping of a generation seems to break the rules for dominant inheritance patterns. In theory anyone who transmits a dominant gene must carry the gene, and anyone who carries a dominant gene must express it. Nevertheless, dominant traits are known that occasionally appear to skip a generation. Scientists frankly admit they do not completely understand the underlying mechanism for this phenomenon.

Penetrance is a concept used in describing the skipping phenomenon. It refers to the ability of a gene or its phenotypic consequence to affect the person who carries it. It may be thought of as the relative power of a dominant gene to express itself in the presence of a normal recessive allele. There are probably a number of normal genes that may be more chemically powerful than others at balancing the effects of the abnormal dominant.

All degrees of penetrance have been observed. If the abnormal dominant gene invariably is expressed at least in part, it is said to be completely penetrant. The abnormal gene for Huntington's chorea is completely penetrant. If an abnormal dominant expresses itself to some degree in only a fraction of the individuals who carry the gene, the gene is said to have a reduced or partial penetrance. In those individuals who carry an abnormal dominant gene but have apparently escaped any expression of its potential effects, the gene might be called impenetrant or be said to have zero penetrance. If an apparently unaffected individual is examined closely, however, some symptom can usually be found that indicates the presence of the defective dominant, especially if the person has both a parent and a child with an abnormal dominant genetic trait.

An example of variable or partial penetrance occurs in *osteogenesis imperfecta*, a condition in which the bones are very fragile and fracture easily. This condition is caused by a dominant gene, but its penetrance is such that only about 60 percent of those carrying the gene have anything detectably wrong with their bones. This same gene causes the sclera or white of the eye to have a bluish cast, an effect that is almost completely penetrant and is phenotypically present with rare exception. The presence of the abnormal gene can be confirmed clinically by the color of the sclera, even when the disease of the bones appears to have skipped a generation.

The most rigorous application of the term penetrance refers to the presence or absence of a gene's expression or effect. Variation in the degree of expression is referred to as *variable expressivity*. Certain kindreds, or groups with a close genetic relationship such as a large family, inherit a form of minor brachydactyly or shortened index fingers. This trait is expressed because of an abnormal dominant gene. Because all individuals who inherit the gene have some form of shortened fingers, it is evident that the gene is completely penetrant. However, because the degree of shortening is variable, this completely penetrant gene is said to have variable expressivity. Some affected individuals have index fingers shortened because one bone is entirely missing and the remaining two are smaller than normal. Others with reduced expressivity for the abnormal gene have the usual complement of three bones, but the last two are shortened.

The gene for *osteogenesis imperfecta* is incompletely penetrant in producing the bone abnormality but is almost completely penetrant in producing blue sclera. Expressivity for this gene varies in one instance in relationship to the degree of bone fragility and in the second instance in relationship to the intensity of coloration of the whites of the eyes.

The concepts of penetrance and expressivity explain a great deal that would otherwise be puzzling. An explanation for how these mechanisms work would be of considerable interest and importance to geneticists. Partial penetrance and zero penetrance exist. They have been observed. What eases the expressive impact of an abnormal dominant gene is not known. The most inviting explanation is that the interaction of the dominant gene with the rest of an individual's genetic makeup is in some way mitigating. In genetic diseases in which environmental factors affect gene expressivity, this same mechanism is probably at work. The presence of sugar in the diet of a diabetic provides a familiar example. Interactions among genes have been observed in single-celled organisms, such as bacteria and yeasts. It seems reasonable to infer that degrees of interaction in a much more complex organism such as man would be much greater.

Another exceptional phenomenon observed in dominant conditions has been called *anticipation*. Anticipation is thought to occur: when a hereditary dominant disease seems to manifest itself earlier with each succeeding generation. A grandparent may be affected mildly. A parent may be affected earlier. A child may be affected even earlier and more severely.

Anticipation is more often a creation of man than nature. In any kindred that is really sizable, genetic counselors consistently report considerable variation in the time of onset of dominant disease. There is no clear evidence for the existence of anticipation. In some branches of a large kindred, children have been affected earlier than the parent; in others they have been affected later. There is a tendency to remember the former phenomenon because it has been honored with a name. Its logical opposite is not so honored. Also, anticipation may seem to occur because a disease that has occurred for generations is watched for earlier and more carefully. Many of the children of affected parents, long after they knew they had escaped a disease such as Huntington's chorea, have admitted that when younger they were often sure they had the disease. They were ever vigilant, often misinterpreting their stumblings of speech and gait. The experiences of individuals at risk for a disease with a late onset are nightmarish. Such individuals seek medical attention earlier than their parents or grandparents.

The question of increased severity with subsequent generations is explained by the tendency to avoid going to a physician unless a medical problem is overwhelming. Almost any child who is brought to the offices of a genetic counselor is apt to be severely affected by his disease. Only when the counselor begins checking family history do traces of the condition become evident in a parent or other forebear. The parent who carried the dominant gene may be the fortunate beneficiary of incomplete penetrance or expressivity and may never have required medical assistance. The severity of the child's condition tends to remain in the physician's mind, reinforcing the idea of anticipation. The opposite case, a severely affected parent with a mildly affected child, is less memorable. Most genetic counselors feel that people should not be worried about the possibility of anticipation.

Establishing dominance for a given trait can be difficult if there is variation in penetrance or expressivity. At first glance the determination of dominance seems simple. The geneticist examines a family history, looking for affected individuals in each generation. In a kindred of reasonable size there should be a 50 percent incidence of the trait in children of affected individuals. If there is a variation in penetrance or expressivity, the job is more difficult. The apparent incidence may be considerably less than 50 percent. The key in such families is usually provided by an intensive study of the family history. Both the maternal and paternal lineage must be considered. If there are signs of the trait in only one and if there are affected members in each generation of that line, the trait is almost certainly dominant. Individuals who appear to have been skipped must be examined very carefully. Usually some sign of the deleterious trait is uncovered.

Although Huntington's chorea is the best known of autosomal dominant diseases, whose symptoms first appear after the age at which a person usually has children, it is only one of a family of related genetic disorders. Many similarly inherited and expressed diseases are now being identified. Others undoubtedly await recognition. Many sociological, psychological, medical, and scientific factors cause delay in recognizing that disease symptoms may be inherited. Many afflicted individuals have an understandable reluctance to seek medical help or to involve their families in the larger issues of their disease. Physicians are primarily concerned with relieving a patient's suffering. Diagnosis or recognition of a late-onset inherited disease is made difficult by the similarity of symptoms to those expressed in infectious or environmental disorders.

Once a set of symptoms is suspected of having a genetic origin and once the reticence of the affected individuals and their kindred is overcome, a lot of work must be done. A family history must be compiled in order to determine the pattern of inheritance of the disease, to locate potentially affected individuals, to reassure those who have not or cannot inherit the disease, and to counsel those at risk who are of reproductive age. The work requires the skills of sensitive but persevering people. Interpretation of the resulting genetic history is complicated by features of variable penetrance and expressivity and requires the skills of a geneticist. Diagnosis of the disease, knowledge of its mechanisms for expression, and its prognosis require a neurologist if the disease affects the nervous system. Other specialists are needed if the disease affects other systems of the body. The kinds of cooperative effort required to bring a late-onset dominant genetic disease to light may be illustrated by the Joseph Family disease. It was initially described in the fall of 1975.

Antone Joseph was a Portuguese seaman born in the early nineteenth century on the island of Flores in the Azores. When his whaling vessel tied up in San Francisco in about 1850, he and his brother and others of the crew jumped ship and made their way north. It was the time of the Gold Rush, and they went to work in the mines of Shasta and Trinity counties. Both brothers earned enough money to go back to Flores, where they married. They brought their wives back to northern California. Antone and his wife had six children. Their children and their children's children established a kindred of ever increasing numbers. Most of them still live in the beautiful country north of San Francisco.

The good life that Antone intended for his descendants in the New World was ominously marred by a progressive disorder that resulted in his early death at the age of forty-five. Mary Grant, his eldest daughter, suffered and died from her father's disease but not before she bore fourteen children, twelve of whom survived infancy. Eight of Mary's children were felled by their mother's and grandfather's disease but not before they, too, had borne children. This tragic legacy continued to appear with each new and expanding generation.

The family scourge was variously explained through superstition, half-truths, and folklore. Some had suggested that female members of the family had "strong genes" and would not transmit the disease. Others thought the disease was filtering itself out of existence. Others believed it was caused by syphilis. Most members of the kindred knew about the disease and were anxious about it, yet for a host of reasons they did not discuss it openly. Its fateful presence could not be hidden. When the first symptoms of the disease appeared, the family knew another of its members would follow the inexorable pattern. Simple problems with balance would be succeeded by the need to use a cane, a walker, and then a wheelchair. Speech would become slurred, thick, and indistinct. The fine coordination required for precise hand movements would deteriorate, and muscle stiffness, particularly in the legs, would increase. In time swallowing and the control of saliva and other secretions would be impaired. Death from pneumonia or a similar respiratory disease would follow.

The familial bond of public silence was broken by a courageous individual, Mrs. Rosemary Silva. She had seen a magazine article describing our work on an autosomal dominant genetic disease in a midwestern family. The pattern was all too familiar. At the time she read the article, her brother was dying of the family disease. Their father had died of it. Since she knew her brother was beyond hope, she did not seek assistance. He died when he was thirty-nine. Mrs. Silva continued to carry a copy of the article in her purse for almost three years. During that time her brother's three children had married and two had infant sons. These young people brought her worries into sharp focus. She decided that it was time "to bring all of this into the open."

Mrs. Silva wrote to the National Genetics Foundation in New York and asked for help. Ruth Y. Berini, executive director of the foundation, coordinates requests for genetic counseling and assistance with genetic referral centers throughout the country. Ruth is a woman of enormous compassion, energy, competence, and sensitivity. On receipt of Mrs. Silva's letter, she took immediate action based on three considerations apparent to one skilled in these matters. The family needed immediate assistance. The disease itself was probably not treatable with present techniques and would have to be approached through genetic counseling. Because of the kindred's size, assistance would have to be provided in California. Ruth communicated with the same geneticist and neurologist who had worked effectively with the midwestern family. We were pleased to volunteer our services.

The next months were filled with the painstaking assembly of essential information. Most of this spadework was done by Mrs. Silva working with Ruth and her staff. Mrs. Silva found family members, told them what she had in mind, sought out old records, and interested her many relatives in coming together for help. Through a masterful job of keeping records straight, a detailed pedigree of the family was prepared by Carolyn Bay of the University of California San Diego and Elinor Frank of the foundation. It began with Antone Joseph.

All members of the team examined both the pedigree and ancillary evidence with care. The gene that originally caused Antone Joseph's disease could have been inherited or could have arisen through spontaneous mutation. The fact that the disease had since been inherited by descendants was scientifically established. In the seven succeeding generations a clear pattern was determined for the inheritance of a completely penetrant autosomal dominant gene. The predicted 50 percent occurrence of the disease was exactly confirmed in the offspring of affected parents. This statistical precision was to be expected in so large a family. We were ready to take our findings to the family (Figure 10).

The gathering of the kindred was scheduled for a weekend in September

1975. Nearly one hundred of Antone Joseph's descendants gathered at the Children's Hospital of Oakland, California. Some of those who stayed away were bedridden with the disease. Those who came traveled from as far as Washington, Oregon, and Nevada. Although two-thirds of them lived in northern California, many had never before met.

Friday we began assembling the team in the Bay area. Dr. Roger Rosenberg, a member of the team, was chairman of the department of neurology at the University of Texas–Southwestern Medical School in Dallas. Carolyn Bay and I met him in the San Francisco airport. None of us had ever seen a patient with this disorder. Soon we were to examine more of them than anyone had ever seen. We were met at the airport by Mrs. Elizabeth Munro, a member of the family and a nurse, and she drove us to Petaluma, where we saw some family members who were too sick to attend the reunion in Oakland.

We began in this way to learn about the disease, about the subtleties of the neurological examination, and about how it affects the lives of its victims. Friday night Eileen O'Farrell Borgwardt, who has done most of the artwork for this book, drove over from Davis with the pedigree she had drawn in beautiful order so we could use it in working with family members. It covered all of one wall in the clinic. We spent all day Saturday examining people, obtaining specimens, and gathering data. We were at it from early in the morning until late at night.

By Sunday morning we had learned all we were going to learn about the disease that weekend, and we were ready to talk to the family members. Extensive neurological examination of those family members with the disease and those who were at risk because a parent had had the disease involved about forty people. Ten were found to have the disease; one may be expressing early clinical symptoms; and twenty-six others—children of parents who have or had the disease—were at risk.

Dr. Rosenberg had concluded that the problem is a striato-nigral degeneration. This means that brain cells die out in very specific areas of the brain, called the *corpus striatum* and *substrantia nigra*, which lie deep within the brain tissue. When the cells die, the patient has problems making his muscles behave properly. Coordination and fine movements become impaired. Destruction of cells in these areas of the brain occasionally had been reported in the medical literature, but had never been linked with an inherited disease. The mechanism by which the faulty gene produces nerve cell deterioration is unknown. The typical course of the disease was confirmed—beginning with mild symptoms of disequilibrium and ending with death from respiratory disease. Many affected individuals have died within ten years of onset in their early thirties. In some branches of the family symptoms have begun as early as the sixteenth year; in others as late as the forty-first. There is no known treatment.

We found working with this family a profoundly moving experience. The

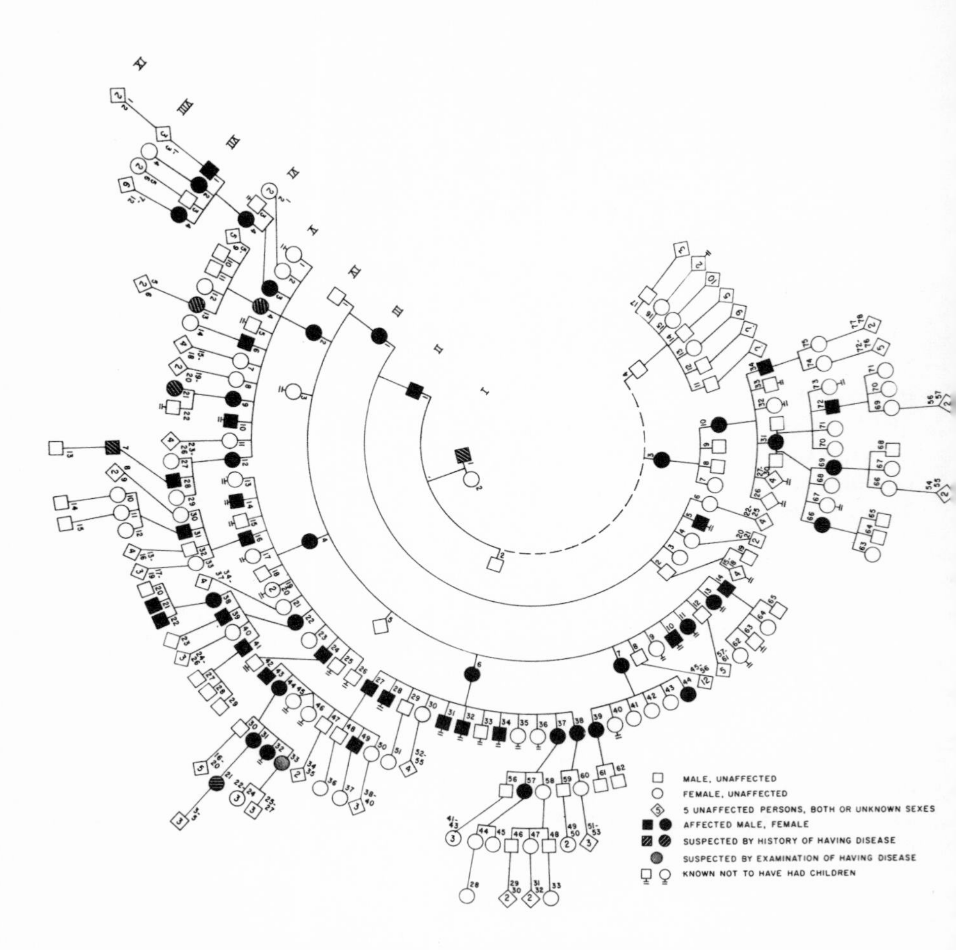

FIGURE 10. *Pedigree of a large family with a dominantly inherited striato-nigral degeneration. Patients with the disease are illustrated by the black squares for males and circles for females. With each generation the number of affected individuals increases. In branches of the family in which the disease is not being transmitted the numbers of unaffected children are indicated by numerals within a diamond.*

family in turn found it reassuring to talk about their disease as a distinct entity and to learn some definite expectations about its character. One of the problems in the past had been with the diagnosis. Many affected members were thought to have multiple sclerosis, Friedrich's ataxia, or congenital syphilis. We believed the disorder was unique and therefore called it the Joseph disease. The family had found it difficult to live with the various conflicting or socially unacceptable explanations for the disease. Elmer Joseph reported, "I had to wait until I was seventy-two to find out what was wrong in my family." Doris

Nusbaum, who has the disease, has a thick, husky voice. She first knew she had the disease when her voice changed. She said, "I couldn't scream anymore." She went on to describe a patient's problems in an uncomprehending world. "I am so tired of having the cops pick me up. They always think I am drunk or a dope addict. I can't convince them I'm sick." Even some of the family members had suspected that Doris with her elegant cane might be putting them on. She was not.

Vincent McKeown had sought a good deal of advice about family planning because he had a parent with the disease. He sought an examination by a neurologist before he married. The examination was negative, and the doctor reassured him. Not entirely satisfied, Vincent sought the advice of a priest, who told him to go ahead and have children. The priest compared Vincent's situation to that of any man about to cross the street. In all probability he would reach the other side. The possibility of being hit by an automobile was remote. Vincent later wrote, "What he didn't realize was that I was already in the middle of the street." Just knowing that the disease does not skip generations provided welcome relief for many family members whose parents had safely passed the age of onset. They will not have to live in fear for themselves or their children. Many thought they might be susceptible to the disease simply because they were related, no matter how remotely, to someone who was affected. For these people there is no chance they could have inherited the disorder.

Carolyn Allekna, who was eighteen, observed: "This is the first time I've ever seen my relatives sit and talk about our disease. My father split from home when he was fifteen because people were dropping dead all around. When I was little, my family would say the disease skips generations. They also said it was filtering out. But I'm too analytical to believe that."

The Donahue brothers, Dennis, Kerry, and Rick, were practically orphans. Their mother had developed the family disease when they were children. Their father responded by leaving town. When their mother could no longer care for them, they were placed in foster homes. She died three years before the study began. During the course of the weekend Rick and Kerry had to be told that they had the disease. For Kerry at twenty-one this was not a surprise. His symptoms were far advanced. Although not previously diagnosed, signs of the disease had been evident since he was sixteen. Rick at twenty was something else. No one, except possibly Rick, himself, had previously suspected he had the disease. When we gave him the news, he said as he walked out of the hospital, "It was heavy, it really was." We were worried he might not return the next day but he did. He explained, "I had to leave and just walk." At the end of the session he still felt that he probably would marry and have children. His older brother, Dennis, is twenty-three. The results of his neurological examination were perfectly normal. In view of the very early pattern of onset in his brothers, he is probably free from the disease though it is too early to be certain.

He has a steady girl whom he met in an institution for homeless teenagers. She attended the session. They have decided never to have children.

The variable times of disease onset in this family makes family planning difficult. The disease could be eliminated only if all those at risk, that is, all those with an affected parent, decided to have no children. This kind of decision is, indeed, "heavy" and must be theirs to make.

Physicians, even geneticists, often wonder what they can do for a family like the Josephs. It is easier for them to work with disorders in which treatment is curative. Today the only viable alternative for the Josephs is preventive. The disease could be wiped out in a generation with the cooperation of the entire family. It cannot be done in one counseling session. Continuous reinforcement is necessary. Because there is an enormous reserve of strength and determination in the Joseph family, one can dare to be optimistic. Among its members are individuals who would make ideal genetic counselors. They possibly might galvanize their relatives into working together for a common cause. It could work.

5.
Autosomal Recessive Inheritance and Its Hidden Defects

The couple is young. They are healthy. They are the proud parents of a happy, vigorous child. The most careful review of medical histories in both families turns up nothing abnormal. They have another baby. Lightning strikes. Their second child is afflicted with a crippling disease. In the midst of their grief and bewilderment they find the child's disorder is inherited. They both carry abnormal genes responsible for their child's condition. This knowledge engenders an insidious sense of guilt and responsibility in both of them. They have caused their child's suffering. They hear the phrase "autosomal recessive disease" without really understanding. They are told all future children run a high risk of having the same disease. In an incomprehensible moment they have been transformed from a happy married couple into a family unit marked by an inescapable stigma.

People in this situation easily believe they are different from everyone else. They may feel they have been singled out or that they are being punished by divine powers. Nothing could be further from the truth. Except for an unfortunate twist of fate, the couple who bears a child with an autosomal recessive disease is no different from any other. Hidden diseases can appear in any family without warning. They are the consequence of recessive, abnormal genes that everyone carries. Defective genes are part of the price paid for being human and for being part of the evolutionary chain of life. The element of blind luck involves the choice of a marriage partner. If by chance two people marry who both carry an abnormal gene for the same trait, fortune has indeed been unkind. Nearly all defective genes are very rare. The disorders they produce are even rarer. Yet the statistical misfortune that unites two defective genes to produce disease can happen to anyone.

A parallel might be drawn between the human body and a spacecraft. Both are designed for a long and independent voyage. Built into the original design of both vehicles are master programs that control the functioning of every component. These programs exist in duplicate. Should one version of a program prove faulty or inappropriate, there is a second program available to intervene and direct proper functioning.

The only time there is a real problem is when both of the duplicate programs are defective. Because a spacecraft must be compact, it carries no spare parts. If a defect in the identical programs is minor, the craft most likely can continue its voyage. If a defect in these identical programs is major, the spacecraft will be lost. This is a relatively remote possibility since the master programs have been naturally selected and repeatedly tested for ruggedness and reliability.

Nature has selected compactness as a desirable trait in the human vehicle. Vital organs such as the heart, liver, and brain do not come in duplicate. The master genetic programs that direct their operation do. The alternative master programs are found in the genetic material with its two full sets of chromosomes and two full sets of genes. Since one alternative set of chromosomes with its genes is inherited from a father and another alternative set from a mother, a child is equipped with a margin for genetic error or malfunction.

The margin for error is explained by the functioning of Mendel's principles for the inheritance of dominant and recessive traits. Although Mendel described traits in pea plants and our description is for characteristics in humans, the fundamental patterns are the same. The classical principles are again illustrated with the familiar inheritance patterns for brown or blue eyes. The dominant gene (B) is specific for the brown-eyed trait. The recessive allele (b) is specific for the blue-eyed trait. Both alleles and their phenotypic expression are perfectly normal and viable alternatives. For the blue-eyed trait to be expressed, an individual must inherit two recessive alleles (bb), one from each parent. If either of the parental genotypes is homozygous dominant (BB), even if the other's genotype is homozygous recessive (bb), none of the offspring will be blue-eyed. Each child will express the brown-eyed characteristic because of the presence of at least one dominant allele (B). If both parents are brown-eyed but heterozygous (Bb), one-quarter of their offspring may be expected to have the homozygous dominant genotype (BB), one-half may be expected to have the heterozygous genotype (Bb), and one-quarter may be expected to have the homozygous recessive genotype (bb). The last will be blue-eyed. Because the presence of a single dominant gene is sufficient to express the dominant phenotype, three-quarters of the offspring will be brown-eyed and one-quarter will be blue-eyed.

These fundamental patterns of inheritance are repeated thousands of times in determining the thousands of traits that characterize a single individual. In the case of eye color both the dominant and recessive alleles and their phenotypic expressions are perfectly functional. So are the vast majority of dominant and recessive alleles. They code for variations, neither of which is abnormal. They have been naturally selected for their ruggedness and reliability on a long voyage.

The effects of inheriting an abnormal or defective dominant gene have been demonstrated in various diseases and conditions. If the degree of aberration is very great, a fetus usually does not survive pregnancy and is spontaneously aborted. If the degree of abnormality is minor, the phenotypic results tend to be as insignificant as the shortened fingers associated with brachydactyly. Many levels of abnormality occur between these extremes, but generally autosomal dominant diseases tend to be less severe than autosomal recessive diseases.

When an individual inherits two abnormal recessive genes, the margin for error breaks down, and the result is a clinical disease. Scientists predict that every man, woman, and child carries from five to ten potentially fatal recessive genes out of an estimated hundred thousand genes contained in each cell. This complement of lethal genes is known as the *genetic load*, an irreducible potential for genetic disease.

Just as the existence of two alternative master programs protects a spacecraft, the presence of two sets of chromosomes and genes—one complete set from each parent—tends to protect the individual against the expression of an often lethal autosomal recessive disease. A perfectly healthy individual may carry a defective recessive gene without knowledge or impairment because he is completely protected by a normal dominant allele. If this individual marries another healthy individual with a similar genotype, some of their children may not be so fortunate.

The system is not perfect. Some people do inherit two abnormal recessive genes and suffer from a genetic disease. Sometimes the disease is severe enough to make normal life impossible. Sometimes it is severe enough to kill. At present the occurrence of autosomal recessive conditions is in most cases unavoidable because the recessive genes are hidden in parents protected by a normal dominant allele. The sudden expression of an autosomal recessive disease is like a bolt from the blue.

There are some things science can do to help. Medical geneticists can now identify persons who carry certain recessive genes before they are expressed in offspring. In these cases it is possible to tell whether two persons who intend to marry have the same harmful, hidden gene. When both parents are known to carry a lethal gene, pregnancies can be monitored by amniocentesis. The unborn child with two inherited abnormal recessive genes can be identified in time for the parents to decide whether to terminate or continue a pregnancy. Early diagnosis and treatment can permit a normal life for some persons born with autosomal recessive conditions. With knowledge and counseling, families with a child affected by an autosomal recessive disease can make the most enlightened decisions about future pregnancies.

The inheritance of recessive genetic disease in people follows the patterns described by Mendel in his classic work with garden peas. The same well-established Mendelian numbers apply in human genetics. If a husband and wife are both perfectly healthy people who carry the same abnormal recessive gene, their individual genotypes are identical (Aa) for a given trait. In each pregnancy there is one chance in four that the child they produce will inherit both abnormal genes and suffer from the genetic disease caused by two recessive genes (aa). There is also one chance in four that the child will inherit a normal gene from each parent. The child will then be normal (AA). There are two chances in four that the child will inherit one normal gene (A) and one abnormal gene (a) and thus become a carrier (Aa). A carrier is a perfectly healthy individual. He or she possesses an unknown, hidden potential for producing genetic disease among future generations. Because the presence of a single normal and dominant allele ensures normal phenotypic expression, the chances are three in four that children of this and every future mating will be entirely healthy. The chances are one in four that a child will have the disease specified by the abnormal gene.

Possible genotypes for the ova, or eggs

Possible genotypes for sperm	A	a
A	AA Healthy	Aa Healthy Carrier
a	Aa Healthy Carrier	aa Affected

A—The dominant normal allele
a—The disease-producing recessive allele
AA—The homozygous dominant; healthy
Aa—The heterozygous; healthy but a carrier
aa—The homozygous recessive; affected with the disease

Another way of describing this pattern of inheritance is shown in Figure 11.

Because of the normal dominant safety factor, a husband and wife who carry the same recessive abnormal gene have a 25 percent risk of bearing an affected child with *each* pregnancy. It is essential to realize that this sentence means exactly what it says. Misinterpretation of genetic information is easy and can cause personal tragedy. Some people have thought a 25 percent risk for recessive disease means that one child in four of such a marriage will be affected while the other three will escape the disease. They have assumed that since they have borne one affected child, their dues have been paid. Nature does not work that way. Nothing could be further from reality. A family reasoning in this fashion could easily bear four affected children.

The 25 percent risk applies to each pregnancy. A couple who has borne one affected child has suffered from unfortunate odds for that particular pregnancy. Those same odds for health or disease hold true for each succeeding pregnancy. Each pregnancy is like an independent toss of the dice. Each is unaffected by

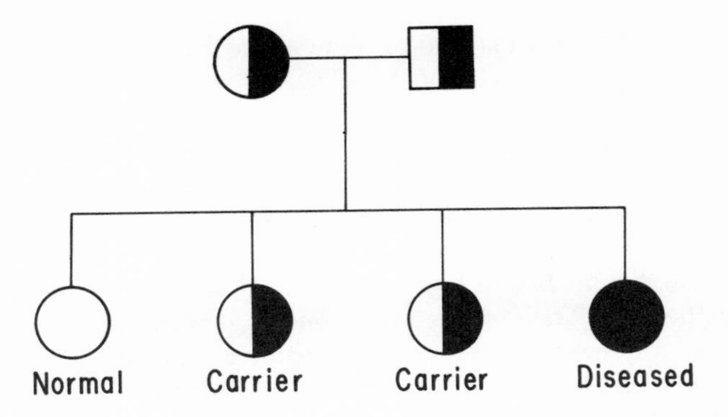

FIGURE 11. *Pedigree illustrating recessive inheritance in man. The affected individual at the lower right is illustrated by the shaded circle. In this family all the children were drawn as girls. They could have been all boys or any mixture. Inheritance patterns here occur similarly for both sexes. The parents, at the top, were heterozygous carriers, as indicated by the half-shaded circle and square. The other children included one normal and two carriers. This is the standard proportion of possibilities for such a mating.*

the outcome of previous tosses. Gamblers and geneticists know that "chance has no memory." The probabilities remain the same for each and every child.

In the case of a couple who both carry the same recessive gene, the physical reality is that the chromosomes are separately shuffled by nature in each pregnancy. It is a matter of pure chance whether the fertilized egg receives two normal genes, two abnormal genes, or one of each. Where fertilization is random and two kinds of genotype exist for each parental sex cell, the following combinations are equally probable:

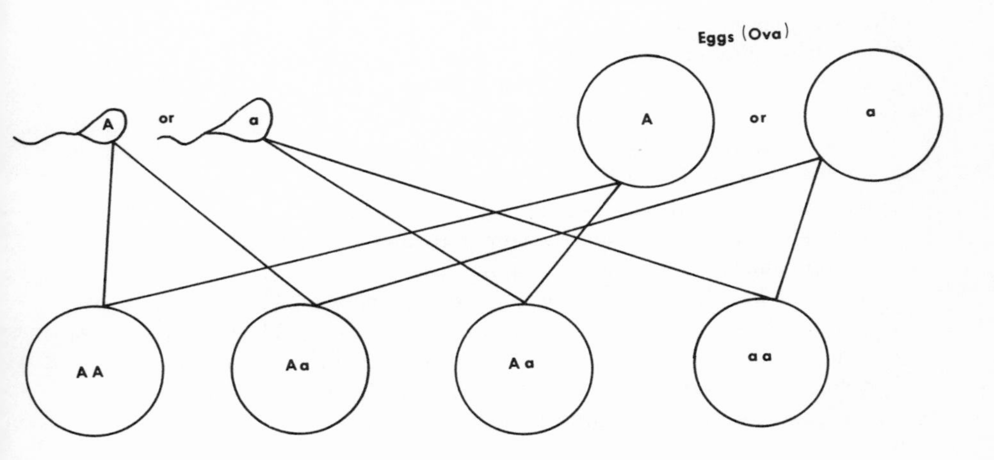

Some couples like this may have several affected children; others may have none at all.

Mr. and Mrs. Pierce lived on Long Island in New York. They had a three-year-old boy with the Hurler syndrome. The Hurler syndrome is one of a family of mucopolysaccharide storage disorders. Mucopolysaccharides are large sugar molecules. They are normally present in all cells, and they provide the material that holds cells together. Mucopolysaccharides are continuously made in the body. Their production is controlled by specific enzymes that are themselves synthesized according to the directions of specific genes. Too great a buildup of these mucopolysaccharides is prevented by the activity of distinctly different genes and enzymes. The second set of enzymes break down mucopolysaccharide molecules into waste products that can be eliminated from the body. A fine balance is normally maintained. In individuals with the Hurler syndrome the gene controlling an enzyme that degrades mucopolysaccharides is faulty. It is an autosomal recessive gene.

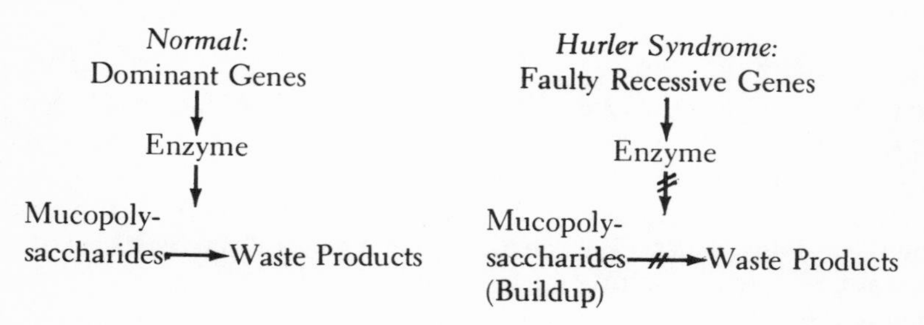

Children with defects in enzymes responsible for mucopolysaccharide breakdown store excess quantities throughout the body. Storage in the tissues of the face gives people with this disease coarse, heavy features. Storage in the bones causes them to be misshapen. The joints become stiff, the spine beaked, and the hands claw-like. The liver and spleen enlarge greatly. Storage in the heart and blood vessels leads to early death, often by five to ten years of age. Storage in the brain causes defective mental development. Hurler children are severely retarded. Mucopolysaccharides are also deposited in the cornea of the eyes, causing poor vision. The disease is heartrending.

When Mrs. Pierce became pregnant again, all the resources for amniocentesis and prenatal diagnosis were at hand. Her doctor discussed them with Mrs. Pierce, but for religious reasons the couple simply could not consider the possibility of abortion. They turned down amniocentesis. The pregnancy went to term, and they had a little girl. The test immediately showed that she, too, had the Hurler syndrome. She went on to develop all the signs of the disease, just as her brother had. Lightning may strike twice.

Not all recessive genes are as hidden as they once were. Exposure of these silent factors is becoming possible as genetics begins to be studied on a molecular level. Because this kind of research is still in its infancy, the chemistry of many defective recessive genes remains obscure. For those genes whose abnormal functioning has been revealed, we can test for the presence of an abnormal molecule or a normal molecule in abnormal concentration.

The messages contained in genes are expressed through proteins. Some of these proteins are enzymes, which are essential to the normal functioning of the body. Enzymes must be present for the thousands of chemical reactions that enable the cells of the body to perform their necessary tasks: metabolize food, utilize oxygen, dispose of waste material, and so on. An abnormal gene causes trouble by producing an abnormal protein. It is when the protein is part of an enzyme that we are best able to see the influence of an abnormal gene.

In alkaptonuria, urine turns black on exposure to light or air. In early adult life patients with this disease develop serious arthritis. Archibald E. Garrod recognized that alkaptonuria is caused by a recessive gene. He postulated that this gene produces an abnormal enzyme. It is now known that the enzyme in question is homogentisic acid oxidase. Its job is to break down homogentisic acid, a molecule normally synthesized in the body. In alkaptonuria, the faulty enzyme cannot do its job. Large amounts of homogentisic acid accumulate in the body. Some of the excess spills over into the urine. Exposed to light and air, the molecule turns black, giving the urine its characteristic appearance. Homogentisic acid that remains in the body accumulates in cartilage, eventually causing arthritis and stiffened joints. Homogentisic acid oxidase, the enzyme, is present only in liver cells. Enzyme assays, analysis of liver tissue obtained by biopsy, from patients with alkaptonuria show essentially no homogentisic acid oxidase activity. When the livers of parents of affected patients are biopsied and assayed for enzyme activity, they are found to contain approximately half the usual amount of enzyme.

The same pattern is true of Tay-Sachs disease. This disorder is caused by an abnormal structuring of the hexosaminidase A enzyme because of a faulty autosomal recessive gene. The presence of the hex A enzyme is easier to measure than homogentisic acid oxidase because it is present in every cell of the body. It can be assayed by testing the blood. Patients who have Tay-Sachs disease show virtually no hex A activity. Their parents have enzyme activities about halfway between those of normal individuals and those of patients with the disease.

This pattern of enzyme activity is explained by the functioning of each allele in an individual's genotype. Each parent of an affected child is heterozygous (Aa) for the trait in question. His or her dominant allele (A) is normal and directs the synthesis of a certain amount of normal enzyme. The amount is about half the usual amount because equal amounts are specified by each gene in a homozygous, normal individual (AA). The recessive allele is faulty. It usually produces a different protein that will not work as an enzyme. The child who inherits two faulty recessive genes, one from each parental carrier, is a homozygous recessive (aa). Lacking any normal gene for the needed protein, this child exhibits none of the requisite enzyme. Lack of the enzyme produces the disease.

In some diseases the abnormal protein can be distinguished from the normal by using a technique known as electrophoresis. In this process two similar molecules exposed to an electric field can be identified according to highly specific patterns of movement. Electrophoresis is useful in tracing the hereditary patterns of sickle cell anemia. In this and other disorders, the heterozygote (Aa) can be shown to produce two quite different proteins. One might wonder why the heterozygote, with only half the normal enzyme concentration and activity, is not half sick. The answer lies in the enormous efficiency of enzymes. Even a concentration of much less than half would be enough to prevent any expression of abnormality. Only when an individual inherits two recessive genes that both code for an inactive protein does an enzyme deficiency become evident.

These inborn errors of metabolism are rare recessive diseases. Since the body is such a complicated biochemical machine, the possible number of different metabolic errors is great. New enzyme abnormalities are being discovered at an accelerating rate. If the present rate of discovery continues, there will be information about more than twelve thousand specific enzyme deficiencies by the year 2009—exactly one hundred years after Garrod first published his findings in book form.

When scientists examine a recessive abnormality, they often find they are looking at a family of abnormalities all related by the fact that they involve different degrees of function for the same enzyme. The variation may be qualitative or quantitative. This is called genetic polymorphism. A family of variant or mutant genes, often at the same point on a chromosome, is specific for a family of different enzyme proteins. Each enzyme differs fundamentally from the others by only one amino acid in the long chain of amino acids that makes up the proteins. The different enzyme proteins may have different levels of chemical activity. Medical geneticists may see patients with very different disease symptoms, depending on the enzyme's level of activity. The inborn errors of metabolism have shown the fundamental mechanism by which all recessive diseases must act. Each recessive gene codes for an abnormal protein. The affected patient has two of these. His or her heterozygous parent has one.

There is an important statistical question that arises with autosomal recessive conditions. What are the odds that two people who have the same abnormal recessive gene will meet and marry? The answer to the question usually depends on the frequency or occurrence of the gene in the general population.

Most abnormal recessive genes are quite rare. The possibility of two of them meeting at fertilization would be remote if mating patterns involved an equal possibility of marriage among all peoples of the world. The idealized model for the chance commingling of all human genes is called *random mating*. For most people, mating is not random. People meet and marry others from the same geographic area. They often marry only those of the same religion or of the same ethnic group. Some populations are physically and genetically isolated. Such groups are described as *isolates*. They include people living on an island who intermarry only among themselves. Another group of isolates are the Amish, who by only marrying other Amish illustrate a social genetic isolation rather than one that is geographic. The smaller the group in which mating occurs, the less random is the coupling of genes and chromosomes and the greater is the likelihood that two parents will share a common defective gene and produce children with autosomal recessive diseases.

The degree of randomness in mating patterns is relevant to what plant and animal breeders describe as *hybrid vigor*. Plant or animal organisms of different strains or genetic heritage, if crossbred, will produce offspring that tend to be hardier than the offspring of organisms from the same strain. This is understandable because closely related organisms have a greater likelihood of carrying the same recessive abnormal genes. Their offspring run a higher risk of inheriting a lethal or injurious recessive abnormality. The chances of such an abnormality are much smaller when the parents come from different genetic backgrounds.

It is common to find genetic diseases that are limited almost entirely to specific ethnic groups. Tay-Sachs disease occurs almost exclusively in Ashkenazic Jews whose parents came from eastern Europe. Sickle cell anemia in America occurs almost exclusively among blacks. Thalassemia, a chronic hemolytic anemia, is found in persons whose ancestors came from Italy, Greece, and other countries around the Mediterranean, which the ancient Greeks called Thalassa. A peculiar type of dwarfism that is accompanied by polydactyly is found almost entirely in an isolate of the Amish of Pennsylvania. This extra-fingered condition has been traced to three couples who came to America before 1770. Such single-gene defects tend to concentrate in isolated populations. The smaller the gene pool in which matings occur, the greater the likelihood that two abnormal genes will unite and produce a disease.

The fact that specific autosomal recessive conditions tend to concentrate among specific ethnic groups is useful in one way. It allows medical geneticists to focus their efforts on a fixed, limited, and well-identified target. Most of the hundreds of autosomal recessive conditions are extremely rare. When one of them occurs, a good deal of detective work may be needed in identifying the disease as genetic. More work is required in establishing its pattern of inheritance. Because autosomal recessive conditions are both rare and complex, there is often difficulty marshaling enough resources to master the problem.

A patient with Tay-Sachs disease in a family of Ashkenazim provides the medical geneticist with a finite number of genetically related subjects with whom to work. The knowledge that certain diseases are found in certain groups with close ties and patterns of communication, sympathy, and understanding facilitates preventive medicine. It may be possible to test for carriers of an abnormal gene if not everyone in the entire population must be tested. It is possible to test or screen for almost any genetic disease if the identifying test is sufficiently inexpensive and simple. At present, screening a random population for a random genetic disease is, as Albert Einstein once remarked in a different context, "like shooting at birds in the dark in a region where there are few birds." A specific target population ensures that there are birds.

The logical extrapolation of this argument is a consideration of inbreeding. The worst step anyone can take toward increasing chances that both parents will carry the same rare autosomal recessive gene is to marry within a family. Intermarriage is known as consanguinity.

Most human societies have placed strong social and sometimes legal impediments against inbreeding. The strongest penalties are usually reserved for incest. This makes excellent genetic sense. An incestuous couple has the highest probability of bearing the same abnormal recessive genes. They run the highest risk of having children with genetic disease. Frequent incestuous breeding could be disastrous for a society.

Many recessive genes are so rare that they occur only in a single family group. Once mutation has produced an abnormal autosomal recessive gene in an individual, that recessive tends to be transmitted from generation to generation. It becomes part of the genetic load and usually is not observed because it has little chance for phenotypic expression through coupling with an identical allele. If members of the family group, first or second cousins, for instance, marry and bear children, their children are likely to inherit two abnormal recessives. Then the potential disease becomes a reality. Sometimes the first clue that a new or rare disease is genetic and of an autosomal recessive nature is the presence of consanguinity within the families of affected individuals.

What applies to families applies to larger and more loosely related communities like the Amish, as well as to other ethnic groups. Some rare genes are found only in a single family. Some are found almost exclusively in one ethnic group. In some disorders there is a *founder effect*. If a group is small enough, its origins might be traced to a handful of first fathers and mothers. If one of these founders carried an unusual and defective gene, the incidence of that gene would be abnormally high after several generations. If marriage occurred commonly within the group, the likelihood of two parents having the abnormal founder gene would be much greater than if mating were randomly distributed through the general population.

The genetic problem inherent in marrying within a family is what happens to the risk of bearing children with rare recessive disease. I have encountered people contemplating marriage with a first cousin or a second cousin who have been aware that genetic problems were possible. They had carefully examined family histories for both sets of parents. Finding nothing to indicate the presence of genetic disease, they thought they could marry and produce offspring with impunity. For the kinds of risks involved with consanguinity the history of the family is irrelevant. A search of genetic histories is useful only for diseases that have been expressed and offer clear warning. These tend to be diseases caused by dominant genes, occasionally by genes on the X chromosomes, and more rarely by common recessives. It is the rare recessives, the ones that seem to strike from the blue, that are not usually revealed in a family's history. Everyone can be sure that he or she carries some defective genes for some insidious recessive disease.

It is impossible to overemphasize the problems people have in accepting the hidden dangers of recessive inheritance when they themselves are involved. I have talked with very intelligent, highly educated parents who understood perfectly the explanations, diagrams, and pedigrees for recessive inheritance. Then one or the other would break down and say, "But no one in my family ever had anything like this" or "I could understand it if someone in my family had been retarded" or something similar. The hiddenness of defective recessive genes makes the potential for disease hard to grasp on a personal, emotional level.

Consanguinity is the most powerful force for revealing hidden recessive genes. The mathematics of risk in intermarriage have been carefully determined and are illustrated in Figure 12. In general a parent transmits half of his or her chromosomes to each child in a random fashion. A parent and child share half their genes. One-half of a child's genes are exactly duplicated copies of one-half of the genes found in each parent. When this child has children, he transmits half of his genes to each of his children. Each grandchild has one-fourth of the genes of the original grandparent. With each generation the figure is halved. A great-grandchild and his great-grandparent have one-eighth of the same genes. The numbers can be easily kept in mind because everybody has two parents, four grandparents, and eight great-grandparents. These are the proportions of genes a person has in common with these ancestors. Siblings predictably share one-half of their genes.

Let us examine the pedigree in Figure 12. In generation II, II_2 and II_3 are sisters. Their children, in generation III, are first cousins. They reasonably can be expected to have one-eighth of their genes in common. It is statistically probable that the two sisters have one-half of their genes in common. Each of them has transmitted half of her genes to each of her children. The rule is simple; with each succeeding generation the numbers are halved. In the next generation, IV_1 and IV_2 are second cousins. It is probable that they have one-thirty-second of their genes in common. Third cousins predictably duplicate one of every 128 genes.

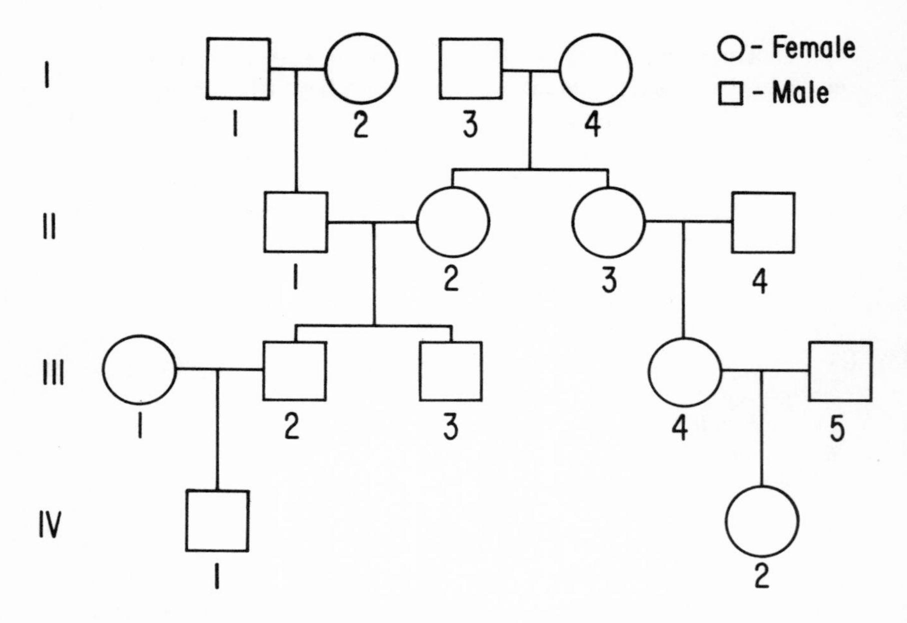

FIGURE 12. *Pedigree of a family. The generations are specified by roman numerals (I–IV) and individuals in each generation by arabic numbers (1–5). A marriage is indicated by the direct horizontal line between individuals and children descending from them in a vertical line. The illustration is discussed in the text in terms of how a consanguineous marriage, for example between III_3 and III_4, might take place, or one between the second cousins, IV_1 and IV_2.*

If III_3 and III_4 had considered getting married, possibly before III_4 met and married III_5, theirs would have been a first-cousin marriage. Their mothers were sisters. If III_3 carried a single recessive gene for albinism, a condition phenotypically expressed by a lack of pigmentation, this is what could have happened. Possibly he was, and generations before him had been, heterozygous (Aa) for this recessive gene. For generations no one would have been aware that this recessive gene even existed. Its phenotypic expression with the usual characteristics of milk-white skin, fine white hair, and pink eyes would have been impossible because of the presence of a normal dominant allele. Since the gene for albinism is found on an autosome, he might have inherited it from either his mother or his father. The chance it was from his mother is exactly one-half. If his mother were heterozygous (Aa), the chance that her sister was also heterozygous is one-half. The combined chance then is one-quarter, the product of the two individual probabilities. The possibility that II_3 had transmitted this gene to her daughter III_2 is again one-half. The chance that the two first cousins who contemplated marriage both bore the gene for albinism is 1 in 8. If each possessed one defective allele for albinism and if they married each other, the possibility they would bear an albino child would be 1 in 4. The product of these two probabilities of 1 in 4 and 1 in 8 would represent an overall risk of 1 in 32 that a child from this mating would be an albino (aa). If the incidence of phenotypic albinism in the general population were 1 in 10,000, although the real figure is smaller than that, 1 person in 50 would be a heterozygous carrier for the gene. The possibility that anyone was a heterozygote would be 1 in 50. The frequency of predictable marriages between heterozygotes would logically be the product of both individual probabilities, that is, the product of 1 in 50 times itself. The resultant probability would be 1 in 2,500. The likelihood of an offspring with albinism from such a marriage would remain the familiar 1 in 4. Therefore, the product of these two probabilities, 1 in 2,500 and 1 in 4, would result in a predicted incidence of 1 albino birth for every 10,000 individuals. This would be the predicted incidence of albinism for random mating in the general population. The difference between a probability of 1 in 10,000 and 1 in 32 is the difference in risk between that for albinism in the population as a whole and that in a first-cousin marriage. The difference in likelihood is enormous.

The same kind of reasoning is applicable to any intermarriage and to any of the genes that might be shared. Second cousins like IV_1 and IV_2 probably share one-thirty-second of their genetic material. A second-cousin marriage carries 1 chance in 128 of producing a child with a rare recessive abnormality. Most of the rare recessives have an incidence that is closer to 1 in 100,000 than the 1 in 10,000 of albinism. It is easy to see that some rare recessive diseases are practically unheard of except in families in which there is inbreeding. In cultures like the old-order Amish, among whom inbreeding is a way of life, the incidence of recessive diseases of all sorts is common. It is also common in many isolated communities, for instance, in Switzerland. Inbreeding is also widespread in the Middle East.

Some recessive disorders, like a number of their dominant counterparts, do not manifest themselves at birth. Late-onset recessive diseases may appear at any time in infancy, childhood, adolescence, or adulthood. There are all types. One of the most variable in its time of onset is the Wilson disease.

Joan and Jim Austin had grown up together in a small midwestern city. Their mothers were close friends who brought their families together for frequent birthdays, holidays, and vacations. Over the years Jim grew into a strapping blond, blue-eyed six-footer. He was a superb athlete and president of the senior class. His was an outgoing personality that netted him many friends. A year younger, Joan grew into a petite brunette with luminous eyes, flashing smile, and an enviable figure. Hers was a restrained nature, delightfully leavened by a sparkling, dry wit. No two individuals could have seemed less alike in appearance or personality. The attraction of opposites worked its predictable magic. A year after Jim went off to the state university to study law, Joan followed to pursue a major in the humanities. No one was surprised when they announced plans for marriage following Jim's graduation.

Joan's parents were naturally pleased with their future son-in-law. Jim had for years been like a member of the family. In the surrounding glow of the engagement festivities Joan's parents noted that history seemed to be repeating itself. They, too, had been childhood sweethearts—but with a difference. They were also second or "kissing" cousins. Although they had been aware of the dangers of intermarriage, all concerns had been laid to rest by Joan's radiant good health, a family history free from disease, and the striking contrast in physical type between their daughter and her fiancé. This looked like a wedding made in heaven.

Within five years Joan and Jim Austin graduated from college, married, and bore two delightful children. They had moved to mid-Manhattan where Jim was achieving success with a Wall Street firm, and Joan, between her chores as a mother and homemaker, became a valued editor in a publishing house. The Austins' professional achievements were complemented by an equal success on the social front. Their company was actively sought by members of Jim's firm and Joan's contacts in the publishing world. They seemed perfect representatives of the ideal American couple.

Shortly after their fifth wedding anniversary, Jim noted that his wife lost interest in her personal appearance, often failing to keep her beautiful hair in its usual glistening condition. With increasing frequency he observed her grimacing and contorting her normally serene, beautiful features. At an important business dinner given by one of his senior partners, Joan behaved in a peculiar and damaging fashion. Before leaving home Jim observed that his wife's dress and grooming were so far from her usual standards of elegance that she seemed almost unrecognizable. He said nothing, knowing that a hectic day with a difficult author and the energy of two lively youngsters on arriving home could dampen anyone's enthusiasm for an evening among professional associates.

Following predinner cocktails, the party moved to the dining room—all except Joan who, on rising from her chair, stumbled and lurched into a nearby table. Jim was instantly at her side and guided her to her seat. He was immediately sensitive to the possibility that she might have had too much to drink following an exhausting day. Inebriation was unlike Joan, but Jim was on his guard.

During the meal Joan displayed no interest in her food, had difficulty managing her dining utensils, and spoke with the slurred speech of an intoxicated individual. Jim was aware of the knowing glances of his colleagues and their wives. More embarrassing was the solicitude of their hostess when the Austins effected an early departure.

In succeeding weeks Joan's behavior deteriorated rapidly. If it had not been for a devoted mother's helper, Mark and Linda, the Austins' children, would have been woefully neglected. Joan's skills in managing both a home and a profession completely evaporated. Her eyes were often glazed, her speech garbled, her movements awkward, her clothing disarrayed, and her mind apparently vacant. Jim was confounded. His once vivacious wife had vanished in some mysterious way, replaced by an ill-kempt, untidy individual who was a complete stranger. Jim racked his brain. He could find no reason for this dramatic alteration in Joan. Could she be an alcoholic? Could she be entering early menopause? Could she be going mad?

One afternoon in May matters reached the breaking point. Joan's senior editor called Jim to report that she had just sent his wife home in a cab. She and Joan's coworkers had become distressed by the same behaviors which had so distressed him. Jim raced to their apartment to find Joan collapsed on the floor, disheveled, trembling, and incoherent. He wasted no time in phoning the family physician who had Joan admitted immediately to the hospital.

Joan's physicians were initially baffled by her physical symptoms as well as her personal behavior. Continued disorientation accompanied by garbled speech, bizarre movements, and an absence of any clear evidence of neurological injury suggested acute schizophrenia. The possibilities of treatment involving shock therapy, heavy medication, and prolonged detention in a psychiatric hospital loomed large. Jim was stunned. His disbelief in a psychological origin for Joan's behavior impressed the doctors. They pursued his concerns about the possibility of alcoholism. The results of the biochemical analyses were devastating. Joan was suffering from cirrhosis of the liver. To Jim, acute schizophrenia induced by alcohol seemed an inescapable diagnosis. The doctors were not so easily satisfied. Repeated examinations and tests for a host of possible disorders were carried out. The results were entirely negative until a consulting neurologist noted that Joan's very striking eyes resulted from a greenish ring around the rim of each cornea. Within hours her doctors had their answer. Joan was suffering from the Wilson disease, a relatively rare recessively inherited disorder characterized by biochemical changes in the brain and by cirrhosis of the liver.

Joan was neither an alcoholic nor a true schizophrenic. She was a victim of that chance meeting of two hidden recessive and defective genes. In Joan's case the possibilities for the tragic coupling of these same disordered alleles had been considerably heightened by her parents' consanguineous marriage. Although each parent was entirely healthy, each bore a defective recessive gene along with a normal, dominant allele. The latter protected each of them from disease, but every time this couple conceived, they ran an unwitting one-in-four risk of bearing a homozygous, genetically handicapped child. Joan was suffering the results of those very unfavorable odds.

Fortunately for the Austins, Joan's genetic handicap made its phenotypic appearance in 1974. Her disorder, which links liver and brain deterioration, was originally identified and described by Dr. S. A. Kinnier Wilson in 1912.

During the intervening years a great deal had been learned about the disease: its cause, its effects, and its potential for treatment.

For reasons that remain unknown, the inheritance of the two defective recessive genes involved in the Wilson disease produces a major disruption in the ordinary metabolism of copper. This mineral is regularly ingested in such familiar foods as chocolate, liver, nuts, and shellfish. It is a common constituent of drinking water that passes through copper tubing. Ordinarily, copper is metabolized by the liver, where it is either incorporated into a protein known as ceruloplasmin and released into the bloodstream, or if in excess, it is excreted through the digestive tract or kidneys. Absence of the gene essential to proper copper metabolism leads to the accumulation of the mineral, principally in the liver and brain. The effects of excessive concentration are devastating.

The rate of copper buildup in the body varies considerably. Evidence of toxicity may first appear in youngsters as early as five years of age or remain hidden until the fifth decade of life. In Joan Austin signs of copper poisoning appeared when she was twenty-seven. The doctor who correctly identified her condition recognized the greenish border that surrounded the cornea of each eye as the so-called Kayser-Fleischer ring. This extraordinary coloration indicates an abnormal accumulation of copper within the various body tissues. It is the identifying hallmark of the Wilson disease.

Less obvious symptoms of the disease may manifest themselves in a number of ways. The liver may fail to function properly. The nervous system may react abnormally, producing tremors, rigidity, or spasticity. The emotions may be affected, producing apparently schizophrenic or hysterical behaviors. In general the disease may appear in one of two ways. In its juvenile form, primary symptoms tend principally to involve liver dysfunction. In the adult, late-onset form suffered by Joan Austin, the symptoms tend to be primarily neurologic, although liver impairment is also present.

In the past many individuals who inherited the Wilson disease simply died because no effective treatment was available. Many were wrongly treated as schizophrenics or alcoholics. Following World War II, investigators began using a drug known as BAL (British anti-lewisite) in treating the disease. It was developed as an antidote for arsenic poisoning. BAL ties up the arsenic metal into a harmless molecular complex that can be excreted. It binds some copper as well. The idea of using BAL was to eliminate copper from the body tissue as rapidly as possible. The addition of further copper could be at least partially controlled by careful attention to diet. Some patients with the Wilson disease improved with BAL treatment. Others did not. The therapy is not easy or pleasant. It requires frequent, painful injections.

In 1956 Dr. John Walshe of Cambridge, England, found a new drug, penicillamine, which has a dramatic impact on the Wilson disease. Although related to penicillin, penicillamine has no antibiotic activity. It does absorb and eliminate copper from the body. Because it can be taken orally, it has tremendous advantages over BAL. Individuals often develop pseudo-allergic rashes early in penicillamine treatment. Some may also experience fever, drowsiness, and debilitation. If an individual can tolerate penicillamine during the early stages of treatment, the side effects disappear and do not return as long as the drug is administered.

Joan was treated with penicillamine. The results were startling. In a few short months her slurred speech and awkward gait disappeared. With excessive copper withdrawn from her system, Jim again recognized the woman he had married. Joan returned to her job. She and Jim took pleasure in entertaining the same people who had witnessed her unfortunate copper "intoxication" the previous year. The hostess sparkled. The Austins were lucky. Many patients with the Wilson disease are not diagnosed before irreversible brain or liver damage has occurred.

With Joan restored to health, she and Jim began to ask serious questions about their children. They sought the advice of a genetic counselor, who explained that since Joan has the disease each of her children would be a carrier of the defective allele. If Jim were a normal homozygous individual, Mark and Linda would be free of the disease. As carriers of a defective gene, it would be essential to be aware of their peculiar genotype before marrying and bearing children.

A more critical question concerned whether Jim is a carrier of the defective allele. There is a blood test for the heterozygous genotype. It appears to be reliable when positive. Sometimes a ceruloplasmin determination, a measurement of the concentration of the molecule in the blood, will achieve the same end. It will tell if someone is a carrier. Mark and Linda are indeed carriers. What Jim Austin requires is a test that will reliably tell him he is not a carrier. These tests cannot do that. If a test is negative, there is still doubt. Liver biopsy and analysis of its copper content are more reliable. The procedure is formidable, and there are factors that make a diagnosis of normality less than certain. For these reasons Mark and Linda must be carefully monitored for the Wilson disease throughout the rest of their lives. Joan will continue to take penicillamine until a more effective treatment is found.

There will be further advances in understanding the Wilson disease. The answers now available make an enormous difference in the lives of people like the Austins. We've seen patients who couldn't write their names, couldn't light a match, couldn't walk—all restored to normal. Inmates of psychiatric institutions have been treated and restored to productive lives. It is important that the affected be diagnosed as early as possible. Success in treating this disease serves as a model for the understanding and management of other autosomal recessive diseases.

6.
Common Recessive Diseases

Despite all that has been written about genetic diseases in recent years, many people find it difficult to understand the affected individual and his problem. In contrast, they readily extend understanding and sympathy to those suffering from an infectious disease. Most people comprehend the nature and behavior of both viral and bacterial disorders because such infectious diseases occur commonly and frequently. Everyone has had an infection of some kind, if only a common cold.

The situation with genetic disorders is different. It is even difficult for personally involved people to understand and accept what has gone wrong when a genetic disease occurs. There are a bewildering number and variety of different genetic disorders, too many of them with unpronounceable names. Most occur so rarely that each may seem like an isolated tragedy. Even persons who are struggling with one genetic condition often cannot make emotional contact with individuals affected by another. Lack of understanding by the general public is not surprising.

Not all genetic diseases are rare. Some abnormal genes and the disorders they produce are relatively common. Two autosomal recessive diseases are familiar to most Americans. That they are of genetic origin is less well known. Although one may not have heard of the Hurler syndrome or alkaptonuria before opening this book, virtually everyone has heard of sickle cell anemia and cystic fibrosis.

Sickle cell anemia is the most common autosomal recessive disease among American blacks. An estimated one in ten carries the recessive gene for the disorder. One black baby in every four hundred suffers from the disease. An estimated twenty-five thousand to fifty thousand persons in the United States have sickle cell anemia. One in twenty-five white Americans carries the recessive gene for cystic fibrosis. This disease occurs once in every two thousand births among white people of European descent. Neither of these diseases can be considered rare. In fact, advances in public health have so reduced the incidences of some infectious diseases that sickle cell anemia and cystic fibrosis are now more common than such better known bacterial or viral diseases as poliomyelitis, diphtheria, and smallpox. The incidence of many dreaded infectious diseases has dropped to the vanishing point. The incidence of sickle cell anemia and cystic fibrosis has remained unchanged.

The sickle cell anemia story has a definable beginning in the year 1904. A young black student from the West Indies walked into the office of Dr. James B. Herrick, a cardiologist from Illinois. The student complained of shortness of breath, weakness, and dizziness. He had ulcerations of the leg and anemia. He had experienced these problems for years.

The young man's disorder was new to Herrick. When he examined his patient's blood under a microscope, he realized he had found something unusual. Normal red blood cells, whose function is to carry oxygen to the cells of the body, are disc shaped. The red cells of this patient were distorted into long, pointed shapes resembling sickles. In a report written for a medical journal, Herrick emphasized the diagnostic importance of the distorted, misshapen cells. The significance of the abnormal cells in relation to the symptoms of the patient remained to be established.

Following Herrick's report, other physicians began identifying patients with the disease. By the end of World War I, sickle cell anemia had acquired its name. In 1923 John G. Huck of Johns Hopkins University summarized what was known of its genetics. Sickle cell anemia was a disease seen only in blacks. It was distinguished by the sickling of red blood cells. It appeared to be transmitted as a dominant genetic trait since only one faulty gene appeared enough to cause sickling.

Dr. James V. Neel, an outstanding geneticist, ultimately defined the genetics and inheritance patterns of sickle cell anemia. Working at the University of Rochester after World War I, Neel determined that sickle cell anemia is really an autosomal recessive disease. Individuals with only one abnormal gene and one normal allele (Aa) have red cells that sickle under the standard test conditions, but they simply do not have the symptoms of sickle cell anemia. They have the distinctive sickled cells but are free of the disease. Neel described these individuals as having the sickle cell trait. Individuals with two abnormal genes (aa) have cells that sickle spontaneously. They also have clinical manifestations of the disease. The distinction between a person who carries but one abnormal gene and has the *trait* and one who has two abnormal genes and has sickle cell *disease* is important. It is not possible to distinguish between individuals with sickle cell anemia and those who are carriers by examining red blood cells under the microscope. Victims of the disease have symptoms and other manifestations of the clinical illness.

The relationship between the sickling of cells and the symptoms of the affected individual became clearer in 1927 when E. Vernon Hahn and Elizabeth B. Gillespie of Indiana University Medical School found that the red cells of patients with sickle cell disease remained normal in shape so long as they were saturated with oxygen. When the supply of oxygen to the red blood cells decreased, sickling occurred. Normal hemoglobin supplies oxygen to body cells. Sickled red cells are not found in the well-oxygenated arteries where blood is pink. They are found in the veins, where blue, oxygen-depleted blood flows back to the heart.

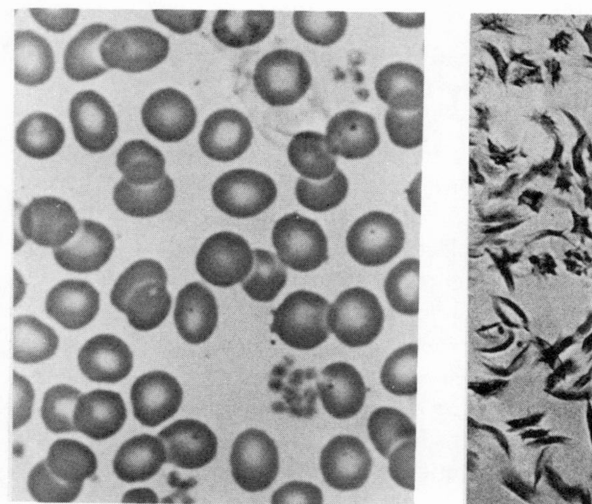

FIGURE 13. *Normal and sickled red blood cells, or erythrocytes. The sickled cells are shown on the right and the normal cells are shown on the left.*

Real understanding of the nature of the sickle cell problem came after World War II with a brilliant discovery by Linus Pauling, already a Nobel laureate, who at the time was a chemist at the California Institute of Technology. It seemed to Pauling that the inherited defect that produced both the sickle cell trait and the sickle cell disease had to lie in the hemoglobin molecule. Hemoglobin is an iron-containing protein that does the actual work of picking up oxygen and bearing it to the body's cells. Oxygen is absorbed in the lungs and is carried by the hemoglobin to all tissues where it is released. Pauling's keen mind envisioned an abnormal hemoglobin molecule that might be held in shape when it contained adequate supplies of oxygen and might collapse into an abnormal sickle when the oxygen was released. The result might be distortion of the entire blood cell.

Pauling began his research in 1945. In 1949 he and colleagues, J. Singer, H. Itano, and I. Wells, published a landmark paper in *Science* entitled "Sickle Cell Anemia, a Molecular Disease." They reported the results of experiments with hemoglobin extracted from the red cells of various sources: normal persons, individuals with the sickle cell trait, and people with sickle cell disease. The key to the disorder was found by using the technique of electrophoresis. Proteins and other biological molecules that carry an electrical charge will migrate or move at different rates in an electric field created by an electrical current. Hemoglobin from patients with sickle cell disease had a distinctly different pattern of migration from that of hemoglobin from normal persons. Pauling and his colleagues designated the normal hemoglobin as hemoglobin A and the abnormal, sickling hemoglobin as hemoglobin S. Persons with the sickle cell trait but not the disease had both hemoglobin A and hemoglobin S in their red cells. This was a sure indication that the two alleles governing the production of hemoglobin in these individuals were different. It also provided the first evidence of the molecular expression of a recessive gene in heterozygotes (Aa). The work of Pauling and his colleagues launched the field of molecular medicine.

Other scientists began the painstaking search for the exact difference between the normal hemoglobin molecule and the sickle cell molecule. At the Cavendish Laboratory of Cambridge University in England, Dr. Vernon M. Ingram used a technique he called fingerprinting in which the hemoglobin molecule was chemically chopped or digested into small peptide segments by enzymes. The segments were then analyzed. It was immediately apparent that most of the fingerprints of the two hemoglobins were the same. But there was an important difference. The different peptides were then further broken down or digested into their component amino acids.

Ingram eventually found that the sickle cell hemoglobin molecule differs from the normal molecule in a single amino acid. The significance of this finding and the complexity of research required are apparent when one learns that there are a total of 574 amino acids in the entire hemoglobin molecule. In the beta chain of hemoglobin S, a polypeptide portion of the molecule, there is an amino acid called valine in the same position in which the amino acid glutamic acid is normally present in hemoglobin A. That is all. The rest of the molecule is unchanged. This substitution creates a less acid protein and accounts for its slower migration or movement during electrophoresis. Although the difference seems small, it is enough to cause the complex phenomenon of sickling. In the complete absence of hemoglobin A it results in all the manifestations of disease.

These discoveries in sickle cell anemia were important to the history of medical and genetic research. They provided insights to the structure of the hemoglobin molecule. Some one hundred abnormalities of that molecule have now been discovered. In addition, the sickling hemoglobin, S, provides a model for genetic and evolutionary studies. All these advances, wonderful as they are, do not help the patient who suffers from sickle cell anemia. With all we know about sickle cell anemia and its inheritance patterns, there is no definite cure. This places a major burden for control on preventive medical techniques.

The disease is lethal. For patients and their families, sickle cell anemia can be painful and expensive. It can cause a wide variety of symptoms. Most of them are attributable to the abnormal shape of the red cells. The capillaries, the body's smallest blood vessels, are so narrow that red cells have to pass through them in single file. Sickled cells, because of their jagged shape, tend to become trapped in these small blood vessels. Sometimes they entirely block the flow of blood, causing a thrombosis or occlusion that leads to oxygen deprivation. Lack of oxygen destroys all cells in a deprived area. Cellular or tissue death from oxygen depletion is known as an infarct or an infarction. Because sickled cells are also more vulnerable than normal red blood cells, they are more quickly exhausted or destroyed. The result is the characteristic anemia.

Children with sickle cell disease tend to be underweight, and their growth is slow. Thrombosis, the blockage of blood vessels by sickled cells, can affect any tissue or organ in the body. Among children, blocked blood vessels often cause painful swellings of the hands and feet. Thromboses in the brain can produce retardation, epilepsy, or death. The spleen and kidneys are often severely damaged. Thromboses in the bones can become very painful. The symptoms of this skeletal involvement may be indistinguishable from infection of bony tissue; in fact, sickle cell patients are unusually susceptible to the serious bone disease osteomyelitis. Because their resistance to infection is generally lowered, many sickle cell patients succumb to pneumonia, meningitis, or other infectious diseases.

Sickle cell patients learn to live with what are called *crises*. In a crisis an affected individual may experience an acute attack of pain, often in the abdomen or back or in a specific bone. Abdominal pain is frequently as severe as in appendicitis. Crises are sometimes accompanied by a temporary halt in red blood cell production by the bone marrow. They sometimes are associated with increased blood cell destruction and jaundice. Sickle cell crises are usually of a finite extent and duration, but they often require hospital admission and emergency treatment. They can cause death. Frequent transfusions are the only definitive measure for the alleviation of symptoms and may be temporarily lifesaving.

Carriers of the sickle cell trait are not entirely immune to manifestations of abnormality. Certain kinds of stress, particularly violent exercise and exposure to high altitude, may cause thrombotic crises. Army recruits carrying the sickle cell trait are reported to have died during basic training. Although black athletes with the sickle cell trait had no problem in the 1968 Olympic Games at Mexico City, where the elevation is 7,000 feet, sudden death did occur in four young carrier males exercising vigorously at 4,060 feet. Most persons with the sickle cell trait go through life happily unaware of their condition. They should become aware of their condition and consider the remote risks involved in air travel. They certainly should avoid flying in unpressurized aircraft.

In the United States public awareness and national commitment to the problem of sickle cell anemia have undergone a major and recent acceleration.

This began in 1970 with what appeared to be the arousal of a white liberal conscience. "It is fair to say," declared Senator John V. Tunney of California in 1970, "and research figures prove the fact, that if sickle cell anemia afflicted white people, we would have made a commitment long ago to end this disease." Tunney was then a sponsor of the National Sickle Cell Anemia Act, whose purpose was to increase research spending substantially.

The history of the act is a study of the interaction between medicine and politics. In February 1970, President Nixon declared sickle cell anemia to be "a targeted disease for concentrated research." He proposed an increase in spending for research and treatment from one to six million dollars annually. The Democrats promptly upped the ante by proposing an extra twenty-five million annually to provide federal grants for sickle cell programs on the local level. The bidding went on, with no one willing to be outdone. By the time the act was signed into law in May 1972, it authorized twenty-five million dollars for the fiscal year of 1973, forty million for fiscal 1974, and fifty million for fiscal 1975. This was certainly a grandiose increase over former levels of spending.

A wave of publicity accompanied the presidential and congressional involvement with sickle cell anemia. Many well-intentioned groups were spurred to action. Relatively simple and inexpensive tests for the detection of the sickle cell trait had existed for some time. Widespread use of these procedures in combination with informed genetic counseling could do an extraordinary job of preventing this disease. Mass screening programs aimed at black adults and children were established. By 1972 seven states and the District of Columbia had gone farther. Laws were passed that mandated testing for sickle cell hemoglobin in blacks. Booklets, pamphlets, television commercials, and other appeals have been used to spread the word.

To many people there appeared to be too much activity too soon. A public screening program, particularly for heterozygote detection, requires a lot of preparation and proper public education. Success presupposes a receptive target population. In an eagerness to publicize the disease and to screen widely, many programs antagonized the target population. The result, according to one black physician, was "a near panic in black communities." Groups that had established screening programs were often not equipped to give a carrier of the sickle cell trait the correct information about his or her condition. That information is vital. Individuals who are carriers have nothing to fear. Their heterozygous (Aa) genotype protects them from sickle cell disease. The only relevance of their genetic condition is to their personal plans for marriage. Should their mates bear the same genotype, they stand a good chance of bearing children with sickle cell disease.

Mandatory screening laws, particularly for heterozygosity, raise serious questions of individual liberties. When they seem to involve the right to reproduce, people become anxious and tense. Even though black legislators have sponsored many of the proposed laws for mandatory screening, other spokesmen for the black community have condemned any laws that are aimed solely at blacks. They have expressed fears that possessing the sickle cell trait would be regarded as a stigma that would adversely affect a black person's life and career. Blacks with the trait have said they have been denied employment or insurance. Some have begun to describe the screening for sickle cell trait as a step toward genocide.

One black woman obstetrician explained the situation in blunt terms: "I can't tell any of my patients not to have children because of sickle cell anemia. Most of them regard birth control as a white plot against black people. I'm not certain that they're wrong." In such an atmosphere of distrust genetic counseling becomes extraordinarily difficult, perhaps impossible. What started out as a well-meant crusade in many areas degenerated into unfortunate and unnecessary chaos. Many physicians have found themselves busy reassuring carriers of the sickle cell trait that there is no cause for panic.

Confusion in the screening programs recently has been compounded by questions in the area of treatment for sickle cell disease. There are a number of newly developed treatments, and all are controversial. A leading figure in the search for improved treatment techniques reasoned that the amino acid valine, which is substituted for glutamic acid in the abnormal hemoglobin molecule, formed bonds with other parts of the molecule. He believed this might distort the hemoglobin molecule and the red cell into the observed sickle shape. He proposed that urea, a chemical commonly used in the modification of proteins, might have the proper molecular properties to prevent sickling. Urea was infused into patients with sickle cell anemia during crises. Urea is a difficult chemical to handle. It causes the body to excrete large quantities of water and may cause severe dehydration. After trials on perhaps a dozen patients, urea therapy was reported to bring patients out of their crisis states faster than other treatments.

These studies omitted one essential feature—the use of controls or comparison studies in which patients with the same condition are divided into two groups, one receiving the medication to be tested and the other not. In a controlled study stringent efforts are made to eliminate all possible variables between the two groups. The only significant difference should be the presence or absence of the medication. If a comparison study reveals that the experimental group markedly improves in comparison with the control group, there is evidence for the effectiveness of the medication. Without such controls, the results of any medical experiment are doubtful.

Other researchers suggested that urea might prove effective because it was chemically transformed into a molecule of cyanate during a crisis. Cyanate, a combination of carbon, nitrogen, and oxygen, was used in a number of patients during crisis situations. Although the original hypothesis that urea was transformed into cyanate has been disproved, cyanate did seem to alleviate symptoms during crises. Controlled studies are now under way in a number of treatment centers. Most experienced hematologists are wary of either urea or cyanate treatment. The mainstays for the treatment of crises remain oxygen, good fluid balance, and blood transfusion.

The possible prenatal detection of sickle cell anemia has received considerable attention. The problems posed by uncovering such a potentially useful technique are interesting. They involve the little understood processes of how a single fertilized egg cell evolves through growth and differentiation into a human being. Hemoglobin beta chains, polypeptide components of the hemoglobin molecule, whether of hemoglobin A or hemoglobin S, are not normally detectable during fetal life. If one could detect these identifying beta chains during pregnancy, whether in the form of A or S or both, one could determine if a developing fetus were normal, a carrier, or affected. Analysis of fetal blood invariably reveals the presence of a third form of the molecule, hemoglobin F. Normal babies, carriers, and those who eventually develop sickle cell anemia all have the same hemoglobin F, with its own unique polypeptide beta chain. Identification of hemoglobin F in a fetus provides no clue to the fetal genotype. The genes for the production of hemoglobin A and/or S must be present since one or both of these molecules is synthesized immediately following birth. Many geneticists thought that effective prenatal diagnosis of red blood cell genotype would somehow require "turning on" the apparently dormant genes in order to identify the kind of telltale beta chains, A or S, that would be produced.

In 1971 a team of physicians working at Johns Hopkins University in Baltimore, Drs. Michael Kaback, Morely Hollenberg, and Haig Kazazian, reported an interesting advance that appears not to require the hypothetical activation of dormant genes. The proposed technique would permit detection of sickle hemoglobin in fetal blood. Tests were done with fetuses from nine- to eighteen-week pregnancies that had been terminated early, either by natural or artificial means. The medical team devised a method for selectively inhibiting the synthesis of the beta chain of hemoglobin F. Under these conditions they found that small amounts of hemoglobin A beta chain and/or hemoglobin S beta chain were indeed being synthesized. The genes are not entirely dormant during the fetal period. By suppressing the formation of hemoglobin F beta chains, it is theoretically possible to identify the kind of hemoglobin ultimately to be found in the individual. In this way one could know if a fetus were to be normal, a carrier, or diseased.

A prenatal test for sickle cell anemia is dependent on obtaining a sample of fetal blood. Some samples have been obtained directly from fetal veins viewed directly through an amnioscope. This instrument looks like a long, slender needle and can be inserted directly into the uterus, permitting inspection and sampling. Most approaches to prenatal diagnosis of hemoglobin diseases have utilized a single needling of the placenta, which obtains a mixture of the fetal and maternal blood. This is followed by an incubation of the blood with a radioactive amino acid that becomes part of the hemoglobin. The radioactive hemoglobin subsequently can be detected by a radioactivity counter. The mixture with maternal cells is not a problem unless the mother has become anemic and carries cells that rapidly synthesize hemoglobin as does the fetus. A useful precaution is to give the mother a blood transfusion so she will not be anemic. After incubation of the cells with the radioactive amino acid, it is possible to separate the beta and alpha chains of hemoglobin. In this way the prenatal diagnosis of sickle cell anemia is safe and not too demanding.

If widespread prenatal detection of sickle cell anemia became possible, a difficult ethical problem would arise. The problem has its roots in the nature of the disease. Most patients with sickle cell anemia die young, after a life of terrible suffering. Not all do. Some live well into adulthood. The development of better therapy for sickle cell crises compounds the ethical problems. Since current research is directed toward the prolongation of life, the ethical issues become complex. Would a medical geneticist suggest an abortion for a condition in which the patient might live long enough to be an adult? He might, since most patients suffer terribly. The development of effective methods for prenatal diagnosis will not automatically solve these problems.

Heterozygote carrier detection and genetic counseling present another problem. It is possible today to identify every individual who carries the abnormal recessive gene along with its dominant allele. It should be possible to know which carriers are married to other carriers. In an autosomal recessive trait, mating of two carriers is necessary to produce children with sickle cell anemia. Counseled intelligently about the disease and the way it is transmitted, such couples might decide not to reproduce. They might instead find all the pleasures and rewards of parenthood through adoption. If one parent has the recessive trait and the other does not, the effect is as if neither carries it. These parents have nothing to worry about other than to educate and inform their offspring about the recessive gene they may carry. For the majority of families, screening programs could provide this kind of reassurance. A real problem with achieving widespread acceptance of the programs is educational. Although sickle cell anemia is the most common chronic illness in black children, there is still a general lack of awareness of the condition, its causes, and its effects.

Useful information about sickle cell anemia is available from the National Sickle Cell Disease Program, National Institutes of Health, Bethesda, Maryland 20014. An excellent question and answer book about sickle cell anemia for parents, entitled *Sickle Cell Anemia and Your Child,* was written by Drs. Roland Scott and Althea Kessler of Howard University. It is available from the Sickle Cell Center, Howard University, Washington, D.C. 20021. It was written for parents of children with the disease but would be useful and informative for any potential carrier.

A variety of testing methods is available to screening programs. Most employ the simplest technique, in which turbidity, a cloudiness of the hemoglobin, is determined. A cloudy solution indicates the possible presence of defective hemoglobin S and the recessive gene. A test is said to be positive when the measurement of turbidity indicates the presence of hemoglobin S. Positive tests are followed by electrophoresis to distinguish patients who have only hemoglobin S from carriers who have both the A and S forms. It is essential that a screening program have this kind of second test to confirm the presence of the hemoglobin S gene and to distinguish those affected with the disease from healthy carriers. It is essential that both groups be provided with a counseling program.

Testing for the sickle cell gene has stimulated more controversy than any other aspect of human genetics today. One of the problems in understanding sickle cell screening programs and discussing them with the public is that people are not clear about what is being investigated and for what reasons.

One type of screening is to test directly for the disease, identifying people with S-S hemoglobin who clearly possess the homozygous recessive genotype. This kind of testing is invaluable. It should be carried out as early as possible, preferably on the newborn. Dr. Roland B. Scott, professor of pediatrics at Howard University in Washington, D.C., has said: "We should screen newborns to find cases of sickle cell disease. They get infections, and we need this diagnosis. And it's a very good thing for the crisis-sick child to have the knowledge and the remedies that will help. Let's focus on the sick child." Dr. Scott is right. These children are constantly in danger of life-threatening episodes, which often are caused by bacterial or viral infection. If physicians know ahead of time that a child has sickle cell disease, they are prepared and can more often come to a life-saving diagnosis and treatment. Screening for sickle cell disease in the newborn is not as easy as it is in later life. It can be done using a special type of electrophoresis. If starting today all newborn infants were screened, there would still be a number of individuals missed who are now past infancy. It is probably not yet feasible to screen the entire black population.

Another important target population is women in their child-bearing years. Drs. Arthur Fort and John Morrison of Shreveport, Louisiana, and Memphis, Tennessee, have written that motherhood for the patient with sickle cell anemia "is not worth the risk." The risk of maternal and fetal death is high. At Memphis Hospital only one of every two thousand obstetrical patients admitted has had sickle cell disease. Yet sickle cell disease has been present in one of every six women dying in childbirth. It is the third-ranking cause of maternal death in that hospital's population. Women with sickle cell anemia also have a higher incidence of fetal loss through spontaneous abortion, a much greater incidence of babies with such low birth weight that they fall into the premature class, and a higher incidence of babies with early life-threatening complications. It is essential for every black potential mother to know if she is a carrier or has sickle cell disease. She should have a thorough knowledge of the risks before undertaking a pregnancy.

Another type of screening is one that looks for the causative gene. The aim is to detect the heterozygote who has both A and S hemoglobins. This kind of testing is controversial. Some of the controversy is unnecessary. A stewardess lost her job with an airline because she had the sickle cell trait, not the disease. It is true that such an individual could suffer from a crisis when flying in an unpressurized plane well over ten thousand feet above sea level. But commercial planes in this country are pressurized. Cabin atmosphere is usually equivalent to that at seven thousand feet, where the pressure is considerably greater than at ten thousand feet. That this stewardess lost her job is tragic. The information that an individual is a carrier should be his or her legal property—a thing to be disposed of only as the individual sees fit.

With increased information obtained about people through screening, we must find ways to protect the confidentiality of such information. There is no earthly reason that the presence of a sickle cell trait should influence anyone's chance for employment or status as an insurance risk. The information should be given only to the individual, who can then decide about marriage, children, and the possible curtailment of the few activities that might prove harder for him or her than for most. The reason for screening programs is to help prevent disease.

If the histrionics can be put aside, it is possible that some control over this common and terrible disease can be achieved. Identification of the presence or absence of the sickle cell gene in all black individuals could be done as a routine premarital or prenatal check. Distribution of information along with a careful educational program could identify all pairs in which both the potential mother and father carry the gene. Some of those who had this information might not marry; others might choose not to reproduce. Combined with enlightened counseling, a program of this sort would certainly reduce the incidence of sickle cell anemia. It could virtually eliminate it. This is the controversial area. It might not be so controversial if those most likely to be affected had all the facts and were permitted a free choice.

Another abnormal recessive gene common to a particular genetic group is the one that produces thalassemia or Cooley's anemia. This disease occurs almost exclusively among Italians, Greeks, and other groups indigenous to the Mediterranean basin. It is sometimes called Mediterranean anemia. It is transmitted as an autosomal recessive trait.

Patients with thalassemia have difficulty producing red blood cells with sufficient hemoglobin. Lacking adequate supplies of functional hemoglobin, their cells are less resilient and more vulnerable than normal red blood cells. They are destroyed faster than usual, while effective replacement is slower. Iron that normally would be incorporated into hemoglobin molecules accumulates in the tissues. Patients with thalassemia may eventually die of iron poisoning.

There is no known treatment for the basic defect. The only relief is provided by blood transfusions, which are required frequently, often once every two to four weeks. Proper administration of blood may require three to four hours. The process may prove very painful, particularly for an infant or young child whose veins are naturally small, hard to find, and often scarred from previous transfusions. The process can be emotionally rough on the child, his family, and the physician.

The patient with this disease is faced with an additional burden. He wears the outward mask of his disorder. In an attempt to correct the anemic condition, a patient's bone marrow responds by working overtime. It enlarges in the process and as a result causes the bones to enlarge. Bones in the face become especially prominent. Michael Iovene, an articulate patient from Connecticut, has said, "People tend to treat me as an Oriental, but I'm Italian." As a child his appearance bothered him, but he has adapted to it. His outspoken efforts led Congressman Robert N. Giaimo of Connecticut to introduce a bill in Congress authorizing funds for treatment, prevention, and research. The bill was passed by both the Senate and the House and signed by the President in 1972. Whether patients will see any results depends on whether the promised funds are affected by the recent cuts in appropriations for health research and science.

Screening for individuals who are thalassemic, those with the homozygous recessive genotype, is not difficult. Any physician or hematologist can make the determination. Effective screening for the carrier is not now possible. Research is required to develop a reliable test for the single recessive gene or trait. With such a test, a program for screening and genetic counseling might not be difficult to develop since there is a finite target population of similar ethnic background. If a screening program could be evolved, the disease might be made to disappear within a few generations.

Prenatal diagnosis of thalassemia is more difficult than that of sickle cell anemia because there is no new identifiable form of hemoglobin synthesized. Variance from the normal is quantitative rather than qualitative. It is possible to identify the thalassemic individual by assessing the differing rates of synthesis for gamma and beta hemoglobin. Monitoring the time required for radioactive amino acids to be incorporated into beta and gamma hemoglobin chains reveals whether the rate reflects normality or is indicative of the retardation in synthesis typical of thalassemia. Drs. David Nathan and Blanche Alter at Harvard and Drs. Yuet Kan and Mitchell Golbus at the University of California, San Francisco, have employed this technique for the prenatal diagnosis of fetuses with thalassemia. Dr. Nathan estimates that monitoring of pregnancies at risk has led to the birth of eight to ten children who would not be alive without this technique.

Cystic fibrosis is an autosomal recessive condition that is very common. It occurs within specific, genetically limited populations. While sickle cell anemia is found almost exclusively among blacks, cystic fibrosis occurs almost entirely among whites. The molecular cause of sickle cell anemia is known; that for cystic fibrosis is not. Many of the genetic lessons are similar. The methods for control that are available but so controversial for sickle cell anemia are simply not available in the case of cystic fibrosis.

Cystic fibrosis was identified as a distinct entity in 1938. The disease affects all of the body's exocrine glands. These are the glands that produce mucus and sweat. They include the many little glands of the skin, the salivary glands, and most insidiously, the pancreas, which produces so many of the enzymes necessary for the digestion of food in the small intestine.

A diagnostically useful symptom is excessive salt in the sweat or perspiration of an affected individual. Patients with cystic fibrosis secrete a sweat that contains from two to five times the normal amount of salt. This permits a fairly simple test for the presence of the disease. The sweat test is the standard approach to a definitive diagnosis. It is precise and produces no discomfort or inconvenience for the subject. At the same time it is true that the test requires careful attention. It should be performed at a center where technicians conduct the test often and are readily familiar with its requirements. Otherwise, inadvertent errors are common. Misdiagnosis is tragic.

Excessive sweating makes hot days dangerous for individuals affected by cystic fibrosis. They must be careful about salt loss and its replacement. The abnormal output of the body's mucous glands is a more serious problem to the affected individual. Instead of producing clear, free-flowing mucus, these individuals secrete a thick, sticky substance that clogs the parent glands. A clogged gland, like a clogged stream, spells trouble. The gland is ultimately destroyed. Difficulties often begin at birth. About 10 percent of those individuals with cystic fibrosis are born with meconium ileus. Meconium is the substance normally found in the intestines of newborn infants. It is the material a baby normally excretes in his stools during the first few days of life. The baby with meconium ileus has such thick, dry, and hard meconium that it produces an intestinal obstruction. Such a baby will die unless the blockage is immediately relieved through surgery.

When thick mucus clogs the ducts of the pancreas, it inhibits or stops enzyme flow into the small intestine. The glands behind the ducts expand to form large lakes or cysts. As they die, the glands become scarred or fibrotic. For this reason the disease is known as cystic fibrosis of the pancreas. Blockage of the pancreatic duct leads to difficulty in digesting food. Food tends to pass straight through the body, producing bulky, foul-smelling stools. The stools are often very fatty because of the lack of lipases, the fat-digesting enzymes produced by the pancreas. The nutritive value of food is lost. Children with cystic fibrosis may eat ravenously yet suffer from malnutrition. Most are thin, although not all of them have major digestive difficulties.

The digestive problems of the disease become easier to treat once a diagnosis is clearly established. Special diets help, and the physician can provide pancreatic enzymes for the patient to ingest directly with his food. The diet must be low in fat and high in protein. Supplementary vitamins are provided, and salt tablets are called for in hot weather.

The most serious problems of this disease involve the lungs. Thick mucus can clog the bronchi, the major passages linking the nose and throat with lung tissue. This condition invariably leads to serious infection. Patients experience chronic coughing, frequent collapse of parts of the lung, scarring, fibrosis, and emphysema. About 90 percent of patients with cystic fibrosis ultimately die of chronic lung disease. Until recently most died early in childhood, their short lives plagued by episodes of pneumonia and bronchitis, frequent hospitalization, and the need for constant medical care. Damage to lung tissue lessens the organ's ability to absorb oxygen. The heart must compensate by pumping additional oxygen to the tissues. Chronic heart strain is a major cause of death.

Families with a child suffering from cystic fibrosis face an almost overwhelming challenge. They must work for long hours with physicians who are skilled in the care of the disease and with physical therapists expert in the function of the lung. Many have moved to climates more suitable to a child with chronic lung disease. These efforts help the patient, but they engulf the life of a family.

A physical therapist must instruct the family about how to relieve the patient's congestion with techniques designed to provide postural drainage. The child is placed in different positions designed to elevate the lungs so that drainage will be downward, while the therapist or parent uses chest clapping and vibration to jar the thick mucus out of the bronchi. This routine must be done two or three times a day. Exercises are added to correct poor breathing habits. Most centers treating cystic fibrosis use mist tents that are made of plastic and are filled with a spray of water and chemicals discharged in a stream of flowing air or oxygen. These are designed to loosen the accumulating mucus. Many patients sleep in a mist tent every day of their lives.

The strain that such a routine inevitably imposes on a family is brutal. "Mechanical masseurs" that can relieve parents of the need to pound and pump their children provide some help, but there is no machine to relieve the psychological pressures. The cystic fibrosis treatment team often includes a social worker who helps with emotional problems. If not, the physician must involve himself with these problems.

The mortality rate in cystic fibrosis is high. Dr. Warren J. Warwick, director of the cystic fibrosis clinic at the University of Minnesota and keeper of a national cystic fibrosis registry, reported in 1972 that half of all patients die by the age of fourteen. In certain medical centers it has been possible to achieve more encouraging results. An increasing number of patients with cystic fibrosis survive into their late teens and twenties.

The most important aim in treatment of cystic fibrosis is to diagnose the disease early and to begin an intensive therapeutic program before serious lung damage occurs. Lung tissue cannot be repaired, and the strain that damage places on the heart and circulatory systems often starts an irreversible physical deterioration. If the lungs are not damaged severely, aggressive use of all available therapies, at home and in the hospital, can make a real difference in the life of a child with this disorder.

This treatment is only partially successful. It creates problems for the patient and for the family. For the patient the disease and the life-style it dictates cause tremendous psychological stress. This stress affects parents and siblings. In 1972 a group from the National Institute of Arthritis and Metabolic Diseases made a detailed study of twenty-seven patients with cystic fibrosis and twenty-one mothers of such patients. They found that many of the affected individuals performed well in school but not so well in psychological terms. Infantilizing of relationships with mothers was common, as was the psychological withdrawal of fathers. Denial of the emotional impact of the illness was thought to contribute to psychological difficulties. There are good reasons for psychological difficulties. Adults with this disease cannot obtain health insurance. They often cannot find jobs. They must somehow live with their disease. Despite this crushing burden, individuals with cystic fibrosis have married and some have had children. They are the minority, for a variety of reasons. One is that cystic fibrosis tends to cause sterility.

Genetic counseling about cystic fibrosis depends entirely on the recognition of symptoms in a family. The earlier this is achieved, the better. Parents can then be counseled about autosomal recessive inheritance and the one-in-four risk of bearing other children with the disease. There is no test now capable of detecting carriers of this recessive gene. The gene is common, rather than isolated among related parents. It is a tough gene to avoid. The hope for the future is that research will produce a test that will detect the carrier reliably. This test could then be used for mass screening purposes.

There have been some encouraging reports about tests that were thought to provide the answer to the screening problem. None has survived a period of evaluation. There is a need for a real breakthrough. The fundamental defect in the disease is still unknown. Some abnormal protein is probably the product of the abnormal gene, just as the abnormal S hemoglobin is the product of a variant gene in sickle cell anemia. Once this protein is identified, testing for carriers will be possible. The corollary is probably also true. Until this fundamental defect is found, it will probably not be possible to detect the carrier reliably.

The same is true for prenatal diagnosis and amniocentesis. The diagnostic techniques are simply not available for cystic fibrosis. They will be needed for a complete program controlling the disease. Effective screening programs will require a real understanding through research of the fundamental causative mechanisms for the disease.

There are a number of problems unique to cystic fibrosis and a number that are common to any chronic, potentially fatal disease. Psychological and emotional difficulties may begin very early, particularly before diagnosis is clear. Audrey T. McCollum and Lewis E. Gibson of Yale University wrote in the *Journal of Pediatrics* about the adaptation of the family to the child with cystic fibrosis. The mother of a baby who eats ravenously and still fails to thrive may have doubts about her capacities to nurture. One parent observed, "The worst part is watching them starve right in front of you. They look like those kids in India."

The establishment of the diagnosis brings other problems. One problem may be disbelief in a diagnosis. "Perhaps this doctor is wrong. The others were." Under these circumstances, it is easy to repress what the physician has said. As awareness of the truth becomes a conscious reality, parents may experience feelings of guilt. When they learn their child's suffering and disease has been genetically determined, their feelings of guilt may be compounded. Anger is a natural reaction—anger with earlier doctors who missed the diagnosis, anger with a mate for his or her genetic abnormality, even anger with an organized church or specific religion whose teachings are apparently inadequate. These resentments require patience and understanding on the part of the physician, the social worker, and other members of the family. They are human and understandable responses.

Reproduction is a particular problem. A natural urge is to have another child to replace the one who is programmed to die. This impulse must be balanced by effective genetic counseling and the competing wish, also natural, not to bring another affected child into the world. Questions arise about the reliability of contraceptive methods. Sexual intercourse begins to assume risks that may strain a relationship between a husband and wife.

Cystic fibrosis often leads to catastrophic medical expense. It is bound to tax the resources of a family. The cost varies, but treatment and care have been estimated to require more than ten thousand dollars a year.

Long-term adaptations are particularly difficult. It is essential not to underestimate the challenge of maintaining a gratifying relationship with a potentially dying child. In every situation like this, denial is practiced. This is how the soldier in combat lives with himself. He denies the likelihood of dying and does not think about it as he goes about his duties. In a similar fashion successful parents treat their affected child in as normal a fashion as possible. With cystic fibrosis there are a number of constantly intrusive characteristics that remind everyone of its presence. There is the nagging cough, the daily physiotherapy, and the mist tent. There is also an undeniable odor. Over 60 percent of parents surveyed have commented about this as a persistent reminder of the disease. Coughing at night may disturb a family's rest. Bed wetting is common. Conflicts over diet and other aspects of care increase as the affected child matures.

The problem of dying must be faced squarely by the family and with the affected child. Questions such as "Will I ever get over being sick?" are asked by at least thee-quarters of all patients. Fund-raising appeals may frighten a child or lead to unwelcome communications from his classmates. It is not uncommon for a child to return from school with the news that "Johnny told me I'm going to be dead next year." One sibling tormented an affected sister with "Never mind, you're going to be with the angels pretty soon." These crises are not easy to handle unless they have been thoroughly thought out before they occur. A good answer to the most ominous questions might be "None of us knows when we're going to die. We all will die one day. The important thing is to do all we can to live as long and happily as possible."

The child with cystic fibrosis demands immense strength and support from a parent. Parents' groups, such as the National Cystic Fibrosis Foundation, can be a source of such strength. There is a local chapter in most areas. Physicians and others in centers devoted to the care of these patients can be a source of support. Working closely with a treatment center can assure parents that their child is receiving the best and most up-to-date care possible.

All autosomal recessive diseases, like their autosomal dominant counterparts, are heartrending. Although a finite number of techniques for detection, treatment, and prevention are at hand, many more are needed.

7.

Genes, Chromosomes, and Chromosomal Disease

Contemporary geneticists estimate that each cell of the human body contains genes, or specific DNA sequences, governing approximately fifty thousand different traits. Since each trait is normally controlled by a pair of genes or alleles, the number of genetically specific DNA sequences compressed into a packet invisible to the human eye approaches one hundred thousand. This exquisite miniaturization has never been equaled by man-made technologies. Nature's economy and virtuosity are underscored as this storehouse of thousands of gene codes provides not only a library of comprehensive information but a dynamic, precisely synchronized set of specifically functioning and independent molecular programs controlling all cellular activities. The mechanisms that orchestrate this array into a precisely coordinated operational cell evoke continuous awe and fascination. They provide the raw material for much of current genetic research.

Had it not been for Walter Sutton's recognition that Mendel's hypothetical genes exist as real physical components of chromosomes, comprehension of the magnificent scheme by which nature precisely concentrates so much into so little might have proved impossible. When Sutton proposed the link between genes and chromosomes, the real number and nature of the different genes was unknown. Although his original explanation did not envision the association and ordering of fifty thousand discrete hereditary units into a much smaller number of chromosomes, the fundamental accuracy of his formulations has been repeatedly confirmed with modern recognition of the magnitude and complexity of the genetic material. His ideas have withstood the test of time.

The nucleus of every human cell typically contains 46 chromosomes dispersed through a liquid medium. At specific times in the life of the cell each of these 46 chromosomes is recognizable as a member of one of 23 different pairs. This recognition is based on the gross structure of each chromosome (Figure 14). Although the specific DNA sequences or genes found on different pairs of chromosomes may vary from individual to individual, the overall shape of each is common to all human cells. Geneticists number each pair according to size. Identification progresses from number 1, the largest, to number 22, the smallest. The twenty-third pair, the sex chromosomes, are considered separately.

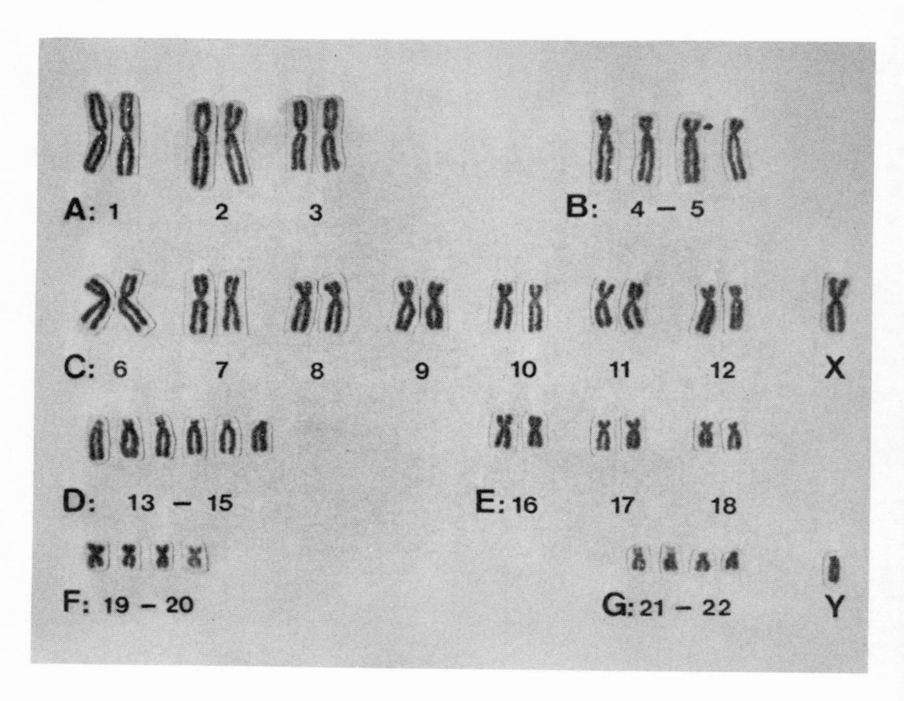

FIGURE 14. *Human chromosomes. A normal idiogram. The chromosomes have been photographed and enlarged. Then each has been cut out and lined up according to size. When this is done, it is apparent that man is diploid, which means that his chromosomes exist in pairs. The numbering and lettering systems for classification are both illustrated.*

Of the 23 sets of complementary chromosomes, one member of a pair is inherited from each parent. Genes for thousands of specific traits distributed over 23 chromosomes are borne by a father's sperm cell, or gamete. At fertilization this complement of 23 different chromosomes is matched or paired with a second complement of 23 chromosomes borne by the mother's ovum, or gamete. Genes for the same thousands of traits are distributed among the 23 chromosomes of the female gamete in the same order and pattern found in the male. Genes for specific traits linked together on a particular chromosome from one parent are similarly found on the appropriate complementary chromosome from the second parent. If two DNA sequences, or alleles, for a particular trait are identical, the offspring is said to be homozygous (AA or aa) for that trait. If the two DNA sequences are different in the number and order of nucleotides, the individual is said to be heterozygous (Aa) for that particular trait. This is true when both alleles code for alternate expressions of the same trait and are found in the same location on complementary chromosomes.

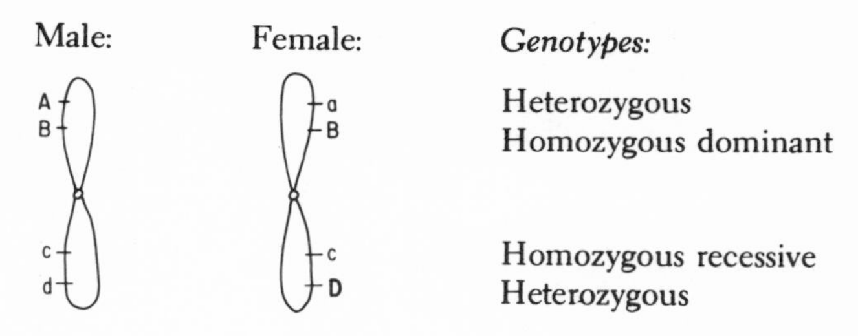

FIGURE 15. *A chromosome pair. The chromosome from parent 1 bears two dominant genes (A,B) and two recessive genes (c,d). The chromosome from parent 2 bears two dominant genes, or alleles (B,D), and two recessive genes, or alleles (a,c). The individual's resulting genotype is (Aa, BB, cc, dD).*

Of the 23 pairs of chromosomes found in a typical human cell, the allelic or complementary members of 22 pairs are virtually indistinguishable from each other on gross examination. It is impossible except with special techniques to identify which member of such pairs, called autosomes, is inherited from the male parent and which from the female. The genes for traits borne on the autosomes know no gender.

One pair of chromosomes, the so-called sex chromosomes, have two markedly different and alternative shapes and sizes. The larger is known as the X chromosome (see Figure 16). The X chromosome has a real resemblance to that letter of the alphabet. Genes linked together on an X chromosome are involved with the expression of primary and secondary sexual characteristics or traits. The smaller sex chromosome is called the Y chromosome. Because of its relatively diminutive size, it bears many fewer genes than the alternative X chromosome. Genes carried on the X and Y chromosome, unlike their autosomal counterparts, are evidently not alleles. They do not carry alternative DNA sequences for the same trait. If an individual inherits an X chromosome from one parent and a Y chromosome from the second parent, he is a male (XY). Genes on the Y chromosome evidently confer qualities of maleness. The single X chromosome in such an individual is not paired with a complementary chromosome bearing allelic genes for the same trait. The same is true for the single Y chromosome. Whatever DNA sequences are to be found on the male's X or Y chromosome should be phenotypically expressed. A gene that is important for the clotting of blood is located on the X chromosome. If a male inherits the recessive gene or DNA sequence for hemophilia, he will have the disease because there is no protective alternative allele. If an individual inherits an X chromosome from both parents, she is a female (XX). Since she has two X chromosomes, a female is usually protected from conditions such as hemophilia by the allele on her second X chromosome.

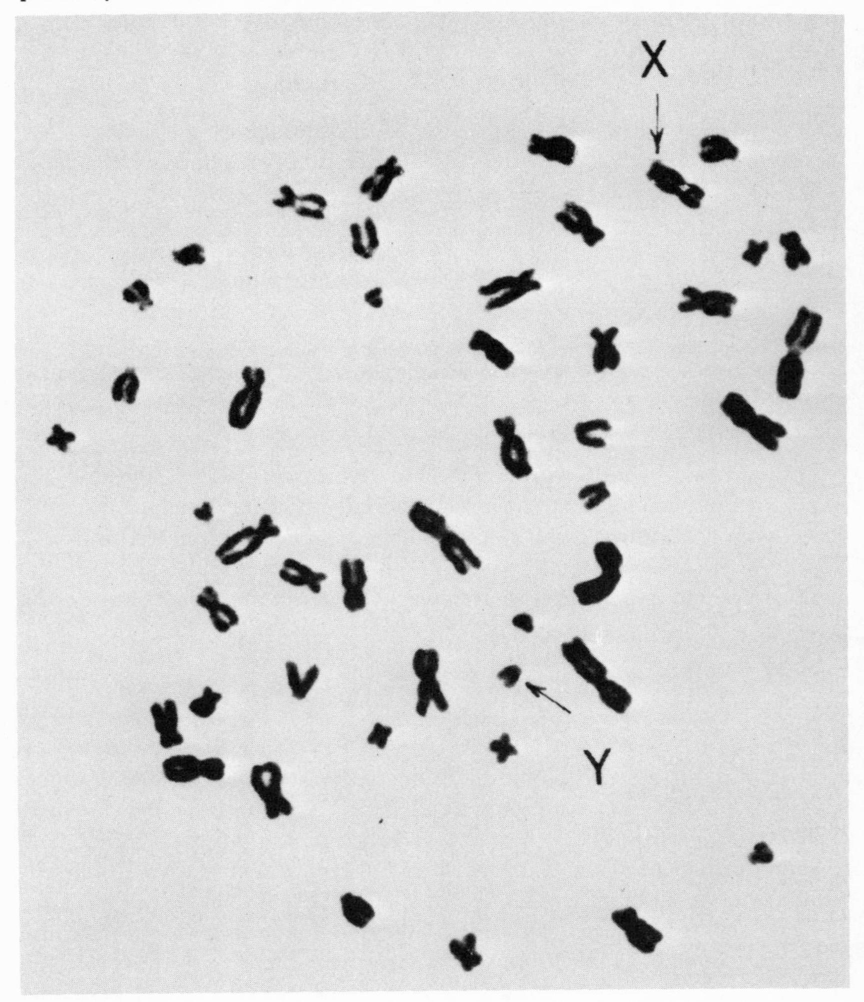

FIGURE 16. *Human chromosomes. This is the appearance under the microscope of the standard squash preparation. These are the chromosomes of a single normal cell.*

Since DNA sequences for an estimated fifty thousand different traits are distributed among only 23 chromosomes, the number of genes on a single chromosome is large. That each of more than a thousand DNA sequences may function with precision and accuracy requires that a chromosome be structured in a highly ordered and efficient fashion. A gene that governs the expression of a given trait by controlling the synthesis of a particular enzyme composed of 60 amino acids must itself be composed of a specific sequence of 180 purine or pyrimidine nucleotides. The chemical identification and positioning of each amino acid molecule at the site of protein synthesis in the cytoplasm requires a triplet sequence of three nucleotides within the gene.

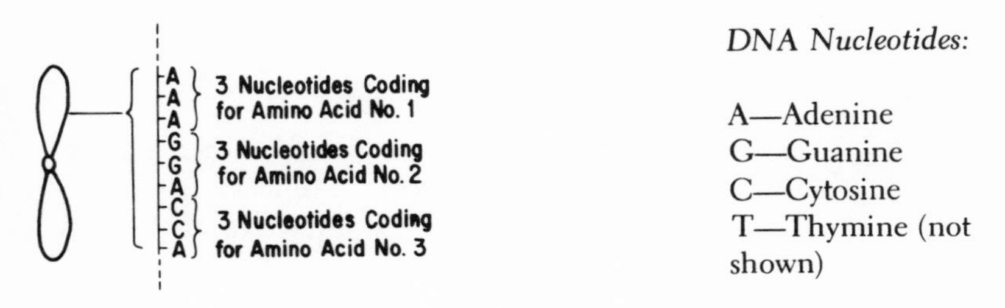

FIGURE 17. *A small portion of a DNA sequence for a gene, illustrating the triplet coding pattern.*

If an error occurs in this prescribed triplet sequence, an inappropriate amino acid may be substituted in the resulting protein. The abnormal hemoglobin S found in sickle cell anemia differs from normal hemoglobin A by the fact that the amino acid valine rather than the amino acid glutamic acid is coded for by the defective gene. This error results from an incorrect ordering of three nucleotides out of approximately seventeen hundred required for the whole hemoglobin molecule. These seventeen hundred nucleotides, representing two pairs of allelic genes, must exist in proper sequence and number if the information is to be properly expressed.

Each gene or DNA sequence of nucleotides is linked in prescribed order with other genes by protein molecules. The protein segments provide structural integrity to the chromosome and serve to separate each DNA sequence into discrete entities of appropriate length. For a hypothetical gene composed of three hundred nucleotides, protein molecules at either end of the DNA sequence serve as a kind of essential chemical punctuation. The messenger RNA that bears the gene's instructions to the site of protein synthesis is constructed as a chemical mirror image of the master DNA gene and will contain exactly three hundred RNA nucleotides in proper sequence.

When a new individual is conceived through the fertilization of an ovum, or egg, by a sperm cell, two sets of 23 chromosomes are united to form one diploid cell. For this single diploid cell to develop into recognizable human form, it must undergo billions of cell divisions. In each division one cell divides into two new daughter cells. Each must be the exact genetic replica of the original. The exactness of replication is a function of the chromosomes' ability to

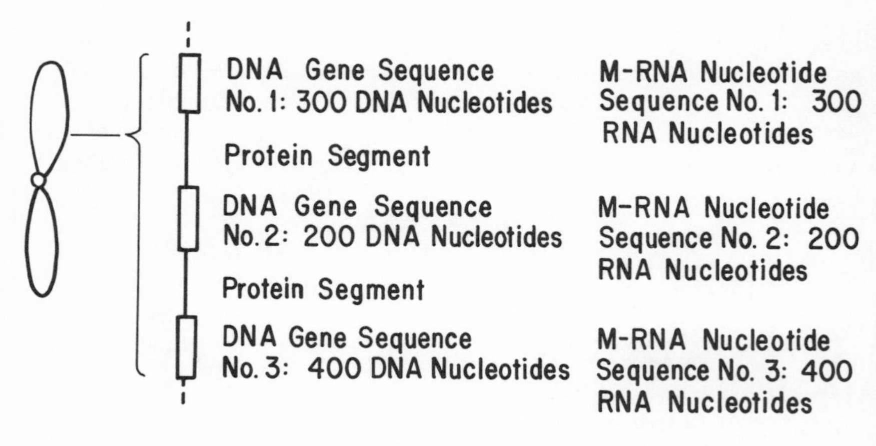

FIGURE 18. *A small segment of a chromosome showing the relationship among DNA nucleotide sequences or genes, protein segments, and the synthesis of messenger RNA (M-RNA).*

duplicate themselves exactly from available raw materials. In the process the nuclear membrane of the parent cell dissolves. Each arm of the chromosome is replicated, yielding two chromosomes, the original and an exact copy.

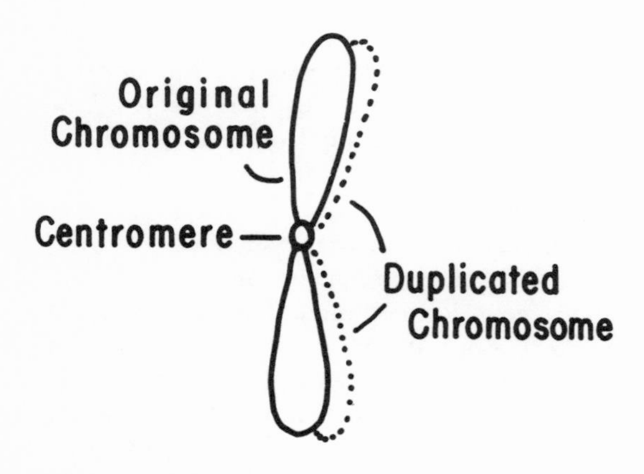

FIGURE 19. *A replicated, or duplicated, chromosome and its copy.*

The two chromosomes are joined by a centromere, the pinched-in portion of the structure. At this stage, the original chromosome and its duplicate are known as chromatids.

Fine fibers become attached to the centromere. They contract, dividing the centromere in half. The original chromosome and its duplicate are pulled to opposite ends of the cell. This same process simultaneously occurs for all 46 chromosomes and their copies. When the resulting two sets of 23 pairs of chromosomes each arrive at opposite ends of the original cell, a new nuclear membrane is formed around each diploid set. The original cell membrane contracts around its equator, dividing the cytoplasm roughly in half. Two new, fully functional cells are formed. Although one-half the size of the original, each contains an exact copy of the diploid number of chromosomes present in the original fertilized egg (Figure 20).

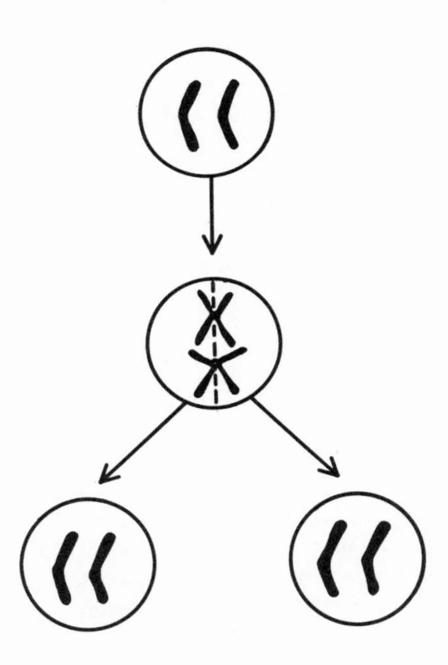

FIGURE 20. *Mitotic cell division. A pair of chromosomes is shown at the top in the normal resting stage of the cell. In the middle each chromosome reproduces itself, the new parts temporarily sharing the same center, or centromere. This stage is called metaphase. At the bottom the chromosomes separate along the vertical axis, forming two new cells, each with the complete pair of chromosomes.*

At the molecular level the weak hydrogen bonds linking each half of the DNA helix are chemically broken. Each unpaired DNA strand duplicates its complementary strand from free nucleotides available in the nucleus. With the addition of appropriate protein segments, two new and identical chromosomes are formed from the original. No other molecules in the cell need be duplicated. The instructions for synthesizing any necessary substances from raw food material are present in the full diploid complement of chromosomes in each daughter cell.

This replicative process is called mitosis. It accounts for the growth and development of an individual from a single cell into an adult. Once full size has been attained, mitosis continuously renews cells that naturally die or are lost through injury. In our tissues, particularly those rapidly formed and replaced, like the skin, the intestine, or the blood cells, new cells are constantly being made as old cells die. The mitotic process of cell division ensures that each new cell is an exact genetic copy of its parent. If the mitotic process has been normal, the nature of the individual's genetic material in old age will be the same as it was at conception.

The process of reproduction in which a new person is produced from two parents is more complicated. The difference is that a diploid organism with 23 pairs or two sets of chromosomes must be produced from the diploid cells of two parents, each of whom also bears two sets of 23 pairs or 46 chromosomes. This could not be done by mitosis. Simply adding the mother's 46 chromosomes to the father's 46 chromosomes would produce children with 92 chromosomes, grandchildren with 184 chromosomes, and so on. What happens instead is a process called meiosis, or reduction division. The reproductive cells, or gametes, are not typical diploid cells. Each has only one set of 23 chromosomes. Since this is half the usual number, they may be called haploid cells. Since they contain only one full set of chromosomes, they are sometimes referred to as monoploid cells. When a sperm fertilizes an ovum to form the cell from which the embryo, fetus, and baby will develop, this new cell will contain the usual diploid complement of 46 chromosomes.

The meiotic process includes one chromosomal duplication and two cell divisions (see Figure 21). These three operations occur in two stages. During the first meiotic division both chromosomes of all 23 pairs are duplicated. Each original chromosome and its exact copy, both called chromatids, are joined by a single centromere. One of the original chromosomes and its copy become part of an intermediary cell destined to divide further into the actual gametes. The second original chromosome and its copy become part of a second intermediary cell destined to divide into different gametes. During the second meiotic division, the centromere is divided by the contraction of the same fine fibers that function in mitosis. Each chromatid, the original and its copy, is segregrated into a separate sperm or egg gamete. In this fashion a pair of diploid chromosomes each duplicates to form four chromatids. During a first cell division each chromosome and its copy becomes part of an intermediary cell. These intermediary diploid cells then undergo cell division without chromosomal duplication, with the result that four gametes, each bearing one of 23 chromosomes, is formed from one original diploid cell. These haploid or monoploid cells are then ready to meet and produce an individual with the required matched sets of chromosomes. The process of reduction division happens only with the production of spermatozoa and ova. All other cells are diploid and produce only diploid descendant cells by mitosis.

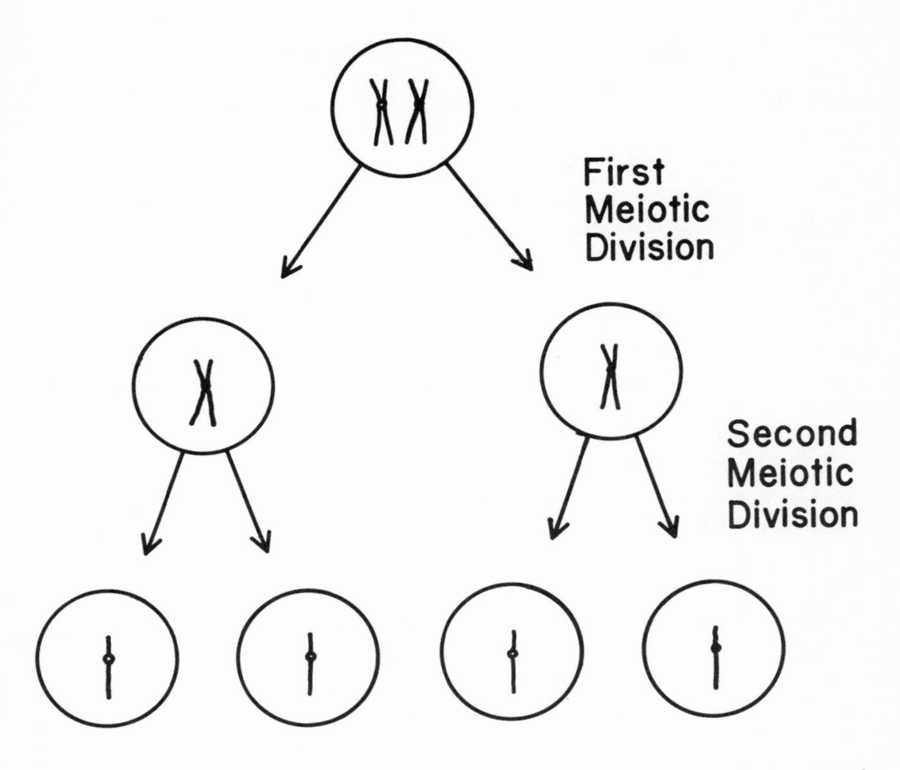

FIGURE 21. *Meiosis. The reduction division by which normal sex cells or gametes (spermatozoa and ova) are formed.*

The mitotic and meiotic processes described above are normal. If they functioned in this fashion one hundred percent of the time, there would be no need for chromosomal analysis in medical genetics. A number of things can and do go wrong. Individual chromosomes can be drawn into the wrong descendant cell. Pieces may break off from chromosomes. The result of even the slightest deviation from exact reproduction of each chromosome is usually genetic disease or death.

The techniques that have led to an integrated understanding of the sophisticated relationships between genes and chromosomes have been evolved only recently. Although chromosomes had been accessible to microscopic analysis for decades, until twenty years ago the exact number of chromosomes in a normal human cell was unknown. During the 1950s cytogenetics, the study of chromosomes, went through a "classic period" in which many fundamental questions were answered. Progress was rapid. Once an accurate count of normal chromosome number was established, diseases were promptly recognized that resulted from or could be associated with abnormal chromosome numbers or characteristics.

Techniques for the accurate counting of chromosomes did not at first reveal the nature of their interior structure. Chromosomes were visible only as X-shaped bodies, distinguished from one another by differences in size and the relative length of the arms radiating from the centromere. More recently methods have been developed that delineate the fine or inner structure of the chromosomes. Scientists are now able to distinguish one chromosome from another with certainty.

The analysis of an individual's complement of chromosomes is called a karyotyping. This is now a standardized procedure that is available in laboratories in most communities. The techniques that reveal the more individualistic structure of different chromosomes are so far available only in a few genetic centers. They are simple enough to perform and will shortly become more widely available. Research is under way that will computerize chromosomal analysis. This should make these procedures cheaper and permit their more widespread use.

Analysis of the chromosomes begins with growing cells in a tissue culture, which can be established using any cell of the body. The most readily available cells are those from the blood, but in some complicated cases it is necessary to obtain cells by a biopsy of the skin. This is a fairly simple procedure that is nearly painless for the patient. A small patch of skin is anesthetized. A dermatological punch, which resembles a steel pencil with a three- to four-millimeter hole in one end, is rapidly rotated on contact with the anesthetized surface. This releases a little button of skin tissue, which is then snipped off with small scissors. In the laboratory this sample of skin tissue is divided many times and placed in glass or plastic bottles containing special nutrients. Within two to four weeks cells from the skin multiply by means of mitosis. When they cover the bottom surface of the container, they are ready for analysis. This technique makes many cells available for a variety of cytogenetic studies. With proper methods of freezing and storing, cultures of skin cells can be kept for years. The culturing process is not easy. Growing cells of this type *in vitro*, or outside the body, takes a kind of cellular green thumb. These skilled thumbs are now available only in specialized laboratories at centers for cytogenetic studies.

The technique using blood cells is much easier and can be done in virtually any laboratory associated with a modern medical center. This is the technique that is routinely used for a patient requiring cytogenetic analysis. The lymphocytes, a form of white blood cell, are the most suitable for culturing and analysis. They will grow for short periods in a culture medium, long enough for most diagnostic procedures.

The technique that permits this widespread analysis of human chromosomes was discovered by Dr. Peter C. Nowell of the University of Pennsylvania. Its essential feature is to encourage specific blood cells to divide and reproduce *in vitro*. Only when the cell is dividing, at what is called the metaphase stage of the mitotic cycle, are the chromosomes discrete enough to study for diagnostic purposes. At metaphase each chromosome has duplicated. The original chromosome and its exact replica, the chromatids, are joined by a common centromere. This linkage, prior to division of the centromere and segregation of each chromatid into a separate cell, accounts for the X shape associated with chromosomes. All of the photographic prints that appear in this chapter and throughout the book are of chromosomes at this duplicated stage in metaphase.

Nowell found that a chemical extracted from red kidney beans causes lymphocytes to divide. This chemical is called phytohemaglutinin because it is extracted from a plant (phyto) and because it causes red blood cells (hema) to stick together and form clumps (glutinin). Before Nowell's discovery this chemical had been used in the laboratory to eliminate red cells from a blood sample in order to isolate white cells for study. The newly identified action of phytohemaglutinin on lymphocytes is of much greater importance. It has made the white blood cells, or lymphocytes, the standard source for chromosomal studies. One of the main advantages of this technique is time. It may take more than a month for a cytogenetic analysis of skin cells obtained through biopsy. The results of the blood test are available in a few days.

Once cells were available either through skin cell biopsy or lymphocyte sampling, a number of additional discoveries were required before chromosomal analysis became a reality. An important advance depended on the use of colchicine, a chemical obtained from the meadow saffron. When added to a culture of dividing cells, colchicine stops cell division. Mitosis can be arrested or frozen at the crucial metaphase stage, before the duplicated chromosomes have divided. The characteristic X shape of the chromosomes at this stage of mitosis is, of course, due to the attachment of a pair of chromatids to a single centromere.

Within two to three days after a blood sample has been taken and phytohemaglutinin added, many cells are found to be reproducing mitotically. At this point colchicine is added to the culture. Then Hsu's technique for separating chromosomes is employed. A dilute salt solution is added to the sample. The cells swell and the chromosomes separate. A stain is usually added to make the chromosomes more visible. A piece of glass, either a microscope slide or cover slip, is put over the cells and pressure is applied, squashing the cell and spreading the chromosomes out as far as possible. The chromosomes are examined through the microscope. Photographs are taken of representative cells.

Each photograph is enlarged three to four thousand times. The print is then cut up by hand so that each chromosome can be isolated and mounted on paper. The chromosomes are matched in pairs, lined up according to size, and classified to form the neat picture illustrated in Figure 22. This is called a karyotype or idiogram.

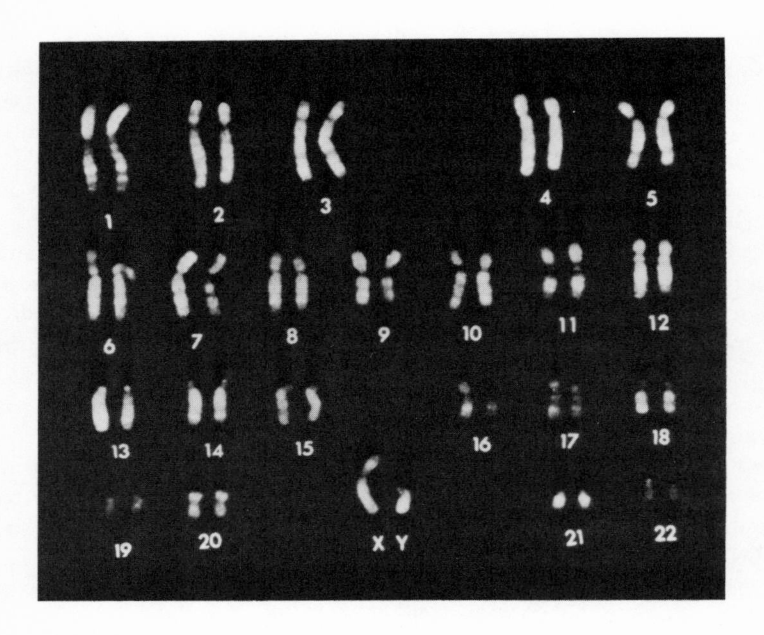

FIGURE 22. *Human karyotype. This is the fluorescent pattern obtained using quinacrine mustard to stain the chromosomes of the cells of a normal male.*

Classification of the chromosomes in this way is trickier than one would like. There is really not much outward difference in appearance among many of the pairs of chromosomes. In the ideal situation, each pair of chromosomes receives a number, strictly on the basis of size. Only chromosome pairs numbers 1, 2, 3, and 16 can always be identified reliably by size and shape alone. Adjoining pairs of chromosomes are so similar that another classification is employed. These chromosomes are divided into seven groups, each of which is identified by a letter. The largest three chromosomal pairs are classified in group A; the next two largest in group B; the next six in group C; and so on through group G, which contains the smallest chromosomes.

The number and letter classifications are not mutually exclusive. They are used almost interchangeably. A physician may speak of chromosome pair number 9, or if he is not certain that the chromosome in question is a member of that numbered pair, he may refer to it as a member of group C. Newer techniques in cytogenetics now make it possible to distinguish all individual pairs of chromosomes with confidence. The letter classification will probably disappear. It is still useful in describing karyotypes that have not been studied by the newer techniques.

The development of cytogenetics had an enormous impact on medical genetics. For the first time large numbers of retarded patients could be chromosomally characterized and clearly identified, even at birth. A reason was now evident for a major percentage of human miscarriages. Chromosomal aberrations are of such magnitude that survival through pregnancy is frequently impossible. Spontaneous or natural abortion is the typical consequence. The products of these new diagnostic techniques were of major significance, and they became part of the established armamentarium for the cytogenetic diagnosis of a number of disorders at most medical centers.

In 1971, after a plateau in research, the first of a new series of techniques surfaced that has since launched a new era of cytogenetic discovery, understanding, and application. The first new technique was the production of fluorescent chromosomes. The breakthrough was the work of the Scandinavian scientist T. Caspersson, who found that chromosomes treated with quinacrine mustard developed brightly banded patterns when examined in ultraviolet light. The banding patterns could be used to characterize individual chromosomes with great accuracy. Quinacrine is the chemical name for the antimalarial drug atabrine. It was the drug routinely used to prevent malaria among American troops in the South Pacific during World War II. Its staining properties were well known to the soldiers whose skin turned characteristically yellow on repeated dosages of the drug. The mustard derivative of quinacrine, a relative of mustard gas, was originally prepared for use in the treatment of cancer. Although better drugs were found for this purpose, the drug during testing displayed various characteristics that had great relevance for the study of chromosomes. Quinacrine mustard was observed to enter into intimate association with DNA molecules. Its fluorescent properties were not lost in combination with DNA. Caspersson reasoned that if chromosomes were subjected to quinacrine mustard, those areas containing DNA genes would appear brightly fluorescent on exposure to ultraviolet light while those areas containing protein, which does not absorb quinacrine mustard, would appear relatively dark. The resulting banding patterns of alternate darkness and fluorescence could be used to characterize individual chromosomes and accurately distinguish them from structurally similar counterparts. Quinacrine alone might produce the same kind of fluorescent banding pattern in the chromosomes, though the effect might possibly be less sharply defined than with quinacrine mustard.

Experimentation dramatically confirmed these predictions. The banding effect is spectacular. Figure 22 illustrates the karyotypes as obtained through a fluorescent microscope. Each of the chromosomes has a distinct pattern of bands or areas of brightness and darkness. For instance, chromosome pairs numbers 21 and 22 are virtually identical in size and shape. No one really knew which was which before. With this technique, pair number 21 is bright and shining, while number 22 is hardly distinguishable. The X and the Y chromosomes are shown in the middle of the bottom row. The fluorescent technique is characterized by the brilliance of the Y chromosome. It really lights up, as no other chromosome does. The brilliant Y fluorescence can also be seen with fluorescent staining of whole cells. The result is a fluorescent Y body that signifies maleness, much as the Barr body signifies femaleness. The Y chromosome is easily identified in Figure 23.

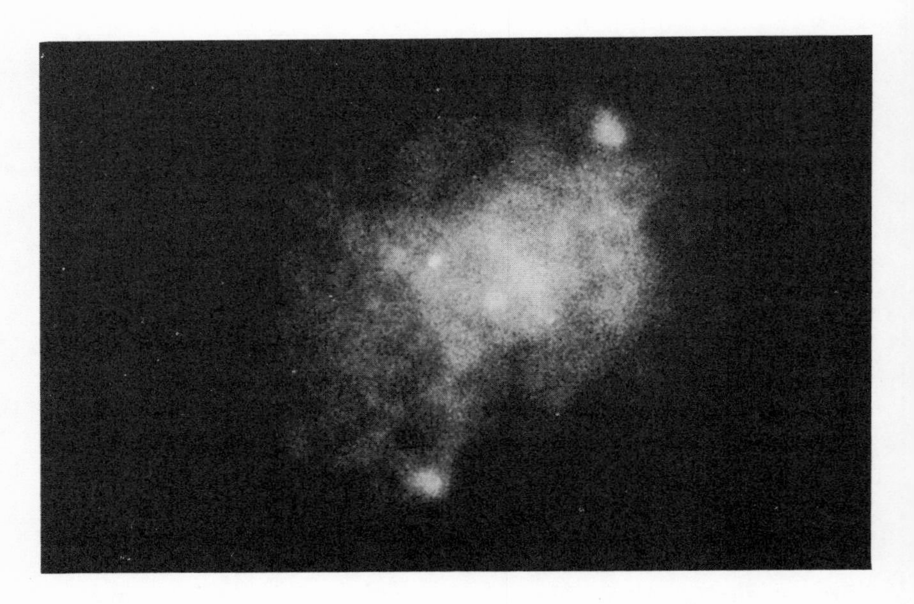

FIGURE 23. *Quinacrine mustard fluorescence of a whole cell reveals the Y body or chromosome. This cell was obtained from a male with two Y chromosomes, the brilliantly fluorescent spots seen at two and seven o'clock.*

Since quinacrine and quinacrine mustard become intimately bound with DNA, the fluorescent patterns produced are far from random. For every chromosome the pattern is highly specific. Each can readily be distinguished from every other. This new technique represented an enormous advance in cytogenetics. At the time of its discovery widespread use was problematic. The technique requires a fluorescence microscope, and preparations must be viewed in ultraviolet light, which is hard on the eyes. There is a pronounced tendency for the fluorescence to fade in time. These problems have been sidestepped by the development of other techniques that produce banded chromosome patterns.

The principle of the newer banding techniques involves the controlled fixation, or denaturation, of DNA with a powerful alkali or heat. This is followed by a slow baking, or annealing, during incubation in a warm salt solution. Chromosomes denature and anneal differentially depending on the relative concentrations of DNA and protein. When a cell is stained with Giemsa, a specific dye, the annealed or undenatured sections of the chromosomes stain darkly, and the characteristic banding patterns emerge. There are now a variety of Giemsa techniques available. The so-called ASG method involves the treatment of chromosomes with an acid (A), a salt solution (S), and Giemsa stain (G). The results of applying such a solution to chromosomes are shown in Figures 24 and 25. These techniques for identifying and characterizing chromosomes are now in routine use at many centers. Their convenience and the amount of information they provide indicate they will become the routine methods of the future. They are much easier to use than the fluorescent methods and will probably supplant them for everything but the recognition of the Y chromosome, which is far more striking with fluorescence. All banding techniques, whether Giemsa or fluorescent, are enormously more specific in the identification of each chromosome than earlier methods. Studies by methods that do not permit exact identification of all the chromosomes are no longer adequate to the demands of clinical cytogenetics.

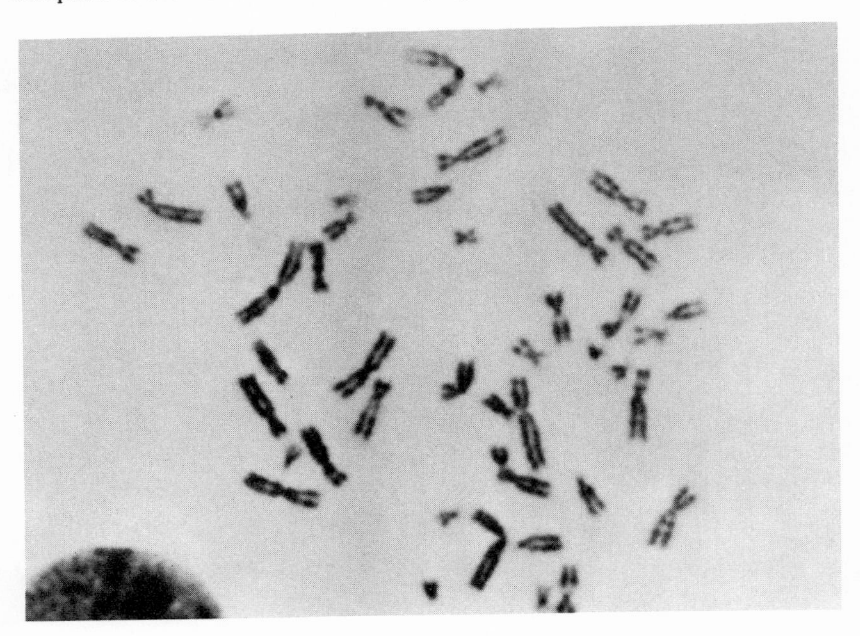

FIGURE 24. *Giemsa technique of producing chromosome patterns. This was a normal cell in a standard squash, air-dried preparation. The distinct banding of each chromosome is evident.*

It is possible with any of the banding techniques to take a photographic transparency of a stained cell and put it into an instrument that will produce a graphic tracing of the various degrees of staining from one end of the chromosome to the other. The instrument is called a densitometer. The kind of enlarged picture it produces makes it easier to compare chromosomal patterns of DNA. It even permits an assessment of the much smaller differences between any two chromosomes of a complementary pair. If information from the densitometer is combined with family studies, a tremendous amount can be learned about the origin and nature of a chromosome pair. One of the two chromosomes of every pair is identical to one of a father's chromosomes and the other is identical to one of a mother's. With the densitometer it is possible to determine which member of a pair was inherited from which parent.

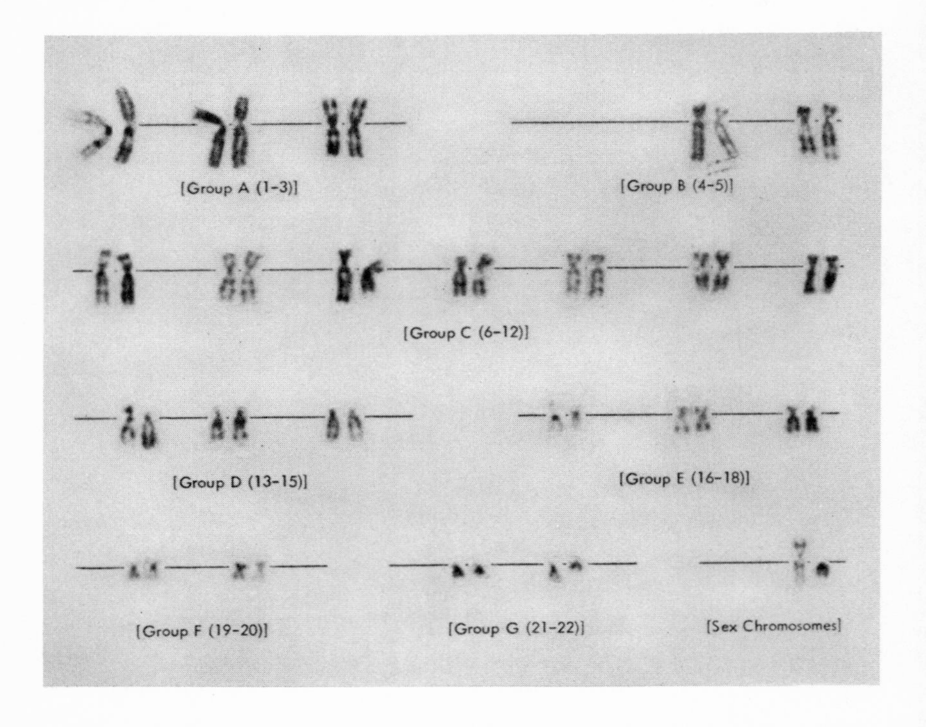

FIGURE 25. *Human karyotype as obtained with the Giemsa technique. It is clear from this picture, as it is in Figure 22 where fluorescent staining was used, that each chromosome has its own distinct pattern.*

Another cytogenetic technique of potential clinical importance is called autoradiography. It is possible to incubate cells with thymidine, a molecule that after a series of cellular transformations is normally incorporated into DNA molecules. Thymidine that contains a radioactive hydrogen atom can be synthesized outside the cell. When radioactive thymidine is fed into a cell, it is readily incorporated into the DNA of different chromosomes. The rate by which this occurs is variable and characteristic for each chromosome. By use of a technique like that of an X-ray film, the location of the radioactive molecule can always be determined. This detection process is called autoradiography. If mitosis is arrested and a cell autoradiographed at various points in time, it can be seen that some chromosomes replicate earlier than others. Using this technique, one can distinguish chromosomes of pair number 5 from those of pair number 4, a very important distinction in the diagnosis of certain chromosomal diseases.

Any of these techniques requires a lot of professional time and a high degree of professional expertise. It seems likely that in the future the various processes will be computerized. This could yield major medical dividends in terms of accuracy and reproducibility. More important, it could simplify the entire diagnostic process, help eliminate error, and reduce costs, making such techniques much more widely available.

Scientists at the Jet Propulsion Laboratory at the California Institute of Technology, who brought us detailed photographs radioed back from the moon, have turned their attention to the automated study of human chromosomes. A recent approach in that laboratory provides analysis of a photographic print of human chromosomes in three minutes. The best time achieved by a highly skilled geneticist for the same analysis is thirty minutes. The computer can sort and match chromosome pairs that constitute a karyotype. It can spot deviations from the normal. This by-product of space research may ultimately make cytogenetic diagnosis or screening available to all.

With the development of highly refined and specific cytogenetic techniques has come the recognition of a whole family of inherited abnormalities and diseases caused by gross errors in chromosome number or composition. The so-called autosomal dominant or recessive disorders like Tay-Sachs disease, Huntington's chorea, the Joseph family illness, sickle cell anemia, and cystic fibrosis result from relatively small biochemical defects in only one or two genes. Diseases of chromosomal origin involve the inappropriate addition, deletion, or rearrangement of hundreds of linked genes, most, if not all, containing perfectly normal and functional DNA sequences.

Although the gross chromosomal abnormality is generally visible in a karyotype, it is not understood how this apparent abnormality causes a patient's condition. While the most unskilled observer can detect the presence or absence of chromosomes in an idiogram, the most skilled geneticist cannot say how the abnormal chromosome number or arrangement causes its symptoms. This is just the opposite of the situation that exists with disorders caused by single abnormal genes. No one has ever seen a faulty gene. Scientists *have* seen faulty chromosomes. Nevertheless, it is possible in many cases to pinpoint the precise molecular defect that is caused by the aberrant gene. The missing or altered enzyme can be localized. It is even possible to describe the precise abnormality of gene structure that causes the defective arrangement of amino acids in the enzymatic protein. In the case of chromosomal abnormalities, it is now possible to tell only how a chromosomal abnormality occurs.

Trouble may begin even before a sperm cell fertilizes the egg. Frequently difficulty takes place during the reduction division, or meiosis, of the parental gamete. As the chromosomes divide in the middle of the intermediary sex cell, two sets of chromosomes or chromatids usually separate and migrate to the two daughter cells. Occasionally a pair of chromatids sticks together and fails to separate following cell division. The centromere does not properly divide. One gamete receives both chromosomes and the other gets none. This process is called nondisjunction. It can probably occur with any chromosome. For reasons not fully understood, it happens most frequently with chromosomes of pair 21. When a gamete containing an extra chromosome is fertilized by or fertilizes a normal gamete, the resulting cell has forty-seven chromosomes instead of the normal forty-six. The extra chromosome will produce abnormalities frequently leading to death or disease (Figure 26).

A mechanism that gives rise to abnormalities similar to the ones produced by nondisjunction is called translocation. In this process part or all of a chromo-

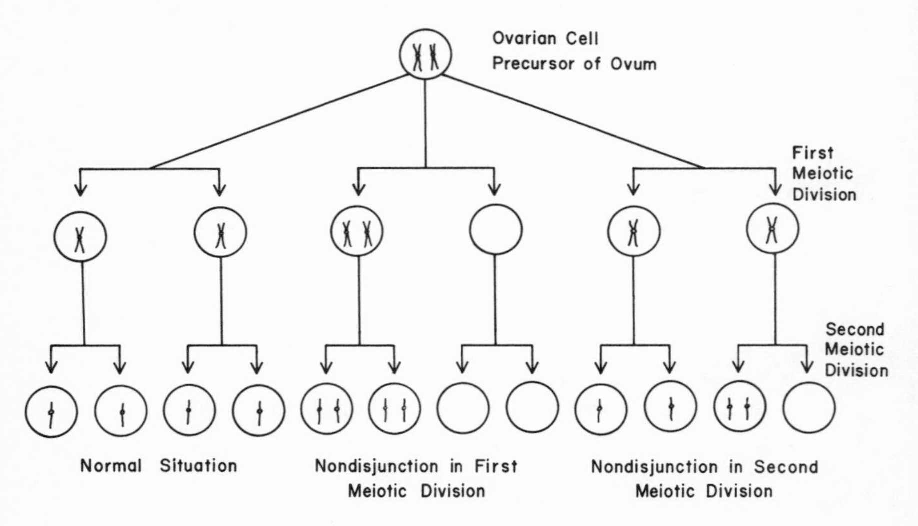

FIGURE 26. *Meiotic nondisjunction. The origin of trisomy. There are two distinct divisions in normal oogenesis or spermatogenesis, and nondisjunction can occur at either of these first and second meiotic divisions. In the normal division a diploid precursor cell with 46 chromosomes is converted to 2 gametes, or sex cells, each containing the haploid number of 23 chromosomes. With nondisjunction the gametes contain 23 plus or minus one. When fertilized by a normal gamete, the former results in a trisomy and the latter in a monosomy.*

some attaches itself to another chromosome. An individual who carries a translocated chromosome often suffers no apparent ill effect because there is a full and normal complement of genetic material in his or her cells. Although the linked genes have been rearranged, what is missing in one place is balanced by its existence elsewhere. The potential for trouble occurs with the next generation when the ovum or sperm is formed and then fertilized.

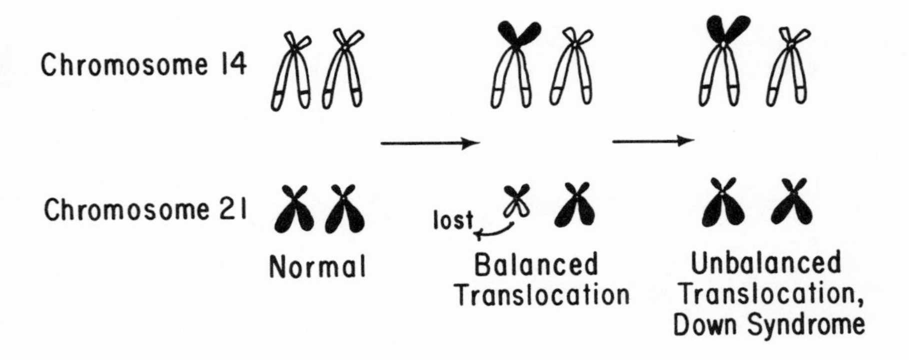

FIGURE 27. *Translocation. The chromosomes 14 and 21 join by centric fusion after each has lost the tiny pieces on the top or short end. The individual in the middle has lost the fragment with the two very small pieces and is in balance even though she has only 45 chromosomes. In mating with a normal person, one possible result is a child who receives both the translocation chromosome and two more number-21 chromosomes. This child is effectively trisomic for the Down syndrome even though he has no more than 46 chromosomes, and he has all the features of the syndrome.*

The person who carries a translocated number-21 chromosome on, for example, the number-22 chromosome has 45 chromosomes instead of the normal 46. However, the genetic material of all 46 is present and functional. Reduction division in such a person produces several different types of sex cells instead of the standard in which each bears 23 chromosomes. Assuming that all but the number-21 and number-22 chromosomes divide normally, and that these cells fertilize or are fertilized by normal gametes, there are four possible genotypes for the offspring. There may be a child who is missing a number-21 or number-22 chromosome; a completely normal child with the proper complement of both number-21 and number-22 chromosomes; a child who is normal but carries the translocated chromosome in balanced fashion; or a child who has two normal number-21 chromosomes and the translocation chromosome that contains an extra number-21 chromosome fused to one of the number-22 chromosomes. This last individual would definitely suffer from a crippling disease.

It is important to appreciate the different patterns of inheritance in nondisjunction as compared with translocation. In the case of translocation, the

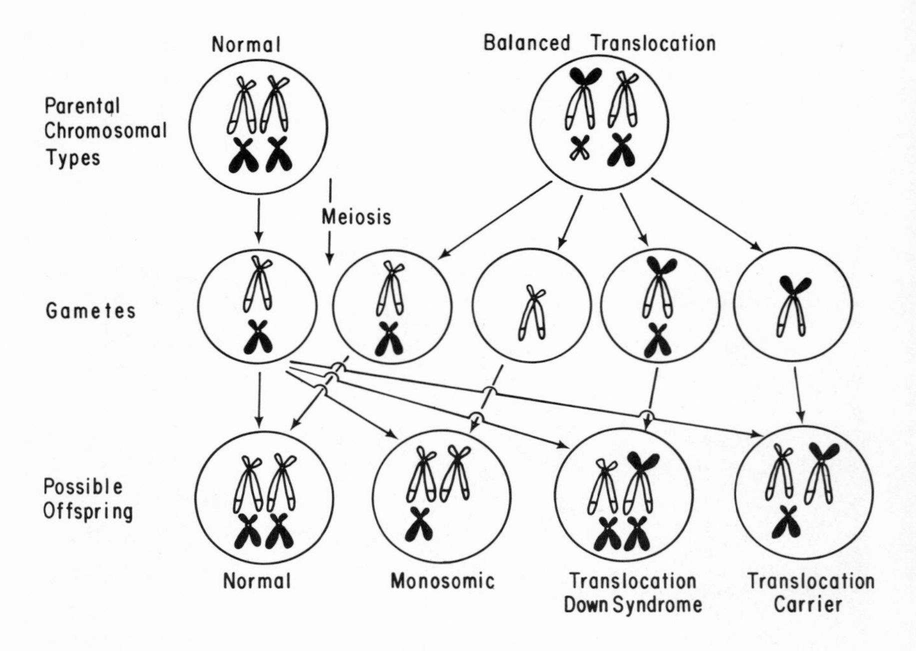

FIGURE 28. *The possibilities that occur when a translocation carrier has children. Schematic representation of the possible outcomes of a union between a person with a balanced 14/21 translocation and a normal individual.*

abnormality is inherited in the majority of instances. It is possible for a translocation to occur by spontaneous chromosomal change, but usually that change results in a balanced translocation. Translocated chromosomes can be transmitted from generation to generation by persons of normal appearance and intelligence when the translocation is balanced. In families in which the presence of a translocated chromosome has been established, it is possible to ensure against the birth of a child with extra chromosomal material. Amniocentesis performed very early in a pregnancy can detect whether or not the fetus has a normal complement of chromosomes.

When nondisjunction or translocation produces an individual with a third autosome, the condition is called a trisomy. In the trisomy described above, which involves the number-21 pair of chromosomes, the genetic condition is known as trisomy 21. In most instances a trisomy for one of the larger chromosomes causes so great a malformation that the fetus does not survive to birth. If the baby does survive, death ensues in early infancy. A certain number of individuals have been reported with trisomy 13 and trisomy 18. These infants have multiple and major defects that usually produce death shortly after birth.

Chromosomes 13 and 18, though larger than chromosome 21, are relatively small in comparison with other autosomes. Trisomies of autosomal chromosomes any larger are to be expected only in fetuses that have been aborted spontaneously.

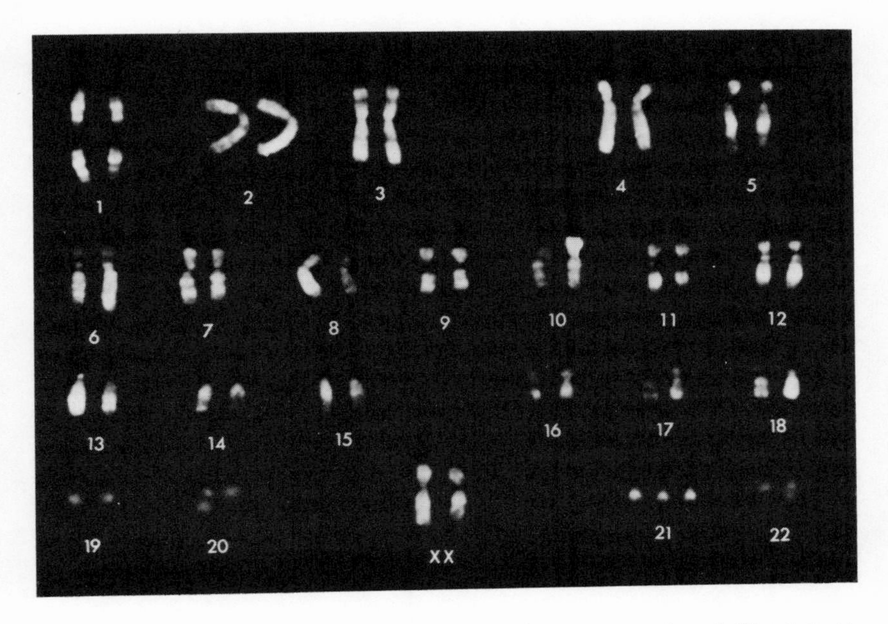

FIGURE 29. *Trisomy 21. The three fluorescent number-21 chromosomes are shown brilliantly in this preparation.*

Monosomies, in which there is only one of a pair of autosomes, have rarely been found. The reason is thought to be that damage caused by a missing chromosome is so great that the fertilized egg is not viable and is never even implanted in the uterus. This assumption may not be correct. Monosomy for the X chromosome is rather common. Such individuals often live into adulthood. At least one individual has been described who is monosomic for chromosome number 21. This child was discovered by Dr. Felix de la Cruz and his colleagues at the National Institute of Child Health and Development. She was retarded but only mildly so and exhibited only the most minor malformations. Her eyes were slanted downward in the opposite direction from that associated with Oriental persons. This is a rather common condition found in people with normal genotypes. It is possible that the absence of an autosome may not be particularly lethal, especially if all the genes on the existing chromosome are functional. The alleles normally present on a complementary chromosome may not be essential for life. It is possible that monosomic individuals may be undetected because of their normal appearance. The results of studies of groups of newborn infants do not support this idea, but there is still doubt about the issue.

Diseases caused by chromosomal deletions are just now being recognized and studied. Deletions are in a way related to chromosomal translocations. In order for a translocation to occur, there must be a prior deletion. This process in itself results in no abnormality as long as the genetic material remains completely balanced. The problem comes with succeeding generations when a child inherits the translocated chromosome with its extra linked genes along with a full complement of the normal chromosomes. Then the child is trisomic for the extra piece. The other possible result occurs when a parent has a balanced translocation and a child inherits the chromosome with the missing piece.

The best known of the chromosomal deletion diseases is the *cri-du-chat* syndrome. It got its name from French workers who first described it and the meowlike cry of the affected child, in whom there is faulty development of laryngeal structures. The patients tend to lose the feline cry as they get older, but they do not develop speech. They are very severely retarded and they have a characteristic appearance. This disorder is caused by deletion of the short arm of chromosome number 5.

Another malformation is a syndrome caused by deletion of the short arm of chromosome number 4. These patients have midline structural defects ranging from clefts of the lip and palate to the genitals. They are extremely retarded and may not live as long as some of the *cri-du-chat* patients.

Another type of chromosomal alteration leads to the development of isochromosomes. This condition is hard to describe but easy to see. It is illustrated in Figure 30. The cause is a horizontal rather than a longitudinal division of the centromere, the point of attachment of the chromatids generally found near the center of a single chromosome. The result of this faulty division is that some of the gametes contain a chromosome with only long arms or with only short arms. If a cell with only short arms is fertilized by a normal gamete, the resulting zygote, or fertilized egg, will be trisomic for short arms and monosomic for long arms. Some genes will be present in but one allelic form while others will occur in the abnormal triplicate. Isochromosomes have so far been demonstrated only for the X chromosome.

A more common condition is mosaicism. This situation is something like the one that occurs in twinning. For unknown reasons, early in the life of a zygote there is a development of two distinct cell populations. In contradistinction to the identical twin condition, these two cell populations are genetically different. Both populations, each with its separate genotype, remain in one individual. Such a person is a genetic composite. The easiest way to understand the genetic condition in such an individual is to think of nondisjunction in

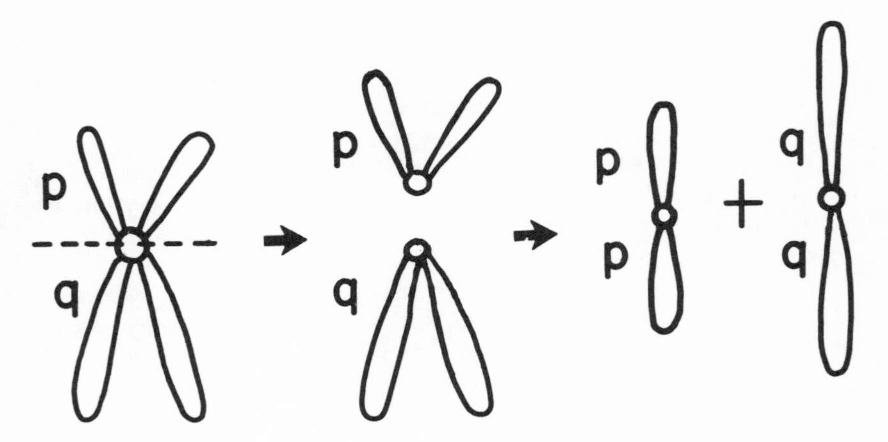

FIGURE 30. *Isochromosomes. The long arms are designated by q and the short arms by p. The misdivision is at the centromere during metaphase. Normally the chromosome divides along the vertical axis, but here it divides horizontally. This leads to the formation of gametes (spermatozoa or ova) containing only long arms (q-q) or only short arms (p-p), whereas the normal situation is for each gamete to have a (p) and a (q).*

mitosis. This is illustrated in Figure 31. A mitotic nondisjunction, let us say for chromosome 21, could lead, if it occurred early enough, to an individual who was trisomic for this chromosome. If the nondisjunction occurred later in the

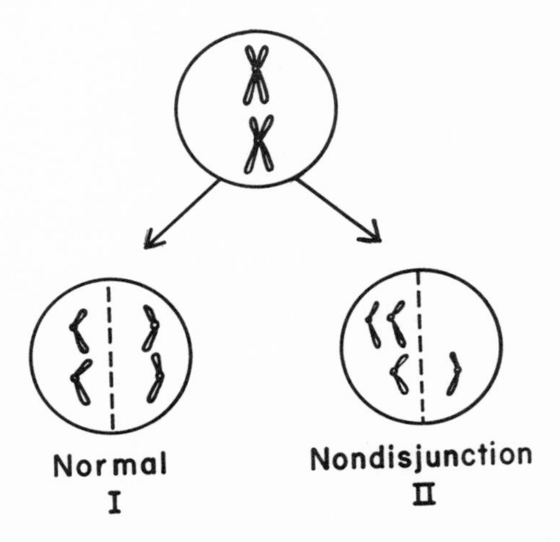

FIGURE 31. *Mitotic nondisjunction. At the top is the cell containing a pair of chromosomes in metaphase that have already replicated themselves. Normally they separate, as in I, and the next step is division into two cells. Nondisjunction is shown in II, in which one of the pairs has failed to separate. This results in one trisomic and one monosomic cell. If either persists along with the normal cell line I, the result is a mosaic.*

development of the embryo, both the normal and trisomic cell populations might prove viable. The baby might end up with a certain number of normal cells and a certain number of cells with trisomy 21. Such a baby would express some signs of disease and some features of normality.

The years to come are expected to bring identification of a whole new group of more subtle chromosomal abnormalities. The defects they cause are believed to be more subtle than the major malformation syndromes now recognized as trisomies and deletions.

Maps of individual chromosomes are making it possible for geneticists to describe translocations and deletions of chromosomes with much greater detail and accuracy than ever before. A condition first thought of as a trisomy might now be seen as nothing of the sort. The extra chromosome could be identified as a broken-off bit of another chromosome. The new techniques have opened a whole new era of cytogenetics.

The development of quinacrine stains that made sections of chromosomes glow in the fluorescence microscope and the methods that followed to produce very different patterns of banding were major advances in cytogenetic diagnosis. For the first time there is a sure way of telling similar chromosomes apart without doubt and of identifying a piece of a chromosome wherever it is present or absent. *Nature,* the century-old British scientific journal that measures its words carefully, said simply: "The implications for human cytogenetics can only be described as staggering."

8.
Autosomes and Disease: The Down Syndrome

A professor of biology was asked how to distinguish a girl student from a boy student. They all seem to wear long denim pants and have equally long hair. He replied, "You look in their genes." "Did you say 'jeans'?" he was asked. Contrary to general belief, it is not always easy or even possible to determine an individual's gender by examining the genitalia. The appearance of the sexual organs and other usual clues to gender may be equivocal or downright misleading. In these cases, a study of the chromosomes is the only way to resolve the question. The pair of sex chromosomes is involved in many abnormalities and diseases.

The consequences of an abnormality of a sex chromosome, by addition or deletion, may be less severe than an abnormality among autosomal chromosomes. It appears that the vast majority of embryos that bear a large abnormality among their autosomes are never born. One recent study found that an abnormality of an autosomal chromosome occurs in 20 percent of fetuses that are spontaneously aborted, miscarried, or stillborn. The damage done even by an extra one of the smaller chromosomes is probably so great that the bearer of the abnormality cannot survive even in the protective environment of the womb. It is believed that a much greater percentage of individuals with sex chromosome abnormalities survive and are born. Many grow up and become adults.

There are exceptions to the rule that abnormalities among autosomes are inevitably fatal before birth. The most important exception is the autosomal abnormality that causes the Down syndrome, or mongolism. A syndrome is a group of symptoms that occur in association, so patients with any one syndrome have a number of characteristic abnormalities that usually permit ready recognition. The most important feature of the Down syndrome is mental retardation. This syndrome is caused by extra chromosomal material associated with chromosome 21. In most patients with the Down syndrome there are three number-21 chromosomes. This abnormal chromosome number is called trisomy 21. The disease occurs once in every six hundred or so births in the

United States. It is the single most common of the defined causes of mental retardation.

The Down syndrome has been called mongolism because affected individuals have slanted eyes that give them a somewhat Oriental appearance. No one likes that name. More properly, the disease is referred to by the name of Langdon Down, the British physician who first described it in 1866.

Most physicians can recognize an older child or adult with the Down syndrome at a glance. Many people who are not physicians can do the same. Recognition in the newborn is not so easy. Immediate diagnosis is often missed for some time. This causes serious difficulties among those concerned. Adjustment to the idea that a child has the Down syndrome is difficult enough once the diagnosis has been made. It is best to begin this adjustment as soon as possible. Essential decisions about care, treatment, and further reproduction should be made early to be effective.

Affected children are diminutive. They are also appealing and eminently lovable. One of the smallest features about them is their little fifth fingers, which are curved inward. Their hands frequently bear creases that run horizontally across the palm. In most people the top crease curves upward toward the index finger while the next line curves downward away from the index finger. In addition to the slanted eyes, these children often have an epicanthus, an extra fold at the inner curve of the upper eyelid. There is often a rather wide separation between the first and second toes, as if affected individuals had been wearing clogs or getas. Faces are very small, and as they grow, the tongue develops more rapidly than the mouth. It is often fissured and because of its size tends to hang loosely from the tiny jaw. In infancy these children are often very limp; their muscles and tendons lack tone. This influences the rate at which they begin to walk and show other signs of physical development. They are mentally retarded. I.Q. usually ranges from twenty to seventy, with a median between forty and fifty, in contrast to a normal rating of about one hundred. Development does occur, but it is slow. Most walk by the third or fourth year. Nearly all have simple language skills by five.

Children with the Down syndrome often have a tenuous hold on life, particularly in infancy. Many of them suffer from major malformations of important organs. The most common is congenital heart disease. Many Down children have symptoms typical of blue babies who have congenital heart disease. The coloration results from defects in circulation that cause the blue color of highly concentrated, deoxygenated blood to be visible through the skin. Many of the children have cardiac defects that are incurable and lead to early death. Others can be helped by surgery. This raises challenging ethical questions for the physician and the family.

If an affected individual has an I.Q. of forty, is it justified to undertake an expensive and major surgical procedure to correct a condition that would otherwise shorten the patient's life and relieve both family and society of an inevitable burden? There are many different answers, none of them right for every situation. For a child who has been living at home and has learned to love and be loved by his parents, the answer is most often in the affirmative. Many of these children are being helped by cardiac surgery. The problem is tougher with some of the intestinal anomalies that infants exhibit. Many are incompatible with life unless surgically corrected. Parents often feel very differently about prolonging life at this early stage. The same is true of physicians and surgeons. Each problem must be individualized. Each requires vision and real understanding. None of the solutions is simple.

One issue is relatively easy to resolve. That is the economic dilemma these children pose. A society as rich as ours and as profligate in its ways of expending national resources can certainly afford to care for all its children and provide each with the best medical service available.

Children with the Down syndrome have a curious propensity for developing leukemia. The disease is three times more common in individuals with this syndrome than it is among normal children. This may simply provide one more argument for the idea that leukemia is an infectious disease, since children with the Down syndrome are much more susceptible than normal children to all types of viral and bacterial infections. Many of them die of overwhelming infectious diseases. This is less frequent an occurrence now that antibiotics are widely available. Yet contagious diseases are prominent among affected children because many infections work very quickly among the susceptible. Antibiotics provide no relief from viral infections. Even if patients with the Down syndrome survive these problems that lead to death at an early age, they experience premature and rapid aging. Their life span seldom exceeds forty to fifty years.

The adjustment of patients and families to the Down disease is similar to that for mental retardation in general. In this disorder the problem is highlighted by the characteristic physical appearance, which reminds parents, neighbors, strangers, and everyone else of the patient's intellectual limitations.

Obvious symptoms of physical and mental retardation do help promote an early diagnosis of the condition. Although diagnosis is not easy and is often missed, the patient with the Down syndrome is usually recognized early, often at birth. Most parents with retarded children realize slowly and gradually that their child is different from normal. For the family with a child affected by the Down syndrome, there may be a crisis while the baby is still in the hospital nursery.

One of the questions that arises concerns institutionalization. This is an area in which physicians, particularly those who are highly directive, may end up at odds with parents. Conflict is not what parents need. They need understanding. All institutions for the retarded have many patients suffering from the Down syndrome. It is also true that most children with this disorder can be handled readily at home. They are usually pleasant, responsive, and affectionate children. They seldom present behavioral problems. There are many community resources in urban and suburban areas—special schools, sheltered workshops, and day-care centers—that are particularly well suited to help with the child or adult suffering from the Down syndrome.

Decisions about the management of a child with the Down syndrome are tough. It is the family who has to make them. Different decisions are right for different families. An understanding physician can be helpful. He can provide information about the particular child's potential and problems. He can supply information about local facilities. It is true that very few communities have institutions that are suitable for the care of a physically handicapped and mentally retarded young child. Direct placement from the nursery may solve a social problem, but it is seldom in the best interests of the infant. The physician can provide a sympathetic ear and a forum in which the family can reason through its problems and come to the solutions that are best for them and the child.

Almost none of these patients is capable of an independent existence. This creates particular problems as the affected individual reaches adulthood. The vast majority of parents with children having the Down syndrome are considerably older than other parents. Although a workable, meaningful life is often achieved with the child at home, no one lives forever. The older parent is forced to make realistic plans for the child's future. Provision for the care and support of such a child after the parents are no longer alive should be considered with a lawyer and should be included in a will.

Parents' organizations can prove helpful to a family. They afford opportunities for people to talk about and seek out solutions to their common problems. Often they can influence the development of community resources. They give parents an opportunity to do something constructive not only about their own child but about the entire problem. For the child with the Down syndrome the National Association for Retarded Children may be the most appropriate organization for help. There are chapters in most communities. Local resources vary from state to state. Information about what help is available can usually be obtained from the state department of health or from a university medical center.

The Down syndrome may be caused by different genetic mechanisms. These mechanisms are typical of many chromosomal abnormalities. The great majority of individuals with the syndrome, as many as 98 percent, have 47 chromosomes. They are trisomic for chromosome 21 (Figures 26, 29). The nondisjunction that produces trisomy 21 is thought to occur most frequently in the maternal gamete. When the egg cell bearing a pair of number-21 chromosomes is fertilized by a normal sperm cell bearing a single chromosome, the resulting child will be trisomic for that chromosome. Although the mechanisms are unknown, it is clear that the presence of the additional chromosome produces the symptoms associated with the disorder.

The conclusion that this nondisjunction is maternal comes from evidence that is indirect but good. Occurrence of the disease is closely associated with the age of the mother. Its incidence rises from one in two thousand births when a woman is twenty-five years of age to one in forty births when she is forty-five. Since there is no similar association with the age of the father, the error probably occurs in the ovum. There is some evidence that certain women are prone to meiotic abnormality. A woman who has borne one child with the disease has a five times greater risk of bearing another.

The mechanism that gives rise to the remaining 2 percent of individuals with the syndrome who do not have trisomy 21 is known as translocation. In this process part or all of a chromosome 21 attaches itself to another chromosome, usually in the D or G group. The person who carries such a translocated chromosome 21, for instance on a chromosome 14 (Figures 27, 28), has 45 chromosomes instead of the normal 46. Because the genetic material for all 46 chromosomes is present, the individual tends to be unaffected and unaware of his or her abnormal autosomal complement. Problems with a translocated chromosome 21 are reserved for the offspring. During reduction division, or meiosis, an affected individual will produce four distinctly different kinds of gametes (Figure 28): one bearing normal chromosomes 21 and 14; a second bearing a normal chromosome 21 and a 14 with an extra translocated piece of chromosome 21; a third bearing a normal chromosome 14 and no chromosome 21; and a fourth bearing a number-14 chromosome with a translocated chromosome 21. If this individual marries a person normal for both chromosomes, the probability is that one-quarter of the offspring will bear normal chromosomes, one-quarter will be monosomic for chromosome 21, one-quarter will be normal but bear a translocated chromosome in balanced fashion; and one-quarter will have the Down syndrome. If a mother has a balanced 21/14 translocation, the odds are one in three that she will bear a child with the disorder. Because translocations can be inherited from generation to generation, prevention of the Down syndrome that is caused by this mechanism can be accomplished by applying the knowledge gained from amniocentesis performed early in pregnancy.

In the 98 percent of patients with the Down syndrome caused by trisomy 21, prevention poses a different kind of problem. The major feature is the age of the mother. There is an increased probability that a woman who has borne one child with trisomy 21 will have another. Nondisjunction can occur in a mother of any age with no prior history of the phenomenon. The numbers of nondisjunctions occurring in older mothers are so overwhelming that amniocentesis and analysis of the fetal karyotype in every pregnancy in which the mother is over thirty-five or forty would markedly reduce the incidence of the disease.

With the development of precise cytogenetic techniques for the characterization of chromosomes, fluorescent and Giemsa methods, answers have been provided to many old questions about autosomal aberrations. Patients with trisomy 21 have an abnormal propensity for leukemia. It is true that the so-called Philadelphia chromosome is associated with one chronic form of leukemia. This abnormal chromosome has been thought to be a partially deleted chromosome number 22. Some researchers assumed that in certain patients with the Down syndrome, the extra chromosome might be a piece that included the deleted genes from the chromosome 22 or that some patients with the syndrome might have trisomy 22 rather than trisomy 21. Either idea would tie the Philadelphia chromosome and leukemia together into a neat package. Since patients with the Down syndrome suffer from acute leukemia, a very different disease from the chronic leukemia in which the Philadelphia chromosome is found, this idea held little widespread appeal. Speculation came to an end with the development of the fluorescence method for characterizing and identifying chromosomes. Banding patterns reveal that the Philadelphia chromosome is clearly a number 22. All patients with the Down syndrome are trisomic for chromosome 21. Thus, there is no relationship between the Philadelphia chromosome and trisomy 21. Although this explanation for leukemia has been disproved, research into the question led to recognition of a separate syndrome, trisomy 22. Its characteristics are quite distinct from those of the Down syndrome.

In counseling families at risk for abnormalities of the autosomes, the problems faced in the Down syndrome apply quite generally. The risk of any kind of trisomy, not just 21, is greatest in the mother over forty. The overall risk of the syndrome in the general population is 1.5 per 1,000 live births. If a couple of unspecified age should come to the medical geneticist having read or heard about the Down syndrome, expecting a child, and worried about the possibility of the disorder, counseling would begin with the fact that in the general population such an abnormality is rare. The geneticist would ask a number of subsequent questions. One is about previous children and the occurrence of the Down syndrome. If no affected child had been born to this couple, the geneticist would be interested in the age of the prospective mother. If she were twenty-five, there would be no reason for realistic worry. This is the time of lowest risk. There is about one chance in 2,000 for the disease. If she were thirty-five, the risk would become one in 250. This risk is cause for real concern. It would be advisable for the pregnancy to be monitored by amniocentesis.

Counseling in the family in which there has been a child with the Down syndrome differs greatly. The parents may have only one child, the affected individual. They are often interested in bearing more children, but understandably do not wish to risk another with the same disease. The geneticist would first prepare a karyotype of the patient's cells. If the child had the translocation type of the Down syndrome, the next step would be to determine if it were inherited. Blood samples from both parents would be obtained and their individual karyotypes examined for translocation. The vast majority of translocations are sporadic, new genetic events, just like the typical nondisjunction producing trisomy. Some are inherited, and in these cases the risk of further childbearing is greatest. The least optimistic situation is that in which either parent is found to have a 21/21 translocation. In this situation 100 percent of the offspring will have the Down syndrome. Counsel for these parents is to seek additional children by adoption. If the father has a 21/22 or other D/21 translocation, the risk of an affected child is less than one in 50. In this situation the couple might cautiously decide on amniocentesis. If the mother has one of these translocations, the risk of another involved child would be 20 to 33 percent. This statistic is so high that only by a commitment to amniocentesis, a readiness to accept therapeutic abortion, and more than one pregnancy, would it be likely that such a couple could bear a normal baby. If the patient is found to have mosaicism, two concurrent cellular populations of different genotype, the risk of recurrence is very low. If the patient has ordinary trisomy 21 or sporadic translocation, the risk for recurrence is slightly higher than that for the general population. The difference is minimal. The same age factors do apply.

In general it is recommended that if one of these lower risk families who has already borne a child with the Down syndrome wishes to have further children, the pregnancy be monitored by amniocentesis. This substitutes definitive information for theoretical risk factors. It can also prove reassuring. Confronted with some of the kinds of risks discussed above, some families, of course, elect not to have further children of their own. This is reasonable, particularly for the older parent. The job of the counselor is to find in conjunction with the parents what is the best solution for them.

9.
An Extra Y Chromosome

Mickey was a hellion, the sort of student whom teachers would rather not have in class. Tall and gangling, not overly bright, he was forever in trouble—throwing tantrums, cursing his teacher, fighting with other students. He often failed to show up for school. He was well known to the truant officer. Teachers considered him a slow learner. Because of his behavioral problems, he was referred to a pediatric clinic. In the clinic a sharp-eyed doctor spotted something that shed a whole new light on Mickey's problems.

It was a rather simple observation that led to understanding. Instead of holding his arms normally at his sides, Mickey held them out at an odd angle. The doctors who had examined him first did not notice this curious rigidity. He was about to leave the clinic when an acute diagnostician recognized that Mickey could not rotate his forearms. An X ray showed the reason. Two major bones of his arm, the radius and ulna, were abnormally fused at their upper end. They obviously had been like this from birth. The only other characteristics that distinguished Mickey from other boys was his considerable height and his below-average I.Q. of seventy-five.

Acting on an educated hunch, his pediatrician ordered a chromosomal analysis of Mickey's blood cells. The doctor found what he had suspected. The laboratory reported a chromosomal abnormality. Mickey's cells contained 47 chromosomes. Instead of the usual complement of two sex chromosomes, a large X and a small Y, Mickey had three sex chromosomes, one X and two Y's.

This discovery removed Mickey from the category of the ordinary behavior problem and put him in a much more troublesome classification, that of the XYY male. The anomaly of an extra Y chromosome has been known for less than a decade. It has raised difficult medical, ethical, and legal problems. It poses questions for society as a whole.

The problem of the XYY male is not primarily physical. Although a variety of congenital abnormalities has been found in such males, including the problem of fused forearms that aroused Mickey's pediatrician, no one common set of defects has been identified in those with the XYY genotype. Such men tend to be taller than average, but so are many men whose karyotypes are perfectly normal. When basketball teams have been cytogenetically screened, the results have revealed no carriers of the XYY defect.

It is the antisocial behavioral patterns associated with the extra Y chromosome that are cause for concern. While the picture is not yet clear, it does seem that some XYY males are predisposed to antisocial and often violent behavior. In children that behavior can take the form of school problems such as those that brought Mickey to the clinic. In adults the extra Y has been associated with acts of violence ranging from assault to rape or murder.

It could be that this association represents a cause and effect relationship. The extra Y chromosomal material may in some fashion program aggressive antisocial behavior in an individual. An exact relationship has not been defined. Environmental and other genetic factors certainly influence the effect of the extra Y. Finding this additional sex chromosome in individuals who have committed crimes of violence is highly provocative. It suggests that at least some males are born with a biochemical predisposition to violence. This inbred, instinctual behavior may exist beyond conscious control.

Medical and social institutions are not yet able to handle such a possibility. If an extra Y chromosome is found in a young boy like Mickey, what should be done? Should steps be taken to prevent him from committing a future act of violence? If an extra Y is found in an adult who has committed a criminally violent act, does that establish grounds for lessening his punishment, or at least for committing him to a medical institution as opposed to a penal institution? In places where the death penalty still applies, would this chromosomal finding commute that usual sentence? These are questions of importance. The answers are not yet available in either law or medicine.

It is perhaps too soon to expect guiding principles to have emerged. The first XYY individual was recognized in 1961. The association of this abnormal genotype with behavioral problems began with a report in the December 25, 1965, issue of *Nature*. Dr. Patricia A. Jacobs of Edinburgh, one of the world's leading cytogeneticists, had begun chromosomal analyses of mental patients hospitalized in Scotland. A pattern relating the XYY condition to exceptional aggression began to emerge.

A study of 197 men who were incarcerated in institutions for the criminally insane was reported under the title "Aggressive Behavior, Mental Subnormality and the XYY Male" by Dr. Jacobs and her associates. She found seven patients who bore the XYY genotype and one who was XXYY. There were eight instances of extra Y chromosomes among the genotypes of just under two hundred men in one institution. This institution brought together individuals who were not only mentally subnormal but who were hard to manage, difficult, or violent. Many were incarcerated following crimes of violence. In a comparison or control group of 266 infants, there was none with an extra Y chromosome. Among all patients previously studied, a group of fifteen hundred highly abnormal individuals, there was only one with an extra Y chromosome.

Among the inmates with the XYY constitution, all were tall. One of every four patients over six feet in height had an extra Y chromosome. All these men had subnormal intelligence. Their I.Q.s were typically in the seventies or eighties.

Shortly thereafter, Dr. M. D. Casey of Sheffield University in England found an incidence of extra Y chromosomes similar to that reported by Dr. Jacobs among the inmates of British special-security hospitals. There followed a number of other studies from both sides of the Atlantic that reported similar results. At last count there were eleven such reports, mostly from the United States and Europe. They provided striking evidence for a higher than normal percentage of XYY individuals among selected male populations in prisons and mental hospitals. Approximately 3 to 4 percent of these males had the extra Y, but the values ranged from 2 to 12 percent in different studies. Almost all the men were tall and mentally dull. Often they were selected for special-security incarceration because they were dangerous or violent. The incidence of homosexuality was considerably higher in one series than in a control group. On the average, the XYY males had been convicted of crimes earlier in life than the average prisoner. Most of them came from respectable families of all social classes. In their respective families the XYY males were the classic black sheep. In contrast, a majority of inmates in any institution reflects a cultural deprivation that also affects other, non-inmate members of the family.

The publicity given to these reports quickly made the XYY condition a legal issue as well as a medical problem. "The implications of gross chromosomal errors for the individual's legal status before the law and for society that must provide either care or parole are fundamental," said Dr. Mary A. Telfer, a biologist at the Elwyn Institute near Philadelphia. "Is society, for example, morally justified in invoking the death penalty against a person with chromosomal abnormalities?"

That question was quickly asked in courts of law. In 1968 in Melbourne an Australian laborer who stabbed and killed a seventy-seven-year-old widow was acquitted of murder after a prison psychiatrist testified that the laborer bore an extra Y chromosome that was to blame for his crime. In Los Angeles a thirty-three-year-old XYY man raped and battered a woman in a parked car. He pleaded innocent by reason of insanity. One of the most sensational cases was that of Daniel Hugon, a thirty-one-year-old French drifter who had spent hours drinking beer and landed in a Paris hotel with a sixty-five-year-old prostitute. He was soon in the arms of Morpheus, not Venus. He slept like a log. When he awakened, his companion asked him for fifty francs, or about ten dollars, for her vigilant labors. He gave her the money but then became madly infuriated and strangled her to death. He was found to have the XYY genotype. The defense did not secure an acquittal on this basis, but Daniel was sentenced to only seven years in prison, much less than the maximum possible in France. If he had been acquitted on the grounds of insanity, he might have spent the rest of his life in an institution for the insane.

An interesting story is that of Richard Speck. It began on July 14, 1966. A man had successively murdered eight student nurses in a southside Chicago apartment. The enormity of the crime in itself was sensational. Its horror seemed more intense because the crime had been witnessed from beginning to end. The murderer had overlooked one potential victim. She eluded the carnage by hiding under a bed. This young woman was terrified but survived and was able to identify the suspect. He was promptly arrested and brought to trial.

Richard Speck, the suspect, was convicted of the crimes. He received an enormous amount of press attention both before and after his trial. He was a tall white male with a low mentality. He had a record of numerous previous arrests and convictions for violent acts: malicious destruction, perjury, forgery, and aggravated assault. He was viewed as a hopeless person, "born to raise hell." He needed an able lawyer. He got one, Gerald W. Getty, the public defender for Cook County.

Because the first report of the XYY syndrome appeared in December 1965, interest was at its height about the time Speck was arrested. A number of cytogeneticists wondered whether or not he might have an extra Y chromosome. One of them, Dr. Eric Engle of Vanderbilt University, wrote to the man's attorney and proposed a confidential study of his client's chromosomes. Mr. Getty promptly accepted the proposal. Blood cells were obtained, grown in the laboratory, analyzed, and the results were reported confidentially to the attorney.

By the spring of 1968 the XYY trials in Paris, Los Angeles, and Melbourne were all in full swing. Major newspapers in the United States carried stories about Speck. They indicated that he was an XYY. Interviews with geneticists and psychologists were carried in reliable newspapers. A well-known laboratory of human genetics was quoted as having determined that Speck's genotype was XYY. The stories suggested that the appeal of the death sentence, which had been imposed during the interim, be argued on the basis of this genetic defect.

In this climate Dr. Engle reviewed the results. He had found the man's chromosomes to be normal, or XY. He communicated with Mr. Getty and found that no other laboratory had studied the genotype. He obtained another blood sample. The results were the same. Richard Speck was an ordinary XY male. All the reports in the press were unfounded.

Appeal was concluded on November 22, 1968, at which time the court upheld the previous verdict and the death penalty. The defense was brilliant. Mr. Getty contended, among other things, that this was a cruel and unusual punishment. He never said anything about chromosomal abnormality. On November 25, 1968, he released to the Associated Press the results of the two chromosomal analyses. Although the facts have been published, the legend tends to live. Richard Speck's name is usually raised whenever the XYY syndrome is discussed.

As these cases were being fought in the courts, new scientific evidence about the significance of the extra Y chromosome was growing. Investigators began describing the presence of an extra Y chromosome in men whose intelligence was in the normal range and who were living normal, peaceful lives. Two such men were found among the ranks of the King Size Club, an organization of exceptionally tall men in Sweden. An unusual report came from London, where physicians at Maudsley described a twenty-six-year-old XYY male whose I.Q. was 118, well above normal. His one crime had been embezzlement, skillfully planned and executed. It was discovered only by a chance change in auditors. These reports have enlarged the spectrum of affected types. Not all XYY males are retarded or violent.

Screening of the chromosomes of large numbers of unselected males has shown that the XYY abnormality is rather common. A study of 2,222 newborn male babies in New Haven, Connecticut, turned up three that were XYY. A study of 3,500 newborns in Scotland found five XYY's. A study of 1,066 newborns in Ontario found one XYY. These numbers are considerably lower than the incidence of XYY in the institutions for those with problem behavior. About one of every 1,000 newborn boys typically has an XYY chromosomal constitution. Since the mortality rate of XYY men is not higher than average, one of every 1,000 adult men should be an XYY male. This would mean that there are 100,000 XYY men in the United States alone. Having an extra Y appears not to be a sure guarantee of a violent, antisocial life. The problem of the extra Y is more complex than it first appeared.

The entire picture of the genetic role of the Y chromosome is only gradually being clarified. It has not always been clear that the Y chromosome had any role in genetics. Early geneticists who studied animals and flies tended to feel that maleness was the result of the absence of a second X chromosome. We now know from human studies that this is not so, since a person who is XO, lacking a second sex chromosome, is certainly not a male. Such an individual has the Turner syndrome and cannot reproduce because of a failure of ovarian development. Her appearance is unquestionably female. So the Y chromosome at least determines that the individual will be male and will have masculine genitals. It does not tell what else the Y chromosome might do.

Before the advent of the double-Y syndrome the only characteristic that even tentatively had been thought to be carried on the Y chromosome was a harmless trait known as hairy pinnae. The term implies an unusual growth of hair from the ends of the ears. If a man with this trait does not shave them, his ears become hirsute. This condition is different from the much more common growth of hair inside the ears. First noted in India and Ceylon in the early 1960s, hairy pinnae have since been found in American males and others around the world. Kindred studies of the incidence within families seem to indicate that the condition may be transmitted on the Y chromosome. All the data are not yet reported, and the condition is certainly very minor. It was the first suggestion that the Y chromosome might carry a share of genetic information.

At the State University of New York's Downstate Medical Center in Brooklyn, Dr. James B. Hamilton has conducted animal experiments that have led him to believe that the Y chromosome determines aggressive behavior. By genetic manipulation of a species of fish called the killifish, Dr. Hamilton has created extra-Y individuals. He has reported that in tests in which the extra-Y killifish were matched against the normal males, the extra-Y fish emerged victorious almost every time. He interpreted this as an indication that the extra Y chromosome conveyed an added measure of aggressiveness. If not more aggressive, Dr. Hamilton reported, the extra-Y killifish were at least more competitive.

It is tempting to apply the results of these experiments to human beings. In general men are taller than women. They are typically more aggressive. If the one Y chromosome of the normal male is responsible for the greater height and the greater aggressiveness, then two Y's should make a male unusually tall and unusually aggressive. This does seem to be the case in many XYY males.

Geneticists are not ready to accept this argument as fact. The general professional consensus, based on analysis of the data provided by Dr. Jacobs and others, may be summed up as follows:

> A) In comparison with an XY male, the male with an extra Y chromosome (XYY) incurs some increased risk of developing a psychopathic personality. Any quantitative assessment of the increased propensity toward antisocial behavior simply can not be made on the basis of data currently available.
>
> B) There is no evidence in hand to suggest that an XYY male is invariably bound to express either antisocial or criminal behaviors. Among those XYY males who have been identified and examined, researchers have found a full spectrum of personality types, ranging from the apparently normal to the severely defective. It would be seriously misleading to conclude that XYY males are inevitably predestined to lead lives of crime.

This is an enlightened point of view. It takes into account the fact that normal individuals have been observed with an extra Y chromosome. It is scientifically sound. It is also consistent with the possibility that new information will become available through the follow-up observation of those individuals found at very young ages to have the XYY constitution.

It is important to deal with this problem on the basis of current knowledge. It is clear that there is an increased chance of sociopathic behavior for an XYY individual. In 1972 Drs. Lytt I. Gardner and Richard L. Neu of the Upstate

Medical Center in Syracuse, New York, gathered together all the statistical surveys about the incidence of the XYY situation in both normal newborn babies and in prison populations. The highest incidence among normal newborns screened was one-third of one percent. The incidence in prison populations ranged from 1.8 percent to as high as 12 percent.

These surveys were carried out in predominantly Anglo-Saxon populations throughout the world. More recently Dr. Primarosa de Chieri of the Fundación de Genética Humana in Buenos Aires began a study of the XYY problem with a small group of twenty men randomly drawn from a prison, the Instituto de Detención de Villa DeVoto. Their crimes were serious ones: armed robbery, murder, theft, and sexual assault. The total prison population was 2,060 men from Buenos Aires. Two of the twenty men were found to be XYY individuals. One was nineteen years old and 6 feet, 2 inches tall, which is very tall for a Latin American. He had an oddly shaped ear. He had had a bad case of acne at fifteen. His I.Q. was below normal. Behavior problems began at thirteen years with a sexual assault on a woman. He was in jail for another similar attack. The other XYY man was twenty-four years old and 6 feet, 5 inches tall. He had a normal I.Q. He was incarcerated for assault. A much broader study is now in progress, but this experience, with a 10 percent incidence, suggests how easy it is to find XYY males in a population of men with aberrant behavior. It also suggests that the problem may be worldwide.

The evidence is convincing that some XYY men are more prone to sociopathic behavior than are normal, or XY men. The extra Y chromosome may be the fundamental cause of the behavior. Environmental influences may play a part in its expression.

Latest conclusions leave many issues unresolved. There are no general guidelines for action. Even if the extra Y does predispose an individual toward sociopathic behavior, it is impossible to tell which individual will be affected. Which environmental factors are important are unknown. There may be other genetic influences to be considered as well, for other aspects of a person's genetic makeup may protect him from the sociopathic influence of the extra Y.

Answers to many questions about the XYY syndrome can be provided only by rigorous, long-term studies. These studies must begin with identification of large numbers of XYY males at birth. Observation must continue over the many years of childhood, adolescence, and maturity. Behavior has to be carefully monitored and compared with that of appropriate numbers of genotypically normal XY males. Both the XYY and XY groups must be large if any conclusions are to have statistical significance. Members of the two groups must be of similar social, economic, and educational backgrounds if resulting comparisons are to have any scientific validity. Only in this fashion will it be possible to assess the chances of XYY males developing abnormal behavior patterns as a result of their genotype.

One approach toward treatment of the problems arising from some cases of XYY syndrome is already being tried at the Johns Hopkins University School of Medicine in Baltimore, where Dr. D. S. Borgaonkar is giving a small number of XYY males periodic injections of female hormones. The men volunteered for the treatment because they feared that without the hormones they might commit violent sexual crimes. Many had committed such offenses already. The treatment is drastic. It may eliminate both sexual desire and potency, and it must be continued for prolonged periods. It is not an answer to the XYY problem, but rather an experiment. Its outcome is anticipated with interest.

The XYY syndrome is interesting. Apparently, many XYY males are born with a tendency to violence. On the other hand, the XYY male may never commit a crime. The factors that influence the expression of the genetic tendency are not fully known.

It is socially and ethically complicated to know how to watch the XYY male, particularly if he is identified by a program of screening of normal newborns. It will be important to avoid a social stigma that might be attached to a boy because a screening program has found an extra Y, labeling him as a potential sociopath early in life; this could in itself have a highly destructive influence.

One thing does not seem to be a problem. That is the inheritance of the XYY syndrome. It does not run in families. The XYY is not handed down from father to son. In many cases the extra Y appears to reduce fertility. This may be a blessing. The extra Y first seems to make its appearance during the meiotic divisions of sperm production; it is thus present when the abnormal sperm fertilizes the ovum. This is a kind of genetic accident in men with a normal chromosome count. Studies of sperm from XYY males have indicated that in nearly all the patients studied the second Y chromosome is eliminated by selective nondisjunction before the sperm is formed.

The important question that is raised is whether some forms of behavior can be genetically determined. The story of the XYY syndrome demonstrates that in some individuals a gross chromosomal abnormality can influence behavior. This raises the possibility that there may be more subtle ways in which behavior can be affected by genetic influences. Most of what we recognize in human genetics and in genetic disease is caused by genes that we cannot see. The XYY syndrome may be the visible tip of the iceberg that is behavioral genetics. It may have created opportunities for the scientific investigation of relationships between the genes and personality of an individual.

10.
The X Chromosome

This chapter is about many things: about genetic disease; about people with too many chromosomes; about the downfall of the Russian empire; about people who cannot eat certain kinds of beans; about children with urges to mutilate themselves; and about multicolored mice and tortoiseshell cats.

The connecting thread is the X chromosome. This is a large chromosome. It got its name because an early observer, uncertain of its function, called it "X," for the unknown. It is the larger of the two sex chromosomes by a considerable margin. Normal females have two X chromosomes; normal males have one X along with the much smaller Y chromosome. The stubby little Y confers maleness and appears to carry very few genes. The X chromosome carries many.

These differences make the two sex chromosomes special in the ways their genes are expressed. Unlike every other pair of chromosomes, the X and the Y are unequal. They do not match. There is not a gene on the Y chromosome for every gene on the X chromosome. The kind of protective balance provided by alleles, one on each autosome in a pair, is theoretically possible for the female with her two X chromosomes. In practice this balance is achieved in females but in a much different way. A duplicate system does not exist in the male.

The relative lack of genes on the Y chromosome and the absence of alleles balancing genes on the X chromosome make males susceptible to some genetic conditions that do not usually affect females. If a harmful recessive gene exists on an autosomal chromosome, the odds are favorable that the allelic gene on the complementary chromosome will be normal. The abnormal recessive gene will not express itself, and the carrier will not suffer from the genetic disease.

If the abnormal recessive gene is located on an X chromosome, the female will generally escape its associated disorder. She has another X chromosome to counteract the disease potential of the first. Since a male has only one X chromosome, the effects of an abnormal recessive gene on this chromosome are unopposed by any normal allele. There is a whole class of genetic conditions described as X-linked or sex-linked disorders. They are diseases usually found in males. They are expressed in the absence of a second X chromosome.

The pattern of inheritance of an X-linked recessive genetic disease is distinctive. Females who carry the harmful gene transmit the disease gene to male children who suffer from the disorder. The affected males do not transmit the disease to their children. The defective gene is inherited by their daughters, who become carriers. Since a father transmits only his Y chromosome, not his X, to his sons, male children inherit the essential, normal X chromosome from their mothers. In this fashion an X-linked condition may skip a generation. A man with the disease may have daughters or sons who are all normal. These offspring constitute a "silent generation." Because the defective gene is carried by the daughters, the gene may reappear and express itself in their sons.

Let us look at a family in which a woman carries an abnormal recessive gene on an X chromosome (Figure 32). The normal gene on her complementary X

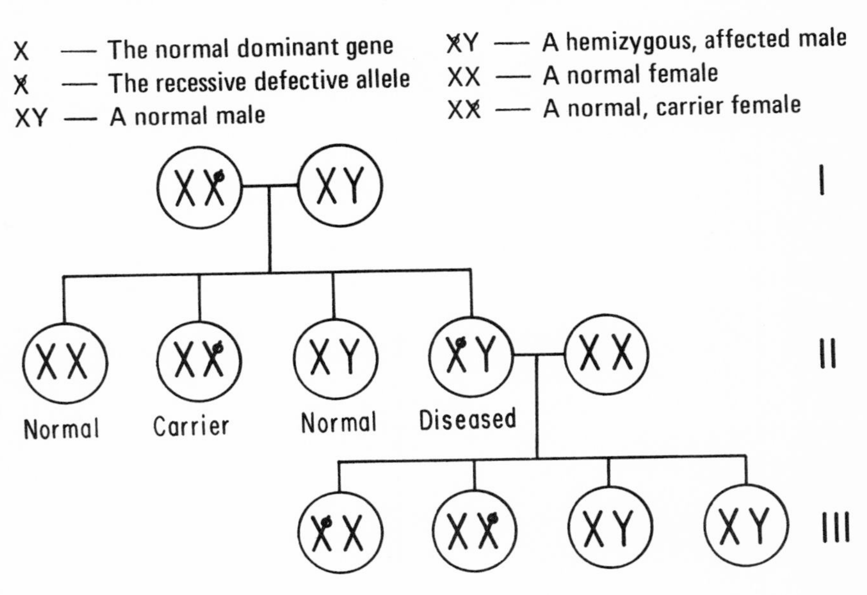

FIGURE 32. *Pattern of inheritance of an X-linked recessive disease in a marriage between a mother who is phenotypically normal but is a carrier of the gene for the disease, as indicated by the circle on one of her X chromosomes, and a father who is normal. The four possible combinations of their genes would be for half the daughters to be carriers like their mother and half the sons to have the disease. This is shown in generation II. If a son with the disease had children, his daughters would in every case be carriers like their grandmother and his sons would be completely normal.*

chromosome masks the effects of the recessive gene, and she appears perfectly normal. If she marries a normal man who does not carry the gene, she will transmit the faulty gene to half her offspring. None of her daughters will show any signs of the disease, but 50 percent of them will be carriers of the gene, like their mother. The sons who receive the gene will have the disease. The risk for inheriting the disease gene among males is such that each time this woman has a son, there is a 50 percent chance of his having the disease. This does not mean that half of the boys in such a family will automatically have the disease or that half of the girls will automatically carry the gene in a family of reasonable size. If there were a hundred children, fifty would predictably bear the faulty gene. If the woman had only two children, neither or both might have the gene. In each pregnancy the odds would be the same, 50 percent each time, regardless of what had happened with previous offspring.

The children of a son who had inherited the disease, both the males and the

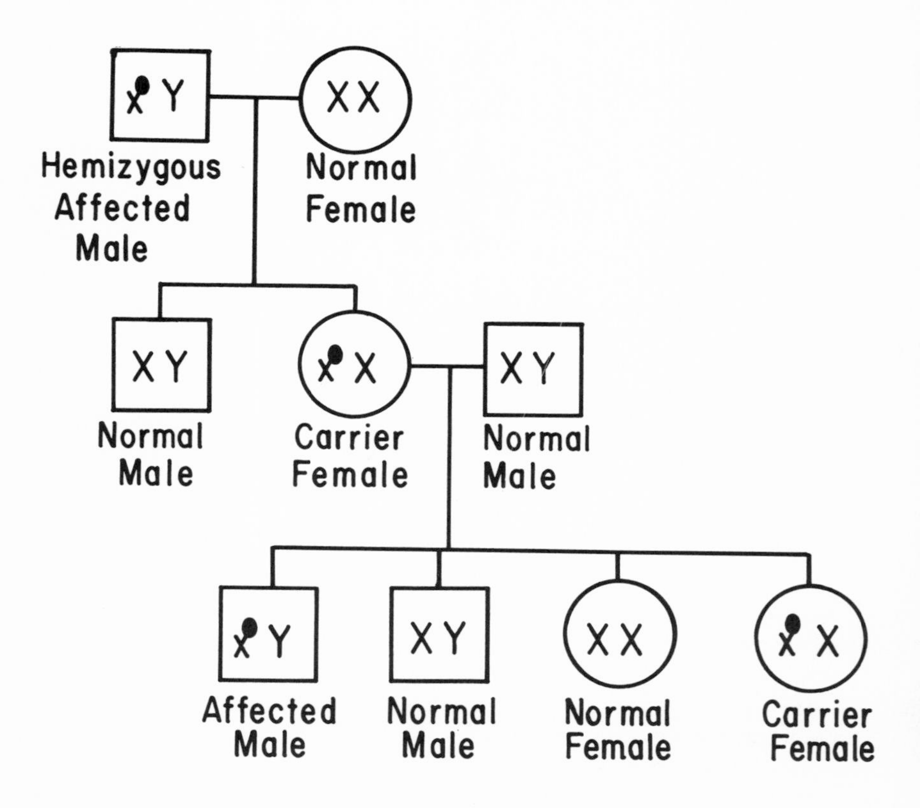

FIGURE 33. *Inheritance of an X-linked disease in a marriage between a normal mother and a hemizygous, affected father.*

females, would be outwardly normal. This would be true if the affected, hemizygous father married a homozygous, normal mother. The male offspring would be genetically sound and could not transmit the gene for their father's disorder to any offspring. The females would all carry the defective gene because each daughter gets her father's only X chromosome. The sons of these females would then have a fifty-fifty chance of inheriting the abnormal gene and expressing the disease. In this way the numbers of individuals involved with an X-linked disease potentially grow with subsequent generations. In this family a single woman carrier may be responsible for the presence of disease among many of her children and even more of her grandchildren. The potential for a wide distribution of a faulty X-linked recessive gene is much greater than for an abnormal autosomal recessive gene.

The best-known family with a serious X-linked disease was that of Queen Victoria and Prince Albert of England. Well-documented royal genealogies suggest that one of Victoria's X chromosomes, inherited from her middle-aged father, had mutated, producing a recessive gene for hemophilia, the dread disease of the blood. Because the normal gene on her complementary X chromosome masked the disease allele, Victoria appeared perfectly normal. Since Prince Albert had a normal gene on his only X chromosome, he was free of the disease.

Victoria's defective gene was transmitted to three of her eight offspring. Five received the normal gene and three received the abnormal allele. None of her four daughters showed any signs of the disease, as each was protected by Albert's normal X. This would have been true no matter how many female offspring the couple produced. Fifty percent of the daughters of such a marriage should be carriers like their mother. Two of Victoria's daughters, Alice and Beatrice, proved to be carriers, which is consistent with the expected ratio. The risk of inheriting the gene for hemophilia among male offspring is such that each time a carrier female bears a son, there is a 50 percent chance of having the disease. Only one of Victoria's four sons, Leopold, had hemophilia. His brothers, Edward VII, Alfred, and Arthur, inherited their mother's normal X chromosome. Leopold inherited the X chromosome with the gene for hemophilia. Unlike his sisters, he enjoyed no allelic protection because he received Albert's Y chromosome.

Victoria and her husband were fortunate that only one son had hemophilia. Had the royal couple borne fifty sons, twenty-five would predictably have been normal and twenty-five would have had the disease. In a family with only four sons, luck might have produced one, two, three, four, or no affected sons. In each pregnancy the odds are the same, 50 percent each time, regardless of what happened with previous offspring.

Leopold married Helena, a normal woman. They bore two children. Their son, Charles Edward, was normal. His sister, Alice, was a carrier. Her son, Viscount Trematon, had hemophilia. Her daughter, May, was normal.

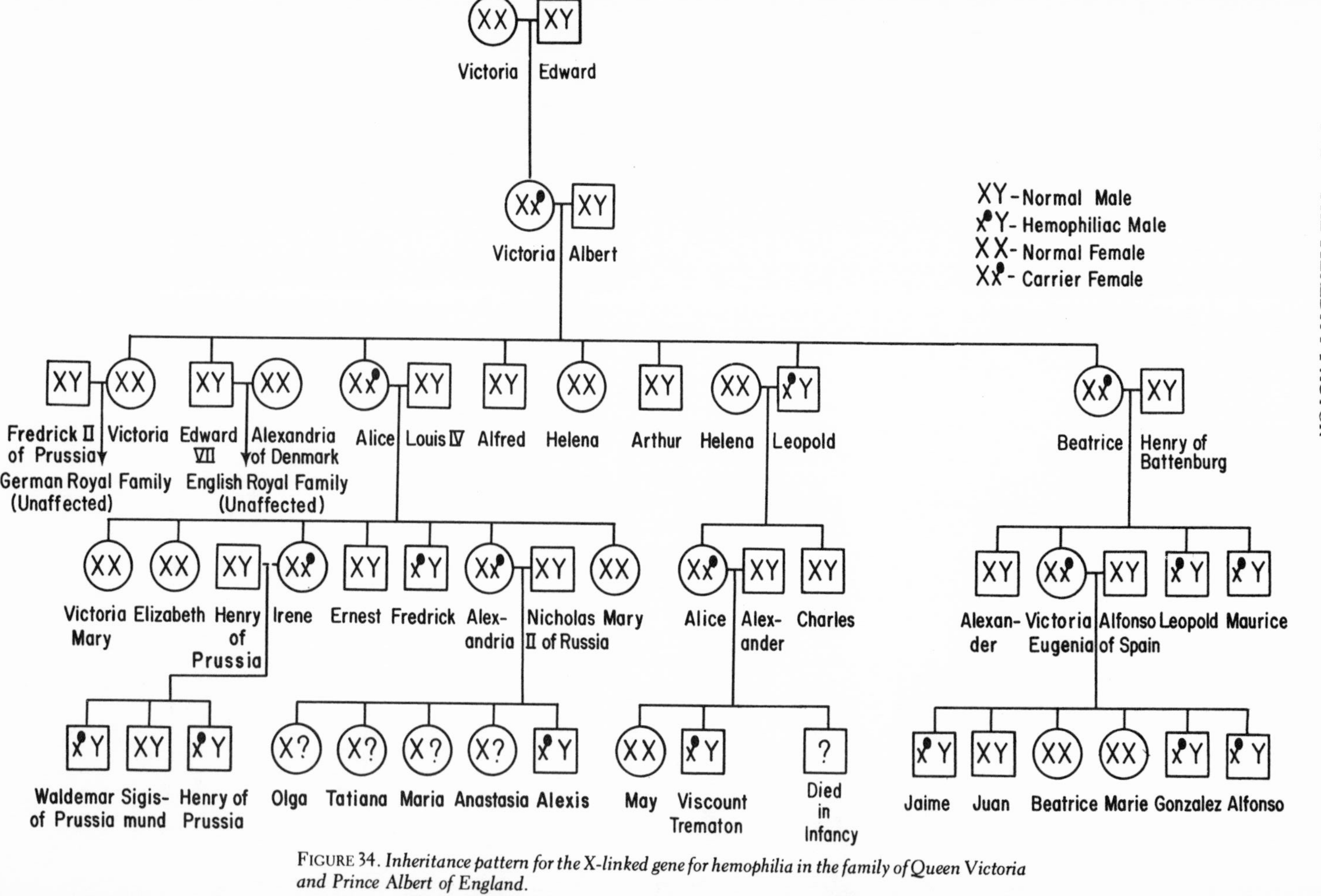

FIGURE 34. *Inheritance pattern for the X-linked gene for hemophilia in the family of Queen Victoria and Prince Albert of England.*

In Victoria's family, this one woman with a recessive X-linked gene produced two carriers and one affected individual within a generation. By the third descendant generation, her single recessive allele had spawned a total of at least five carriers and eleven affected individuals, all males. They illustrate the potential for a wide distribution of a defective X-linked recessive gene.

Among the X-linked diseases, none is more perplexing or unusual than the disorder known as the Lesch-Nyhan syndrome. This disease was first recognized in 1962. At that time I was on the faculty of the Johns Hopkins School of Medicine. Mike Lesch came to my laboratory as a medical student looking for a summer job in research. His background in chemistry was impressive. So was he. I liked him immediately. Although able to work for only half of one summer, Mike got more done than many students accomplish in two to three. As a result, I was able to work him into a Hopkins program in which he spent a year in my laboratory, which did not impede his graduation from medical school at the appropriate time. His research problem was a tough one—the separation of proteins found in cell nuclei. These proteins are thought to modulate the action of DNA. We were hard at work on this research when our first patient appeared. His name was Michael, too.

He was four years old when he was brought to the emergency room of the Harriet Lane Home, the children's wing of the Johns Hopkins Hospital. Although Michael's immediate problem was hematuria, blood in the urine, he had many other problems. He was so severely mentally retarded that he was unable to walk or to sit without assistance. His retardation and cerebral palsy had been present from early infancy. He also had a movement disorder that took the form of uncontrollable spasms of the arms and legs. Physicians call the condition choreoathetosis. The most striking feature of his disease was his badly mutilated lower lip and fingers. Mike had experienced a previous episode of hematuria. At that time his condition was thought to have been caused by infectious microorganisms.

At Johns Hopkins the intern who saw Michael carefully examined his urine. He found no signs of infection but saw that the urine sample was loaded with crystals. Large, jagged crystals, rather than microorganisms, can cause internal bleeding that produces blood in the urine, particularly if fluid intake is reduced and the urine becomes more concentrated. It is sometimes possible to identify crystals by their appearance. Under the microscope the crystals in Michael's urine appeared identical with those of the amino acid cystine. This comparison seemed logical because cystinuria is one of the most common causes of urinary tract crystals and stones in children. Michael was admitted to the hospital with a tentative diagnosis of cystinuria.

This diagnosis had to be confirmed by analysis of the amino acids of the urine. Urine of individuals affected with cystinuria reveals not only large concentrations of cystine but similar amounts of the amino acids lysine, ornithine, and arginine. Analysis of Michael's urine showed the amino acid content to be normal. This was surprising. Our problem then was to identify the crystals chemically. That was not too difficult. They were crystals of uric acid, the chemical that the body uses to dispose of purines. Purines are building blocks of DNA and RNA, but like everything else in normal metabolism, they are subject to breakdown and excretion. Most purine is excreted as uric acid. Michael's blood had a very high concentration of uric acid, while that of his urine was four times greater than normal.

Uric acid abnormalities are associated with gout. This disease is relatively common in adults, particularly males. Most people know someone with the disease. The characteristic swollen big toe has been fair game for cartoonists and other humorists. There is nothing funny about gout. It is an exceedingly painful disease. Crystals of uric acid settle in the joints and cause excruciating pain. They are also deposited in the kidneys, where they may cause organ failure and death. Gout can be effectively treated today. Various drugs are useful, among them allopurinol, which blocks the action of xanthine oxidase and thereby controls the formation of uric acid.

Michael's condition was remarkable. Gout usually does not occur in children. The appearance of its symptoms in a child suggested the possibility of a new or unrecognized disease or syndrome. At the outset the manifestations of disease seemed related: unusual biochemistry, crystals in the urine, mental retardation, neurological abnormalities, and abnormal behavior. His disease seemed an important one that could teach us valuable things, particularly about the brain and behavior. We dropped all other projects. Mike Lesch went to work on this full time.

The child's family was interesting. His mother and father were both twenty-five years old. He lived in his maternal grandfather's house. A sister of his mother and her children also lived there. It was a charming household in a little brick row house with white steps near the Baltimore waterfront. Mike Lesch went down there and drew blood from every family member. Uric acid analysis was performed on each of them. We found nothing abnormal with the samples, but in the process we learned that Michael had an older brother who seemed to have the same disease. He had been institutionalized at Rosewood, a state institution for the retarded just outside Baltimore. We were able to bring Edgar to Hopkins for intensive study and care.

Extensive metabolic analyses were carried out on both boys for more than a year. Their metabolism proved virtually identical. They produced enormous quantities of uric acid. The entire metabolic pathway for purine synthesis was working overtime. Some patients with gout produce exceptional amounts of purine, but the rates found in these two boys exceeded anything previously reported. Production was at least ten times greater than any reported in the medical literature. It was clear that these boys were exceptional. With two affected individuals in one family, it was clear that the cause was genetic.

Our findings were reported in the April 1964 issue of the *American Journal of Medicine*. We concluded that this condition constituted a distinct syndrome. The report generated considerable interest. Patients with the disease were quickly recognized by physicians all over the world. It became rapidly apparent that there were fair numbers of individuals with the disease, all of them boys. Several large kindreds came to light. The pattern of inheritance was unmistakably that of an X-linked recessive disorder. It was a disease of the male, but transmission always occurred through the female. In one family alone there were fifteen males with the disease. No female patients have ever been found.

The Lesch-Nyhan syndrome is caused by a defect in an enzyme of purine metabolism called hypoxanthine-guanine-phosphoribosyl transferase, abbreviated to HGPRT. Its normal function is to reutilize or salvage purines that would be lost as uric acid, making them available for the production of nucleic acids.

In the absence of HGPRT the body machinery gets cranked up and oversynthesizes purine; some twenty times more uric acid than normal is produced. Excess production of uric acid cannot in itself explain the bizarre features of the syndrome. Treating patients with allopurinol effectively reduces uric acid concentrations but has no effect on the neurological symptoms of the disease, even when the treatment is started shortly after birth.

The most striking feature of the disorder is self-mutilation. Patients often show remarkable ingenuity in this. They must be immobilized or they will chew their fingers to pieces. It has been necessary to extract teeth to prevent mutilation of the lips. One mother remarked about what has to be done to protect her son from his self-destructive urges. "He goes to bed," she said, "like Christ on the cross. Imagine how he feels with a fly or a mosquito." Placed in a wheelchair, some youngsters have discovered they can jam their fingers into the spokes of the wheels. Braces prescribed for the cerebral palsy have turned into weapons against the child himself. Patients are outwardly aggressive. They will strike at anyone who comes near them. They are effective at breaking the eyeglasses of nurses and doctors caring for them. They sometimes develop such disconcerting habits as pinching the breasts of their mothers or nurses or grabbing for genitals. Their speech is both aggressive and salty. Four-letter Anglo-Saxon expressions are common.

The mental status of these patients is difficult to assess. While obviously retarded, the degree of retardation is greatly accentuated by the motor and speech problems that go with the syndrome. One child who was asked why he bit his fingers replied, "My uric acid's too high." Several others have answered, "I can't help it." Children with the Lesch-Nyhan syndrome can be quite lovable, apologizing with a big grin or a smile after hurting someone, laughing loudly at funny incidents, showing genuine affection, and exhibiting a need for interaction with others.

A real challenge to the geneticist is to relate the clinical features of the syndrome, particularly those referable to the brain, to their genetic or molecular basis. Uric acid has already been linked to mental ability or performance, but in an entirely different way. Many of the world's great men have suffered from gout. Among them are Alexander the Great, Benjamin Franklin, Isaac Newton, Charles Darwin, Martin Luther, John Calvin, and John Milton. There have been studies in recent years that have examined this propensity. They have uniformly linked high levels of uric acid in the blood to high performance and success. A tendency to elevation of the uric acid levels seems to provide a boost toward the executive suite. The relationship is not clearly correlated with intelligence, but rather with those qualities of drive, work habits, and the like that make maximum use of intelligence.

The aggressive behavior of Lesch-Nyhan patients may be a function of a purine toxicity. A less striking imbalance or alteration in various molecules that end up in uric acid could affect intelligence and behavior in more positive ways. At least in the Lesch-Nyhan syndrome it is clear that the problem is not uric acid itself. Effective reduction of blood concentrations of uric acid has been achieved with allopurinol without influencing neurological abnormalities or stopping self-mutilation and aggressive behavior. This fits with other evidence. Uric acid is not a purine that is found in the central nervous system. It is an end-product molecule. It may reflect events in the nervous system, but it cannot reveal their exact nature.

The Lesch-Nyhan syndrome can be detected prenatally. Testing for HGPRT can readily be carried out in fetal cells grown in tissue culture following amniocentesis. A number of amniocenteses have been done in pregnancies at risk, those in which inheritance of abnormal HGPRT is possible because of a family history. A positive prenatal diagnosis has now been made in some patients. A number of pregnancies at risk have also been identified. It is possible to identify women as carriers of the gene by growing their cells in tissue culture and testing for HGPRT. It is also possible now to identify heterozygous carriers by an analysis of the tiny bundle of cells found at the root of a hair plucked from the scalp. The disease cannot be treated in any effective way, aside from loving care for the patient. On the positive side, all the tools are at hand for prevention by prenatal detection and heterozygote detection.

Mike Lesch has, since our early studies, graduated from medical school and become an internist and cardiologist. He is now on the faculty of the Harvard Medical School. His research is in other areas. The problem he recognized continues to make work for scientists all over the world.

It is reasonable to infer that a woman who carries a gene for the Lesch-Nyhan syndrome should have just half the normal complement of HGPRT activity. Since she has two X chromosomes, one with the gene coding for the normal enzyme and the other coding for a completely inactive enzyme, it would seem logical that, as in those carriers of the gene for Tay-Sachs, one active gene would direct the synthesis of one-half the usual amount of enzyme. The actual situation is a bit more complex. It brings us to multicolored mice and tortoise-shell cats.

Mary Lyon, a British geneticist, made a series of important observations in the late nineteen fifties. From them she developed a theory to explain the expression of genes on the X chromosome. Her explanation is now known as the Lyon Hypothesis. Mary Lyon set out to investigate the genetic mechanisms that produce distinctions between men and women. Her particular focus was on the differing amounts of chromosomal material in the cells of the two sexes.

Since the female has two X chromosomes, she would be expected to have twice as much of the protein specified by genes on the X chromosome as a male. Any enzyme, like HGPRT, would predictably exist in a woman at twice the concentration found in a man. Since some aspects of growth in height are controlled by genes on the X chromosome, one might expect that women should be much taller than men. Because they are not, the assumption that possessing two X chromosomes must necessarily mean a double concentration of related enzymes is in error. Extensive studies have been done on enzymes controlled by genes on the X chromosomes. In every case the activity in normal females is the same as in normal males. Women may have an extra set of genes on a second X chromosome, but they have no excess of the proteins controlled by these genes. Scientists have known for years that some form of compensation must exist to explain this. Several theories had been proposed. None was satisfactory before the Lyon Hypothesis.

Dr. Lyon proposed that there was no imbalance between male and female because one of the X chromosomes in each female cell is inactivated. A female would, in this sense, be like a male in that only one X chromosome is functionally expressed. This inactivation of one X chromosome is thought to occur quite early in fetal life, when the organism has relatively few cells. Whether the paternal X chromosome or the maternal X chromosome is inactivated is a matter of pure chance. Because a female does not exclusively express the traits of one parental X chromosome or its complement, her mother's X chromosome is thought to be exclusively active in some cells while her father's X chromosome is exclusively active in others. In this fashion each female cell has but one functional X chromosome. Because some cell populations are controlled by the maternal X and some by the paternal X, the resulting female enjoys the protection of alternate alleles.

Dr. Lyon developed her theory through observations of multicolored mice. There are a number of species in which one sees mottled, spotted, or brindle coat colors. On closer observation it is clear that the mottled mice are all female offspring whose parents had different coat colors. Fathers may have had white coats, and mothers may have had black coats. Through mating studies Dr. Lyon found that the gene for coat color in these mice is carried on the X chromosome. It seemed reasonable that the coat color in these mice was originally determined by a mutation. This event produced a genetic mosaic in which two populations of cells with different genetic codes grow side by side. Dr. Lyon conceived the patches of coat color as clones, or colonies of cells that arise mitotically from a single cell. These clones would be produced from one or another cell type in a mosaic. From this she reasoned that her spotted female mice were probably also mosaics in which there were two distinct populations of genetically different cells. This explanation might work if one X chromosome in each cell of the female offspring of such a mixed mating was inactivated early in development. The subsequent cells descended from each of these founder cells would have the same inactivated X chromosome as their progenitor cell. One would expect the coats of these mice to be composed of patches of white, because all the cells in the patch arose from one cell in which the mother's X chromosome was inactivated, and patches of black, because all the cells in this patch came from a single cell in which the father's X chromosome was inactivated. Since distribution of the patches in a large sample of these animals was proved to be random, Dr. Lyon proposed that the inactivation of either the paternal or the maternal X chromosome was a chance phenomenon.

Dr. Lyon developed her theory from a broad experience with inbred species of mice. The most popular example of the same process is found in the tortoiseshell or calico cat. These cats are all females. Their mothers are black and their fathers are yellow. Genes for these coat colors are located on the X chromosome. The tortoiseshell tabby is a heterozygous female. She has two populations of hair-bearing cells, one with an active X chromosome specifying yellow coat color and another with an active X chromosome specifying black coat color. The power of Dr. Lyon's observations is impressive. These animals have been observable for a long time, but no one ever recognized the genetic implications of their coat color. Every female, it is reasoned, is a mosaic, a composite of two different kinds of cells. One population of cells has an active X chromosome inherited from the father; the other has an active X chromosome inherited from the mother.

Inactivation of the X chromosome seems to occur quite early in life. A fetus starts as a single fertilized egg that divides to form two identical cells. These each divide to produce four cells, which divide to produce eight, which divide to produce sixteen, and so on. Each cell of the young organism is the parent of an enormous number of cells in the mature body. Inactivation early in fetal life of one X chromosome in each of the cells of a female leads to two genetically different cell lines that then continue to replicate themselves in the individual.

Mary Lyon was able to draw on other evidence to explain what happened to the inactivated X chromosome. This was provided by Dr. Murray L. Barr's discovery of the X chromatin body that could be observed in all normal female cells. In the Lyon Hypothesis, the Barr body is explained as the second or inactive X chromosome, curled into a tight, balled spiral, highly visible because the coiled chromosome absorbs more dye than a normal chromosome.

Precise studies of the inheritance patterns of mottled coats in female mice provided proof for the Lyon Hypothesis. Elegant confirmation of the hypothesis in human genetics has come from enzymatic studies of cultured cells. The first system to be tested was that of the enzyme glucose-6-phosphate dehydrogenase, or G6PD. This enzyme is important in carbohydrate metabolism because it is involved in the breakdown of glucose to release energy for all life functions. It is also an important regulator enzyme, involved in the overall oxidative or reductive environment of the cell. G6PD production is controlled by genes on the X chromosome. It has been established in recent years that there is considerable polymorphism, or variant gene function, at this site on the chromosome. Almost as many kinds of G6PD molecules are known as there are hemoglobins, and the discovery of further variants continues.

One of the most common variants results in G6PD deficiency. The condition it produces is called primaquine sensitivity or drug-sensitive hemolytic anemia. This disorder affects about 10 percent of American Negroes. Involved individuals appear perfectly normal most of the time. The first recognized patients appeared during World War II in programs in which antimalarial drugs were being tested. Some black individuals were found to develop a serious anemia following administration of the antimalarial drugs. The drug primaquine soon became the standard against which others were compared. There were many. A patient with this form of drug sensitivity can develop anemia with hemoglobin appearing in the urine. This may follow ingestion of any of a number of vitamin K preparations, a drug prescribed for urinary tract infection, many drugs given for reducing fever, and even aspirin. Similar reactions may develop following the chewing of naphthalene mothballs, a habit that is common among pregnant women in some ghetto populations. The varied responses reflect a general sensitivity to a large number of drugs. This is an example of the kinds of problems faced in a new field of study called pharmacogenetics.

Pharmacogenetics is involved in defining how different genetic constitutions produce different, often abnormal responses to drugs. It is very important that physicians prescribing drugs be aware of the possibility of genetically determined reactions. It would be ideal if all people with this kind of problem knew they had it. The truth is that practically none do. The person with drug sensitivity has a variant of the G6PD enzyme. The activity of this enzyme is very low. This creates a problem in the chemical environment of the cell, which becomes susceptible to damage by otherwise innocuous compounds.

A related problem is a condition known as favism. It occurs among Mediterranean populations. This disorder is caused by another defect in G6PD in which activity is even lower than in the drug-sensitive variant. People with this defect cannot eat fava beans, particularly uncooked or poorly cooked ones. If they do ingest the bean, they suffer a rapid destruction of the red blood cells. This causes a particularly dangerous form of anemia.

Favism and drug sensitivity are important because the gene for G6PD is located on the X chromosome. Males suffering from favism or drug sensitivity have cells that are deficient in G6PD activity. According to the Lyon Hypothesis, females related to these males should have two types of cells: some cells in which G6PD is deficient because those cells have the abnormal G6PD gene on the active X chromosome and some cells in which G6PD function is normal because the X chromosome with the abnormal gene has been inactivated.

Analyses of large numbers of women, particularly for drug-sensitive G6PD deficiency, which is common, have been consistent with the hypothesis. Because inactivation is random, not every female carrier of the gene would have exactly half the normal G6PD activity. There is an average of 50 percent among a large sample of carriers. In some females the cell populations with normal G6PD activity are greater than those cell populations lacking such activity, and vice versa. Most often activity clusters around the intermediate value, but the whole spectrum is seen in a large population. Some carriers (Xx) have G6PD activities that are virtually normal because close to 100 percent of their cells contain an inactive, abnormal X chromosome. Some carriers cannot be distinguished from patients because nearly 100 percent of their cells have an inactivated, normal X chromosome. In this way some carriers may have the disease just as their sons or fathers do.

Elegant proof of the Lyon Hypothesis was obtained in studies of G6PD deficiency. Cell cultures were established using skin samples obtained from black women known to be heterozygous carriers of the faulty gene. They were chosen because they had borne sons with G6PD deficiency. These cultures were cloned: single cells were selected and put into separate culture dishes so that all cells in one dish would develop into a clone, or colony, derived from that single cell. A large number of clones was studied from each heterozygote. In each case the clones were found either to have normal activity, like the cells of perfectly normal people, or to have no G6PD enzymatic activity, just like the cells of a hemizygous male patient with drug sensitivity. Each heterozygote was proved to be a mosaic of two distinct populations of cells—precisely as predicted by the Lyon Hypothesis.

G6PD also occurs in two different forms that can be separated electrophoretically in samples drawn from perfectly normal people. The more rapidly moving form is called G6PD A and occurs almost exclusively in blacks. The slower-moving G6PD *B* is the form found in most Caucasians. Both G6PD A and *B* have normal rates of enzyme activity. Cell structures from women who were *AB* heterozygotes (X^AX^B) can also be cloned and shown to consist of two distinct cell populations, one population producing only the A form of G6PD (X^A), the other population producing only the *B* form (X^B).

Nearly every X-linked characteristic that has been studied has displayed inactivation of the X chromosome. Inactivation of the entire chromosome may be incomplete. Some gene activity could remain in the curled chromosome.

One characteristic that may provide an exception is blood groups like the A, B, O, and Rh types. The blood factor is X linked and known as type Xg. Some exception to the rule is also seen in carriers of the Lesch-Nyhan syndrome. Unlike heterozygotes in the case of G6PD deficiency, heterozygotes for HGPRT deficiency do not show partial activity. Examination of their blood cells always reveals normal enzyme activity. It is as if all cells arose from a single clone. In that clone it is always the X chromosome coding for the abnormal HGPRT that is inactivated. Geneticists do not believe that there is a selective inactivation, but rather that inactivation is initially random and that it is followed by natural selection against the cell carrying the abnormal HGPRT. Because the cell population with abnormal HGPRT is less fit, its cells are believed to die in competition with populations having normal HGPRT activity. Either mechanism is possible and would explain the observed protection of the carrier of such a deleterious gene. In the case of the Xg blood group, the most likely interpretation of the data is that while most of the second X chromosome is inactivated, a small part retains its genetic activity.

This observation fits with certain clinical observations of a group of syndromes that are caused by extra X chromosomes. Almost as soon as chromosomal analysis became possible, geneticists began finding patients with abnormalities in the numbers of sex chromosomes. Among the most common is the Klinefelter syndrome, in which the affected individual has an XXY chromosomal constitution. This condition probably arises from chromosomal nondisjunction during meiosis. Patients are invariably males with an extra X chromosome. Genitalia are male in type, but the testes may be small or undescended. They never function properly. At puberty the Klinefelter individual often experiences some breast development typical of the female. He usually has some degree of mental retardation. Like XYY males, the patient tends to be taller than average. Sometimes he has aggressive and antisocial tendencies. Not all patients have these problems. Some show normal intelligence and normal behavior. The Klinefelter syndrome occurs once in every 400 to 600 male births. Individuals are known who have larger numbers of X chromosomes. There are some who are XXXY and even XXXXY. In these individuals the degree of physical abnormality is usually more marked than in the Klinefelter syndrome. In general the rule seems to be that the more extra X chromosomes, the more effeminate the patient becomes. Some of these patients have genitalia that make it hard to identify their sex with certainty.

In women there are also syndromes resulting from extra X chromosomes in the genotype. A number of XXX individuals have been observed. There have been studies of XXXX and XXXXX women and even more extreme examples in which up to five extra X chromosomes have been found. Although there is nothing exceptionally feminine about them, these individuals have sometimes been called superfemales. They are mentally retarded in most cases. This tendency is more pronounced as the number of extra X chromosomes increases. There are no obvious physical abnormalities. The incidence of the XXX constitution appears to occur once in every thousand female births.

Medical geneticists have a simple rule for determining the number of X chromosomes in any cell. They count the number of Barr bodies and add one. In any given cell all but one X chromosome is inactivated. If there are three X chromosomes, two are inactivated; if there are four, three curl up into Barr bodies, and so on. The inactivation is discriminating. In patients with the Klinefelter syndrome (XXY), it is never the Y chromosome that is inactivated; it is always an X chromosome.

The fact that abnormalities are found in all these instances of extra X chromosomes is another indication that inactivation of the X chromosome is not complete. If inactivation were perfect, one would expect that an XXY male would be expressed only as XY and be normal. Enough of the additional X chromosome is put out of action to produce the Barr body. Although enzymes like HGPRT and G6PD are always found in amounts consistent with complete inactivation, enough of the inactivated X chromosome evidently remains in operation to cause genetic imbalance. It is possible that most of the problems in these extra X individuals is caused by an imbalance occurring early in fetal life before inactivation takes place.

Problems result not only from extra X chromosomes, but also from too few X chromosomes. A condition known as the Turner syndrome occurs about once in every thirty-five hundred female births. It is characterized by the presence of a single X chromosome. These individuals are designated cytogenetically as XO. The O represents an absent sex chromosome. They look like girls and have external female genitalia. They always have poorly developed ovaries and, like the Klinefelter males, are sterile. In infancy their most prominent features are flabby folds of extra skin at the back of the neck and what appears to be edema, or swelling, of the feet. Closer examination indicates a broadened chest with widely spaced nipples, low-set ears, and a wide angle of the elbows. They grow poorly and remain very short. The intelligence of patients with the XO genotype is usually normal.

The X chromosome is important for the medical geneticist. In addition to conditions caused by too many or too few sex chromosomes, there are over one hundred disorders that are caused by abnormal genes carried on the X chromosome. As in the case of conditions caused by abnormal genes on autosomes, X-linked genes occur as both dominant and recessive alleles.

Since its symptoms occur in both male and female, a dominant X-linked condition may prove difficult to associate with the X chromosome. One dominant gene is enough to produce clinical disease. There are some clues that indicate that a dominant trait is X-linked. The inheritance pattern is unique. While an affected female will transmit the trait to half her sons and half her daughters, an affected male will transmit the gene to none of his sons (since they inherit only the Y chromosome from their father) and to all of his daughters (since they inherit the father's one X chromosome, which carries the faulty dominant gene).

In general an X-linked dominant trait tends to be milder in females than in males. Since females have a normal allele on their second X chromosome, the action of the abnormal gene tends to be balanced. This is the pattern that is seen in the X-linked dominant trait of vitamin D–resistant rickets. This condition begins like ordinary nutritional-deficiency rickets. The bones become misshapen when there is a lack of vitamin D, which is essential for normal bone growth. In vitamin D–resistant rickets patients develop deformities despite a normal intake of vitamin D. The final degree of deformity is always greater than in ordinary nutritional-deficiency rickets. The causative gene is located on the X chromosome and behaves as a dominant. Mothers transmit the faulty gene to their sons, but fathers do not. It is nearly always the case in any family that the heterozygous female patients have less severe disease symptoms than the hemizygous male patients.

There might be corollaries for this type of effect in normal people that account for some of the differences between sexes. Since the defect in this disease involves resistance to the effects of vitamin D, one might reason that there are normal genes on the X chromosome that have something to do with the effects of vitamin D on the bones. If this is so, and inactivation of additional X chromosomes was not complete, one might expect that the extra X of the female conveyed a degree of protection and that males would be more susceptible than females to ordinary rickets. Dr. Barton Childs and his colleagues carried out a survey to test this idea. They analyzed data from patient admission records at the Johns Hopkins Hospital during earlier years when rickets was a common disease in this country. They found the anticipated pattern. Susceptibility to rickets was greater in boys by a factor of almost two to one.

More common than the X-linked dominant disorders are those caused by X-linked recessive genes. Perhaps the most widespread of these is color blindness. It affects an estimated 8 percent of males in the United States. The color-blind person does not have the ability to distinguish one primary color from another. Most often he cannot tell red from green. Color blindness is obviously a handicap in driving automobiles and in piloting aircraft, but the trait is far from life-threatening. This explains its high and continued incidence. Even though recessive, it is expressed with fair frequency in females. Since color blindness does not affect the reproductive ability of a man, there is a predictable chance that a male with color blindness will marry a woman who carries the gene. In such a marriage half the daughters will inherit the gene for color blindness on each X chromosome. Their genotype will be homozygous recessive, and they will be phenotypically color blind.

Female patients with most X-linked recessive diseases are rare. The reason is that most of these diseases drastically reduce the chances of an affected male having children. No child with the Lesch-Nyhan syndrome has reproduced. This has also been true of another unusual X-linked recessive disease, agammaglobulinemia, but may no longer be the case since the disease has come to be understood and treatment has been developed.

Agammaglobulinemia is a formidable word, but if taken apart can be seen to be a medical term for the absence (*a-*) of gamma globulins in the blood. These immunological proteins contain the antibodies that are important to the body's defenses against infection. They are essential for survival. Some individuals are born with little or no capacity for synthesizing gamma globulins. Such individuals suffer many many life-threatening infections. In spite of antibiotic treatment, most of these patients used to die rather early in life.

The discovery of this genetic disease could be made only recently because scientists have known of the existence and function of gamma globulin for a relatively brief time. The first patient with agammaglobulinemia was reported in 1952 by Colonel Ogden C. Bruton, a pediatrician at the Walter Reed Army Hospital in Washington. The patient was a four-year-old boy who had gone through nineteen bouts of serious infection. Tests showed that the boy was synthesizing no gamma globulin. He was placed on a regimen of monthly injections of the protein. This enabled him to survive childhood, go to college, and start a career.

Earlier victims of agammaglobulinemia had not been so lucky. They had died early, often of minor infections that their bodies were not equipped to resist. Dr. Bruton's report soon brought echoes from other medical centers, where more boys with agammaglobulinemia were found. As these boys grow up and reproduce, there may begin to be homozygous female patients with X-linked agammaglobulinemia.

There are other X-linked conditions that are of considerable interest. These include forms of muscular dystrophy; a type of night blindness; and the Hunter syndrome, one of the mucopolysaccharidoses in which these complex carbohydrates cannot be metabolized, leading to abnormalities in abdominal organs, in the bones and joints, and in the brain. Unquestionably the X-linked condition that has affected the most people is hemophilia.

Hemophilia has affected people indirectly as well as directly. It has played a crucial role in history. Hemophilia itself is not a common condition. There are perhaps twenty thousand patients in the United States. The disease is caused by a failure to produce a functional blood protein component called factor VIII, which is essential to the complex process that permits blood clotting. Hemophiliacs have trouble because their blood does not clot readily.

Originally it was thought that hemophiliacs produced no factor VIII. Now most scientists believe that a protein is produced but it is inactive or ineffective because it is coded for by the abnormal recessive gene. When most people are injured and begin to bleed, the blood soon clots to form a tough skin that prevents further bleeding. No such clot forms when a hemophiliac bleeds. An ordinary cut can cause severe loss of blood. A bruise can cause internal bleeding that is both harmful and painful. The bleeding often occurs in a joint in which pain can be excruciating, and permanent disability may result. Bleeding in and around the brain is the most worrisome complication. Hemophilia was first described in 1803. The case of hemophilia that affected most occupants of this planet occurred in Russia. Its origin can be traced to Queen Victoria of England. Victoria became the carrier of the hemophilia gene through a mutation that probably occurred in one of her parents' germ cells. The gene spread through the ranks of European royalty. Of Victoria's eight children, five survived to become parents. They married into almost every branch of royalty on the continent (Figure 34).

One carrier of the gene was Victoria's granddaughter Alexandra, who married Czar Nicholas II of Russia. Their only son, Alexis, was born on August 12, 1904. Alexis was a hemophiliac, and his sufferings were prolonged and frequent. It was to ease those sufferings that Nicholas and Alexandra turned to Rasputin, the rascally monk who played a major role in depriving the Romanov rulers of their subjects' support. Sir Bernard Pares, the distinguished historian, has said that the birth of Alexis "more than anything else determined the later course of Russian history."

If Alexis had lived today, the course of history might have been different. In recent years scientists have learned how to extract factor VIII from normal blood. Some hemophiliacs can keep supplies of the clotting factor in their refrigerators for use in case of emergency. The supply of factor VIII is severely limited, and the cost for treating a single patient ranges up to $20,000 a year. This makes most hemophiliacs turn to other, less expensive sources of clotting factor. But almost certainly enough factor VIII would have been found to treat Alexis.

Whether genetic counseling would have helped Nicholas and Alexandra is an interesting question. It is certainly evident that the disease was present in the family. An uncle and a brother of Alexandra had died of hemophilia, and two nephews had the disease. Because the laws of heredity were dimly understood at the time even by scientists, the Romanovs tended to look upon hemophilia more as a God-given punishment than as a disease.

Even now genetic counseling in hemophilia presents a problem. In cases such as the Hunter syndrome or the Lesch-Nyhan syndrome, the disease can be detected prenatally. But in hemophilia the best that can be done when a known carrier of an X-linked recessive condition is pregnant is to determine the sex of the fetus. If the fetus is female, she will not have the disease if her father did not. There is a 50 percent chance that she will be a carrier. If the fetus is male, there is a 50 percent chance that he will have the gene and be affected by the disease.

Deciding whether this 50 percent risk warrants a therapeutic abortion is an ordeal. There is hope for more available alternatives in the future. At the moment the alternatives are difficult ones, but alternatives are available.

Carrier detection in hemophilia provides another dimension of help for families. It considerably enlarges the scope of genetic counseling. The procedure is complicated. It can successfully be done by Dr. Oscar Ratnoff at Case Western Reserve School of Medicine in Cleveland. One day it is bound to be available elsewhere.

The Keller family lived in a small town in Pennsylvania. Mrs. Keller was worried about hemophilia because her sister had two sons with the disease. When the first of these boys was circumcised, he nearly bled to death. There apparently had been no family history of the disease, but once the boy had survived this episode and was diagnosed, the maternal grandmother admitted that one of her brothers had bled to death at the age of seven. It is not always easy to get a straight story of genetic disease in a family.

Mrs. Keller had a two-year-old daughter and wanted to have more children. She consulted with her physician. He was quoted as saying, "You didn't worry with the last pregnancy, why worry now?" This was not good advice, and fortunately Mrs. Keller didn't stop there. She wrote the National Genetics Foundation, which told her carrier detection was available but that the only way to obtain it was through Dr. Ratnoff because the test is complex and has to be done on fresh blood. With the referral, the foundation wrote a note to Dr. Ratnoff. Some time later Dr. Ratnoff wrote the foundation to tell them that Mrs. Keller had never arrived. With this information, Gay Sachs, counselor for the foundation, called Mrs. Keller and persuaded her to go to Cleveland. She did. The test was positive for the disease. Mrs. Keller turned out to be a carrier. She was counseled appropriately by Dr. Ratnoff. What she decides about having further children will remain to be seen. Now she has all the facts with which she can make an enlightened decision. This is a long way from where she was when she first consulted her doctor.

11. Amniocentesis and the Prenatal Diagnosis of Inherited Disorders

The ability to detect the presence of disease early in fetal life represents a major advance in medical genetics. Its effective use involves a number of simple sequential steps. The first is to know that a family is at risk for an inherited disease. This knowledge may come from previous family history, a defect in an aunt, uncle, or cousin or more commonly the existence of a genetic disease in a previous child. If the potential disease can be prenatally diagnosed, a sample of the amniotic fluid that bathes the fetus must be obtained. Cells from the fluid are grown in tissue culture. These cells are then assayed, or analyzed, for the disease. If it is found that the fetus does in fact have the disease, a therapeutic abortion may be performed.

This procedure may not sound entirely positive on first hearing. It may sound rather negative, but patients do not think so. Although the diagnostic procedure can prevent a certain amount of human suffering, the couples who seek it are generally looking for more than simple prevention. They hope to have a normal child. Before this procedure was developed, their only recourse was to adopt a child or forgo the idea of more children. They now have the option of undertaking a monitored pregnancy. The monitoring is done by amniocentesis. This procedure is usually performed with the understanding that if the fetus is abnormal, they will undergo an abortion and begin again. In the majority of instances the expected baby turns out to be free of the disease. Couples who thought they could not have another child are raising healthy babies of their own.

Women do not usually come to the medical geneticist already pregnant and seeking abortion. Dr. J. Edwin Seegmiller, professor of medicine at the University of California, San Diego, described one of his patients. Mrs. Williams had a two-year-old son who was slowly dying of an unusual inherited kidney disease. This disease had started before birth, but no one realized that anything was wrong until the latter part of his first year. The baby did not seem to be growing as well as he should. He looked pale and thin. X rays revealed skeletal changes like those of rickets. Urinalysis indicated a number of abnormalities. By two years of age the infant had advanced renal failure, the kind that sometimes can be treated with heroic measures like kidney transplantation or chronic dialysis. Sunlight was very disturbing to him, and even a little light caused him to squint and hide his eyes. His doctors realized that a critical analysis of his bone marrow was required. They found that he had cystinosis.

Cystinosis is a disease of metabolism in which the amino acid cystine accumulates in body cells. Cystine is an amino acid that is insoluble in water. Whenever it is present in large concentrations, it forms crystals. That is what the doctors found in the bone marrow—crystals that could be seen under the microscope. In the bone marrow these crystals do no harm, but elsewhere they may be devastating. This is particularly true in the eye and kidney. Kidney impairment is relentless. Mrs. Williams could expect her child to die within a few years, after a great deal of suffering. When she learned of this, she was already pregnant for a second time.

Discussion with her doctor revealed that cystinosis is an autosomal recessive disease. There was a 25 percent chance, or one chance in four, that the baby she was carrying also had cystinosis. She decided to have an abortion.

At that time Dr. Seegmiller, then at the National Institutes of Health, and his colleagues had just developed a test for cystinosis that was applicable to cells grown in tissue culture. They did not know whether or not the test would work on amniotic cells, but Dr. Seegmiller was willing to try. He knew that certain connective cells from a patient with cystinosis had one hundred times the normal amount of cystine. Dr. Cecil Jacobson, Mrs. Williams' obstetrician, performed an amniocentesis. The fetal cells grew well in culture, and while they were growing, a technique was evolved by Dr. J. D. Schulman in Dr. Seegmiller's laboratory for testing amniotic cells for cystinosis. The effectiveness of this new method was confirmed by analysis of normal fetal cells. Mrs. Williams had been quite understanding about the importance of this research and had been happy to contribute to furthering it, but she was unwilling to chance an untested procedure. She still wanted her pregnancy terminated. Dr. Jacobson persuaded her to wait until her baby's cells had been tested and the resultant chemical data were in hand.

The wait was relatively short. The amniotic cells behaved normally. The investigators tested the fibroblasts of Mrs. Williams' two-year-old boy. They were quite abnormal. The doctors believed they had found a significant marker for the disease. They discussed the implications with Mrs. Williams. Since no one had then diagnosed cystinosis *in utero*, they could not be sure. In every instance in which they or others had found a biochemical abnormality in fibroblasts, it had been detected in amniotic cells. Although they could not guarantee anything, the negative odds were now markedly reduced. They thought the developing fetus was normal. Mrs. Williams could probably sense their optimism. She decided to carry her pregnancy to term. She bore a beautiful baby who did not have cystinosis.

Dr. Jerry Schneider of the University of California, San Diego, has now diagnosed cystinosis prenatally. The procedure in his hands is highly reliable, and this disorder can be added to the list of those in which prenatal diagnosis is available.

For a couple seeking to monitor a pregnancy with amniocentesis, the first step is to find a source for proper assistance. The usual procedure is to ask the family's doctor. This may be all that is necessary to set matters into motion. It is important to ask. Do not wait for the doctor to suggest the idea. Physicians are less likely than patients to think about a genetic referral, particularly at the critical period when prenatal diagnosis can be accomplished safely. The ideal referral is to a medical center with a complete program in genetic medicine. Here the amniocentesis, cell culture, and specific biochemical or cytogenetic diagnosis can be done under one roof. With these data a counselor can interpret the resulting information for the parents and can suggest the best plan of action. If a family doctor does not know where to send a patient for this kind of service, the family should have some available alternatives. Consulting a university medical center will usually be helpful. It may or may not offer some or all of the requisite services, but its staff will usually know where they can be obtained. State health departments often have this kind of information, usually in the Bureau of Maternal and Child Health. This is true in California. Dr. Hayato Kihara at Pacific State Hospital maintains a list of centers on the West Coast where specialized tests can be performed on amniotic cells. The National Foundation–March of Dimes publishes a booklet listing centers where genetic services are available. It can be obtained from a local chapter office. The National Genetics Foundation (250 West 57th Street, New York, New York 10019) will make a direct referral to the closest and most appropriate of a network of genetic referral centers.

Once a prospective mother at risk finds the right place, the procedures may vary, but the diagnostic and counseling program will be essentially the same. Medical geneticists like to see a husband and wife together on the first visit. After getting a clear picture of why they have come to us, we describe the whole process of prenatal diagnosis and how we plan to go about it. We try to answer questions that they may raise and ones that may be anticipated. This interview is scheduled so that the patient goes directly to an obstetrician's office for amniocentesis. We have a coordinating nurse who meets each patient in the geneticist's office and goes with her to the obstetrician. She stays with her and assists with the procedure.

The actual process of amniocentesis is relatively simple. Its essential feature is the insertion of a long needle through the wall of the abdomen into the uterus. The needle is placed in the amniotic fluid that surrounds the developing baby. A syringe full of this fluid is removed. (Sometimes the position of the placenta is first determined by ultrasound techniques. This procedure is not required in every case. Ultrasound can be very useful in the diagnosis of twin pregnancies. It causes no discomfort or damage to the mother or the baby.) The only preliminary requirements are that the woman urinate and have her abdominal skin cleaned with an antiseptic solution. A local anesthetic is injected into the skin in the area of puncture. A long, very thin needle is inserted through the abdominal wall. The stylet that blocks the needle cavity is withdrawn, and a sterile plastic syringe is attached in its place. The fluid is withdrawn. Strictly sterile procedures are observed throughout. The fluid is placed in a sterile test tube.

The prospective mother is now ready to go home. What happens to the fluid is critical. Geneticists have learned to be very careful about the logistics of handling a sample so that none of the precious material goes astray. It is hand carried to the appropriate laboratory by the nurse who has accompanied the woman throughout the procedure. Dr. Henry Nadler of the Children's Memorial Hospital in Chicago has developed a standardized procedure for handling samples from a number of obstetricians throughout the city. Each sample is carried from the obstetrician's office to Dr. Nadler's laboratory by the husband. After the sample is safely in the laboratory, the husband returns to the obstetrician's office to pick up his wife and take her home.

Once in the laboratory, the fluid is centrifuged, or whirled at high speed, in order to spin down and concentrate the cells. The fluid is removed, chemically analyzed if indicated, and frozen. The fetal cells are suspended in fetal calf serum, which contains nutrients required for growth, and placed in small plastic petri dishes. These are covered with microscope cover slips and supplied with the nutrient culture medium containing the calf serum and antibiotics. They are then placed in special incubators that provide an atmosphere rich in carbon dioxide and are maintained at body temperature. The cells are fed by changing the nutrient medium every other day. With this kind of gentle, painstaking care the cells multiply and the culture grows. Ultimately, fetal cells cover the surface of the dish. They are removed, divided, and used to begin cultures in other dishes and flasks. This process is continued until there are enough cells for analysis.

This all takes time. Chromosome studies can be done the most quickly. Often the original cover slip with its fetal cells is available for cytogenetic analysis. On the average this procedure takes two weeks. It may take a few days or as many as four weeks to grow enough cells for a cytogenetic study. If biochemical analyses are required to solve the diagnostic problem, it takes an average of four weeks to obtain enough cells.

This is the hardest time for most parents. It is easy to become anxious while

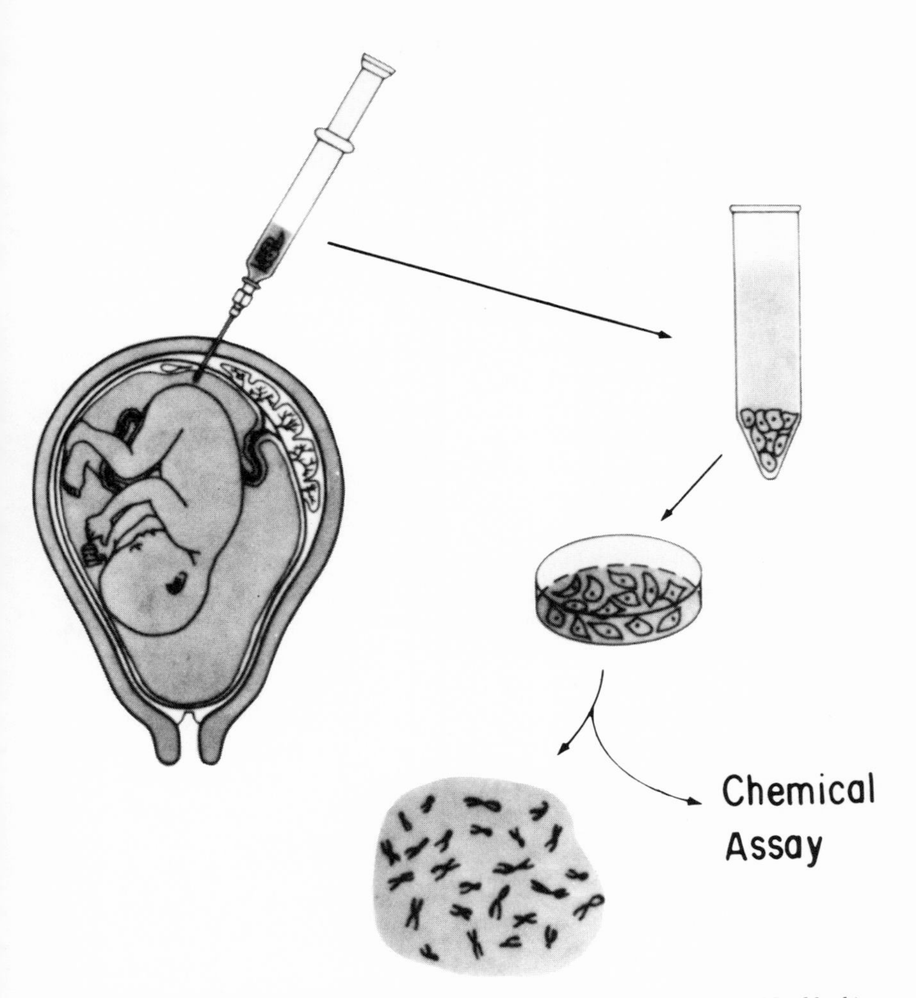

FIGURE 35. *Amniocentesis. The needle inserted into the uterus permits withdrawal of fluid bathing the baby. Cells contained in the fluid are concentrated in the centrifuge tube and then placed in the petri dish in culture. When sufficient quantities have grown, they are analyzed for chromosomes or for their biochemical properties.*

waiting for the cells to grow. We try to emphasize this inevitable and normal time lag during our first interview. If the procedure requires more time than anticipated, we communicate with the parents and urge them to call us whenever they wish.

Sometimes the cells do not grow. This failure can usually be recognized within two weeks, when there is still time for another amniocentesis. Other things can go wrong. A temporary failure of the incubator can cause all the cells to die. This kind of problem can be avoided by splitting each sample obtained by amniocentesis and setting up duplicate cultures in different incubators in different laboratories. This culturing of the cells is the trickiest part of the business. Not everyone can do it 100 percent of the time. Even people who do tissue culture work cannot necessarily grow amniotic cells successfully. In laboratories where amniotic cells are regularly grown, nearly every sample grows well.

Once fetal cells are available in ample supply, ensuing procedures depend on the suspected genetic condition. The vast majority of patients require cytogenetic diagnosis. Fetal cells are prepared for chromosomal study just as described in chapter 7. A chromosome study is performed with every amniocentesis, even if the patient is primarily a candidate for biochemical diagnosis. The biochemical conditions that can be identified are nearly all rare autosomal recessive conditions that produce severe illness in the homozygous patient. Cystinosis is an example. Another is Tay-Sachs disease. The assay of hexosaminidase A, the enzyme that is missing in Tay-Sachs disease, can be performed effectively on amniotic cells in culture.

Other autosomal recessive conditions that can be prenatally diagnosed in this fashion include Pompe's disease, or cardiac glycogenosis; Gaucher's disease; gangliosidosis; the Hunter and the Hurler syndromes; lysosomal acid phosphatase deficiency; maple syrup urine disease; metachromatic leukodystrophy; Niemann-Pick disease; and Sandhoff's disease. The X-linked Lesch-Nyhan syndrome has been diagnosed prenatally in a number of pregnancies.

Once a prenatal diagnosis is made, a number of new problems arise. There are no problems if the fetal cells are free of the suspected disease. The developing baby is healthy. This cannot be too strongly emphasized. In the majority of instances in which a pregnancy is monitored by amniocentesis, the fetus is found not to have the suspected genetic disease. This is the beauty of the statistics. Even in a situation with high risk (the one-in-four risk of an autosomal recessive is high), the odds for a normal phenotype and a normal baby (three chances in four) are higher.

If the diagnosis is positive for the presence of the disease, one option is to terminate the pregnancy. This is a decision for the family, in consultation with their obstetrician. Most people undertaking a monitored pregnancy plan to follow this course of action. There are exceptions. Of the first three pregnancies in which the Lesch-Nyhan syndrome was diagnosed prenatally, two underwent therapeutic abortions. These fetuses were studied and proved to have the disease with its absence of activity for the HGPRT enzyme. In the third pregnancy twins went to term and were delivered. Both boys have the disease.

Abortion itself raises ethical and legal questions that complicate the procedure. In some states it is easily obtained. In some legality is far from clear. In some abortion based on a fetal diagnosis is impossible. There has been an enormous amount of progress in the United States in recent years toward more flexible and enlightened views. Amniocentesis, prenatal diagnosis, and therapeutic abortion are now accepted procedures in most areas.

The results of a four-year study conducted by the National Institute of Child Health and Human Development were reported in October 1975. They should go a long way toward a wider national acceptance of amniocentesis and prenatal diagnosis. The central issue of the study was to ascertain whether or not amniocentesis adversely affected the outcome of pregnancy. The study compared 1,040 pregnant women in whom amniocentesis was performed with a control group of 990 pregnant women. The data showed that amniocentesis is a safe, accurate procedure.

The centers participating in the study were Children's Memorial Hospital in Chicago, Eunice Kennedy Shriver Center in Boston, Johns Hopkins University in Baltimore, Mount Sinai School of Medicine in New York City, UCLA's Harbor General Hospital in Torrance, California, the University of Michigan in Ann Arbor, the University of Pennsylvania in Philadelphia, Yale University in New Haven, and the University of California San Diego in La Jolla. Summation of the statistics from these diverse centers revealed no differences between the two groups of patients in the rates of fetal loss through abortions or stillbirths or in the rates of prematurity. The procedure had no adverse effect on the course of pregnancy, labor, or delivery. Examination of the babies at birth revealed no evidence of fetal injury. There were no differences between the two groups in the incidence of birth defects at one year of age. The infants in the two groups were not significantly different.

In the course of the study thirty-four mothers who had amniocentesis were found to be carrying fetuses with genetic abnormality. Nineteen had chromosomal anomalies and fifteen had metabolic disorders. Eleven others carried male fetuses each of which had a 50 percent risk of an X-linked disease such as hemophilia. Of these forty-five women, thirty-five elected therapeutic abortion. Eight of the aborted fetuses were found to carry the chromosomal abnormality indicating the presence of the Down syndrome. Seven of the women in the control group, who did not have amniocentesis, bore children with the Down syndrome. The results of this study are impressive and reassuring. They should go a long way toward making this technique available to those families who could benefit.

The mechanics of therapeutic abortion are not as simple in the management of genetic disease as they are when the reasons for abortion are maternal health or simply an interest in not having a baby. A pregnancy will have progressed into the second trimester, or fourth month, before there is enough fluid for a successful amniocentesis. An amniocentesis after fourteen weeks of gestation is preferable. It cannot be performed before twelve weeks have elapsed. The fetal cells then require anywhere from two to four weeks to grow in culture. It is best to perform an abortion before twenty weeks of pregnancy for both medical and legal reasons. By the twentieth week a pregnancy is well past the time when an abortion can safely be done by a dilatation and curettage (D and C). The simplest available procedures at this date are the injection of saline into the uterus and the use of prostaglandins. In either case the fetus is aborted. An alternative procedure if the fetus is older is a hysterotomy, an operation in which the uterus is opened and the fetus removed. The choice of procedures depends on the conditions of the pregnancy and requires the judgment of an obstetrician.

An older couple was recently referred to me from another state because they were worried about the possibility of having a child with the Down syndrome. In reproductive terms a parent is "older" if he or she is more than thirty years of age. This mother was forty-one years old. She was six weeks pregnant. The couple had borne a normal child who was four years old. In the interim the mother had had a miscarriage. She and her husband had read about the relationship between age and the Down syndrome. I made an appointment with them for that time when the fetus would be fourteen weeks old. The amniocentesis was perfectly successful. The fetal cells began growing beautifully, but they took their own time. It was nearly a month before there was a definitive answer. In the meantime I received a number of phone calls from the worried parents. When I knew from cytogenetic study that the chromosomes were normal and that the baby would be a boy, I called the parents and told them both pieces of news. Then I wrote them a letter so they would have the information in black and white. A few months later I received their birth announcement. They had had a beautiful, healthy baby boy.

Medical geneticists always determine the sex of an infant when they study the chromosomes of amniotic cells. This information is essential to diagnosis of many X-linked chromosomal diseases. In cases where the gender of the fetus is ultimately of no importance in terms of the presence or absence of genetic disease, it is sometimes best for the physician to withhold this information. One mother expressed the feelings of many when she told physicians not to tell her what the sex of her unborn child would be. She said, "It would be like opening a Christmas package ahead of time."

Dr. Henry Nadler has described an interesting family he helped using amniocentesis. The patient who consulted him was a thirty-eight-year-old practicing attorney who had just gotten married. Her age was sufficient reason for her to be interested in the Down syndrome. She had a better reason. She had three siblings with the disease.

Dr. Nadler first examined her chromosomes. She was a translocation carrier. They discussed prenatal diagnosis, and she elected to become pregnant if he would monitor her pregnancy. Amniocentesis was performed at fifteen weeks. It showed that the fetus had 46 chromosomes including the translocation chromosome. This imbalance would produce the Down syndrome. Pregnancy was terminated, and study of the aborted fetus confirmed the diagnosis.

Three months later she was pregnant again. This time amniocentesis revealed that the fetus was a girl with 46 chromosomes. The translocation chromosome was absent. A normal little girl was delivered at term. At the age of forty-three this mother underwent another monitored pregnancy. She delivered a healthy male infant who was, like her, a translocation carrier. This knowledge of his genotype will prove invaluable to her son when he reaches his reproductive years.

Prenatal diagnosis is now applicable to only a few conditions. It is useful in the detection of every known cytogenetic abnormality. It should be available for the diagnosis of an increasing number of rare recessive genetic conditions of the autosomes and sex chromosomes in which a molecular or enzymatic diagnosis is possible. Although the most common autosomal recessive condition, cystic fibrosis, cannot be distinguished in this way, it does not seem unduly optimistic to believe that one day this condition will be prenatally diagnosed.

The dominant conditions are a challenge. Since the dominant gene is always expressed, a dominant could be eradicated from a family if the condition could be diagnosed prenatally. Among dominantly inherited conditions, many of those that are transmitted from generation to generation are sufficiently tolerable that medical geneticists probably would not recommend abortion even if they knew about the condition ahead of time. Most of the patients with dominant conditions for which we might think about control through abortion arise through new mutations. There are few chemical or physical markers by which the patient with a dominant condition can be identified prenatally. The discovery of some reliable markers would be of great use in the control of conditions like Huntington's chorea.

A considerably less discriminating approach to the prenatal control of inherited disease has been employed in the management of severe X-linked disorders. The approach is to determine the sex of the fetus. As first reported by Dr. Fritz Fuchs of Copenhagen, this involves determination by the presence or absence of a Barr body. Now sex determination can be done by the study of chromosomes or possibly by fluorescent detection of the Y chromosome. If the fetus should be a girl, the parents can relax. If it is a boy, there is a 50 percent chance that he will have the disease. A decision can be made whether or not to abort the male fetus. This is obviously not as satisfactory as a precise prenatal diagnosis in which a test for the abnormal enzyme can be made. It may serve a useful purpose in some families with diseases such as hemophilia or X-linked muscular dystrophy. Its greatest use is in providing a reassuring diagnosis that disease is not present. Decisions are then much easier to make.

There is a real need for the development of techniques that will identify the presence of structural malformations early in pregnancy. X rays can reveal major skeletal abnormalities. They do not reveal the tragedy of malformations such as meningomyelocoele or anencephaly. Babies with meningomyelocoeles are born with defects of the spine. The spinal cord and its meningeal membranes, uncovered by skin, form a large lump on the lower back. A small defect can be closed surgically, and the child can develop normally. This is the exceptional situation. The usual condition involves problems with the lower extremities, inability to walk, incontinence, hydrocephalus (a head swollen by retention of fluid), and retardation. All this results, despite many operations, in serious infections like meningitis and virtually constant medical attention and physiotherapy. Anencephaly is a condition in which an infant is born with little or no brain or skull. Mercifully, such an infant dies within a few days of birth. Either of these conditions would provide an argument for therapeutic abortion if its presence could be detected in good time.

Investigators are working to develop an instrument called the amnioscope. Advances in fiber optics permit some direct viewing of the uterus using a long tube that is thin enough to be inserted into the womb without influencing the course of pregnancy. Perfection of the instrument will take time. It may one day be possible to diagnose structural defects *in utero* by direct observation. Some less direct techniques are now available. It is possible to perform an amniogram, in which a small amount of dye is injected into the uterus. This reveals the outline of the developing fetus. A large meningomyelocoele can be detected in this way. Ultrasound could probably reveal a very large meningomyelocoele. Dr. George Leopold at UCSD has diagnosed prenatally the presence of ascites, or fluid in the fetal abdomen. Amniocentesis was carried out and the ascites was withdrawn from the baby's abdomen.

A woman who had delivered an anencephalic infant became pregnant a year later. She was understandably concerned about the possibility of bearing another anencephalic child. She inquired about amniocentesis, which is of no value in the detection of this condition. She was referred to a small local medical center. Doctors there felt they could be of no help. She communicated with the National Genetics Foundation, whose counselor wrote centers throughout the country about available help. It was decided to try diagnosis using ultrasound. The technique was performed by Dr. Carlo Valenti of Downstate Medical Center in Brooklyn. The technique involves bouncing sound waves off the abdomen. A picture, or sonogram, is produced outlining the shape of the fetus. Measurement of the head can be made very precisely in this way. The technique can also be used for the diagnosis of hydrocephaly. Dr. Valenti found that the fetus had a normally developing brain and skull. He was able to reassure this mother that her infant would not have anencephaly.

Dr. Valenti is also expert in the prenatal diagnosis of cytogenetic, or chromosomal, abnormalities. He was recently involved in an outstanding example of international cooperation in providing genetic services. The story began in Buenos Aires. The Feldmans seemed to have everything a couple could desire. Norberto was a prosperous businessman, a builder of important buildings in that bustling city and a man of vision, full of ideas and projects. Ines, his wife, was beautiful, with dark eyes and jet black hair. They seemed ideally suited to raising a family. They had problems getting this project under way.

Ines had a series of six successive miscarriages. It is not too widely known, but spontaneous abortions, or miscarriages, are sometimes an index of cytogenetic abnormality. It is better known that the incidence of cytogenetic abnormalities in fetuses spontaneously aborted is very high. They are often the result of trisomic conditions that can arise through nondisjunction in a chromosomally normal parent. Repeated miscarriage is common in women who have translocated chromosomes. A translocated chromosome is what was found when Ines was examined, as well as her sister, who had a child with the Down syndrome, and their father, who had a brother with the Down syndrome. Instead of one of these miscarriages, Ines could well have borne a child with the Down syndrome. On the basis of this information the Feldmans adopted three children.

They then heard about the possibilities of prenatal diagnosis. They wrote to a famous cytogeneticist in Paris. His response was discouraging. The French do not believe in abortion and as a consequence have publicly disavowed amniocentesis and prenatal diagnosis. The Feldmans were not ready to take no for an answer. They wrote to Carlo Valenti in New York. He was interested. The Feldmans began a monitored pregnancy. This one did not end in early abortion. At the proper time the couple flew to New York. Dr. Valenti performed the amniocentesis, grew the fetal cells, and in due time provided a diagnosis. The fetus, a girl, had her mother's translocated chromosome in the same balanced fashion. She was genetically sound and would be phenotypically normal. The Feldmans, who had stayed in New York all this time, returned home, and at term their baby arrived. She was indeed normal.

This might have ended the tale, but it in fact provided only the preface to a more far-reaching story. The next chapter began a year after the birth of the Feldmans' baby. A very poor family, the Aragos, living on the outskirts of Buenos Aires, had borne a child with the Down syndrome. The baby was dying of leukemia. He was studied by Dr. Primarosa Chieri, a cytogeneticist in that city who had been a student of Drs. Robert Sparkes and Stanley Wright at UCLA. The affected baby had the translocation chromosome for the syndrome. While studies were in progress, the child died. His mother had loved him dearly and became severely depressed at his death. She required psychiatric help. Dr. Chieri studied her and her family at this point. She found that the mother had a chromosomal translocation, as did her brother. Moved by the woman's grief, Dr. Chieri discussed the possibility of prenatal diagnosis with her. No one in the entire country had ever done an amniocentesis. The Feldmans had had to go to New York for the procedure. Mrs. Arago became interested, and within a month she became pregnant. She waited until the proper time before an obstetrician in Buenos Aires performed the amniocentesis, using syringes and tubes sent from New York by Dr. Valenti. The fluid sample was brought to the home of the pilot of the next plane to New York. He was convinced of the importance of hand carrying the specimen to its destination. Dr. Valenti's laboratory was alerted to receive the sample. All seemed well.

In fifteen days there was an ominous call from New York. The cells looked sound, but they had not divided. Time was running short. A second amniocentesis was quickly performed and the whole process repeated: phone calls to New York, delivery of the samples to the pilot and then to the laboratory in New York. All this produced more anxiety. But this time the cells divided. Cytogenetic analysis was reassuring. There was a balanced chromosomal translocation. Pregnancy went to term, and the baby was indeed normal. The mother no longer needed psychiatric treatment.

Behind the scenes was Señor Feldman. He paid the obstetrician and the phone bills. He assumed all the expenses for getting the work done in Buenos Aires. Dr. Chieri donated her services, and so did Dr. Valenti. This wonderful spirit of cooperation led to the establishment of the Fundación de Genética Humana in Argentina in 1972. The foundation was begun by Norberto, who serves as its president. His wife, Ines, serves as vice president and works at the foundation every day. Dr. Chieri is secretary to the foundation, and her laboratory has been incorporated into it. This is a first in Argentina, and, we believe, a first in South America. It will have an important impact on activities in human genetics that are very broadly based. It had its start with the drama of amniocentesis and prenatal diagnosis.

The miracles that amniocentesis and prenatal diagnosis can bring were described in *Good Housekeeping* of June 1971 by Jean Block and Jane Stein under the title "The Miracle Baby of Carolyn Sinclair." Carolyn was twenty-three years old when she and her husband were driving home from a New Year's Eve party in Quantico, Virginia. There was an automobile accident, and her husband was killed. Shortly thereafter she knew she was pregnant. Carolyn's doctor first told her she was not pregnant and that her symptoms were those of anxiety caused by stress. He was wrong. She was pregnant.

Carolyn gave up her full-time job and began doing part-time proofreading and advertising layouts for a weekly newspaper. The paper was owned by Charles Sinclair. In due time her son was born. Carolyn called him Jeff. He looked and seemed just fine. Carolyn and Charles Sinclair were married in June of the next year.

Jeff turned out to have an inherited disease. By the time he was two years old it was apparent that he was not developing normally. He spoke less than cousins of about the same age. He did not seem to understand as much as they did. He was hyperactive. He could not seem to keep still for a minute. Everyone, even her doctor, tried to reassure Carolyn. They were wrong. Jeff was not normal.

A diagnosis was made by Dr. Aymar Pierre Lechaux, a pediatrician in Alexandria, Virginia, to whom she had been referred. He was impressed with Jeff's coarse features: his large lips and clawlike hands. These were signs of a mucopolysaccharide disorder. Dr. Lechaux ordered X rays. They confirmed his diagnosis. Jeff had X rays typical of a child with the Hurler or Hunter syndrome. Dr. Lechaux ordered a urine test. This further confirmed the diagnosis. Jeff was excreting large amounts of mucopolysaccharide in his urine. The most important consequence of a mucopolysaccharide disorder is limited intellectual development. Another very important consequence follows the infiltration of the heart and circulatory structures by mucopolysaccharide molecules. This invasion leads to premature death. Jeff would not be expected to live beyond fifteen years of age.

This diagnosis meant another tragedy for Carolyn. Her only child was hopelessly retarded. She soon faced another crisis. She was pregnant again.

Dr. Lechaux asked her to seek genetic counsel if this should happen. Carolyn and her husband went to Dr. Cecil Jacobson, the chief of reproductive genetics at George Washington University and one of the earliest proponents of amniocentesis for prenatal diagnosis. Dr. Jacobson wisely decided that the first step was to determine which of the mucopolysaccharide disorders Jeff had. The Hurler syndrome is carried as a rare autosomal recessive gene. The Hunter syndrome is X-linked. If Jeff had the Hurler syndrome, risk of a second affected child with a new husband would be small. In X-linked disease, the husband's contribution of a Y chromosome is irrelevant to expression of the disease. Jeff was referred to Dr. Rodney Howell, then associate professor of pediatrics at Johns Hopkins. Dr. Howell concluded from a very careful examination of Jeff and his X rays that Jeff had the Hunter syndrome.

The distinction between the Hunter and the Hurler syndrome can now be made chemically. It was not possible then. At that time it was also not possible to make an intrauterine diagnosis of either syndrome. The only possibility for assessment of this pregnancy was through fetal sex determination. Dr. Jacobson has said, "The only cure for genetic defects is to prevent birth from happening." Carolyn prayed for a daughter. Amniocentesis revealed that she was carrying a boy. There was a fifty-fifty chance that he had the same disease as Jeff. The Sinclairs thought long and hard. They decided that two defective sons would be too much for them. Carolyn said, "We couldn't afford another child like Jeff, either financially or emotionally. Caring for such a child, even though you love him dearly, is more draining than I ever could explain." A saline installation was performed, and the fetus was aborted. This fetus was studied carefully and found to have the disease. Carolyn said, "We knew then we had done the right thing."

The next time she became pregnant, the state of the geneticist's art had advanced significantly. Carolyn called Dr. Jacobson for an amniocentesis as soon as she knew she was pregnant. That was in June. She had to wait until August. Waiting is hard. "Waiting day after day, not knowing the fate of the baby growing within you, not letting yourself think about what might lie ahead." When the amniotic cells grew, it was clear that Carolyn was again carrying a boy.

Scientists could now prenatally diagnose the Hunter syndrome. This amniocentesis set work in motion in a number of laboratories across the country. The fluid sample was sent to Dr. Reuben Matalon of the University of Chicago, who with his chief, Dr. Albert Dorfman, had developed a chemical test for mucopolysaccharide content in amniotic fluid. The results were normal. That was very reassuring, but the method is not foolproof. The cells went to Dr. Elizabeth Neufeld of the National Institutes of Health. She found that the cells of this fetus did not accumulate mucopolysaccharide as do Hunter or Hurler cells. In a very sensitive test the cells obtained from Carolyn synthesized a protein capable of curing Hunter cells in culture. This evidence provided a clear-cut, definitive answer for the Sinclairs. This baby was not going to have the Hunter syndrome. When he was born, Christopher Sinclair confirmed the prediction. It was a miracle. Carolyn's husband said, "I guess we were afraid to hope for the best." The Sinclairs deserved the best. It is gratifying to report they got it.

12. Public Health Perspectives: Prenatal Diagnosis, Selective Family Planning, and Carrier Detection

Intrauterine diagnosis and selective family planning can provide critical assistance to families at risk for genetic disease. The effective use of these techniques has made an enormous impact on people's lives. Making these services widely available to families who could benefit poses a major challenge to the medical geneticist and to society. There are problems of logistics. If everyone who could profit from amniocentesis and prenatal diagnosis should suddenly appear for treatment, available resources would be swamped. This is not the immediate problem since none of the institutions currently providing prenatal diagnosis is even moderately taxed by this kind of work. An information gap keeps people from what is available to them. It is essential that they become aware of the nature, importance, and accessibility of the help now available to families with actual or potential genetic problems.

Before any massive program for applying scientific advances to human life can be implemented, an understanding of what the new techniques can and cannot do is necessary. At present prenatal diagnosis and selective family planning permit people at risk to have and enjoy normal, healthy children. This is an important objective, and it more than justifies the program. If these diagnostic and treatment services were universally available, what would happen to the incidence of genetic disease in our society? Expectations about the effect of such programs would vary considerably with each type of inherited disorder. Impact on the incidence of the Down syndrome and other diseases caused by chromosomal nondisjunction would be enormous. Since it is known that these conditions occur principally in pregnant women over thirty-five years of age, accurate diagnosis and prevention could be achieved without the birth of a single affected child. If medical geneticists were to perform an amniocentesis and a cytogenetic study of the fetal chromosomes on every older expectant mother, the numbers of individuals affected by these disorders would decrease dramatically.

The potential effect of prenatal diagnosis and selective family planning on the incidence of such autosomal recessive diseases as Tay-Sachs disease or galactosemia is not so dramatic. Among the rare autosomal recessive disorders the first affected child in a family comes like a bolt out of the blue, with no warning. First awareness of the gene is through the birth and subsequent diagnosis of an affected child. Recognizing that a couple is at risk after the birth of one infant with the disease is important. Monitoring of subsequent pregnancies through amniocentesis can prevent the birth of a second affected child and ensure the birth of nothing but normal children. If every positively diagnosed fetus were aborted, families would be relieved of considerable heartache and suffering. Although these preventive measures are of critical importance to the family at risk, it is questionable whether they would realistically diminish the numbers of affected children in the population. The answer depends on many variable and intangible factors, but the reduction in incidence would undoubtedly be slight.

On the basis of the principles of Mendelian inheritance, one of every four subsequent fetuses in a family at risk for an autosomal recessive disease could be expected to have the disorder. If the goal of each family were to bear two normal children, two of every three such children would predictably be carriers of the disease.

A theoretical example with some actual numbers will show how this would work. In an initial study of 480 pregnancies in which both parents are known carriers (Aa) of an autosomal recessive gene, 120 affected children (aa) would be born. Among the 360 couples who bore a normal first child, none would be aware they were both carriers of a recessive disease gene. In a second pregnancy among these people, the birth of about 90 affected children could be expected. Approximately 210 children with the disease would be born before the mechanisms of amniocentesis and intrauterine diagnosis could be set in motion.

Ideally, the first 120 mothers who bore affected children would have their second pregnancy monitored by amniocentesis. Thirty fetuses, or 25 percent of those conceived, would be diagnosed as having the disorder and be aborted. A third pregnancy would have to be undertaken by 240 couples in order to reach their goal of two unaffected children. These 240 couples would include the 120 with an affected first child, the 90 with an affected second child, and the 30 who had required an abortion of their second pregnancy. Two hundred forty amniocenteses would have to be performed, and 60, or 25 percent, would predictably require abortions. These last 60 mothers would hypothetically proceed to a fourth pregnancy. Fewer than four of the original group of 480 would have to undertake a sixth pregnancy in order to reach their objective of two normal children.

Achieving the goal of two healthy offspring for each family at risk would have required 440 amniocenteses and 110 abortions. In the process 210 affected children would have been born. If this same group of people had simply borne children without amniocentesis or abortion until they had had two normal children, they would have had 920 normal children and 320 affected children. A reduction in the incidence of disease from 320 to 210 for a program of prenatal diagnosis and selective family planning would be 34 percent. This is an important reduction but not an overwhelming one. If such couples each bore two children without such a program, regardless of whether or not these offspring had the disease, the total number of affected children would be 240. The reduction then achieved through amniocentesis and therapeutic abortion would be from 240 affected children to 210. This is a reduction in incidence of about 10 percent. In actual practice the difference would probably be even smaller because not every known mother at risk could be expected to have an amniocentesis.

A number of couples with one affected child would probably elect to bear no more children. Diagnosis of the disease condition at birth is the exception rather than the rule. If the affected child were not recognized until five or six years of age, most couples would have decided to bear no more children or would have completed their families. In either case there would be no opportunity for a program of amniocentesis to exert an impact on the incidence of genetic disease.

Thus, programs involving prenatal diagnosis and selective family planning cannot be expected to reduce significantly the occurrence of autosomal recessive disorders in a population. Although the potential reduction in the incidence of X-linked disease with an amniocentesis program is much greater, it is realistic to expect detection to be less than complete. Even in the X-linked conditions there would be little to gain in terms of reducing the absolute numbers of affected children. If a family at risk for an X-linked recessive disease proceeds to bear two children who appear clinically normal, the incidence of heterozygous carriers is bound to increase in the population. Therapeutic avoidance of a second affected child is important to a family. Its effectiveness in reducing the incidence of genetic disease within a population is balanced by the discouraging effect of an involved first child. Further reproduction for families without access to amniocentesis or selected abortion is relatively unlikely.

A significant reduction in the occurrence of genetic disease within a population is possible, but more than prenatal detection and selective family planning is required. To effect such reduction one cannot wait for the birth of the first patient to detect the presence of the disease gene. The medical geneticist would have to identify the gene in the heterozygous carrier of a recessive condition prior to reproduction. Amniocentesis could then be performed in every pregnancy involving two parents who are both known to carry the recessive gene. In this way only normal infants would be born, and the disease could be eradicated. One might even imagine that if there were complete and early detection of heterozygosity, some people who were carriers might not marry. A more romantic conclusion might be that they would marry and decide to adopt rather than reproduce.

If heterozygote detection were available for such common autosomal recessive diseases as sickle cell anemia or cystic fibrosis, a major reduction in their incidence could be achieved. Five percent of all Caucasians in this country carry the recessive gene for cystic fibrosis. Among any ten thousand people, five hundred bear the defective gene. The chance for two carriers to meet, marry, and reproduce is relatively great. Among a thousand known carriers, fifty would be expected to marry people who were also carriers. One-fourth of their children would predictably have cystic fibrosis. Sickle cell anemia is even more common among the population of American blacks. The incidence of carriers is about one in ten. If it were possible to find all the carriers of these two conditions and make a prenatal diagnosis, both diseases could be eradicated.

It is not yet possible to eliminate these inherited disorders. In cystic fibrosis there are neither the methods to recognize carriers nor a prenatal test for the disease. No doubt the techniques for detection will be developed in time, but that does little to reduce the current incidence of the disease. Sickle cell anemia is more promising. Although difficult, it is possible to detect the disease *in utero*. The carriers are easy to identify. If this technique for heterozygote detection were put into practice on a broad scale, even without a program of amniocentesis and selective abortion, the disease could be largely controlled.

The only inherited condition in which a broad program of heterozygote detection seems feasible today is Tay-Sachs disease. In this disorder the availability of prenatal diagnosis and the possibility of selective abortion have been met. The disease is common enough among its target population to make a screening program both feasible and desirable. Technically the same is possible for galactosemia. Heterozygote detection methods are available. They are not as simple or economical as in Tay-Sachs disease. Intrauterine detection is possible and has been accomplished. The question of selective abortion is not as clear-cut with galactosemia since effective treatment for the disorder is possible. The most important problem with mass screening programs for galactosemia is the question of relative incidence. Galactosemia occurs approximately once in every one hundred thousand births. There are only six carriers per thousand individuals, in contrast with the one hundred carriers of the sickle cell trait per thousand blacks. Millions of people would have to be screened to detect a relatively small number of carriers. Such a massive testing program is probably not feasible and may not be desirable since the potential for marriage among carriers is relatively remote.

The target population for a Tay-Sachs prevention program is concentrated among descendants of the Ashkenazim. One in thirty of these people carries the gene for Tay-Sachs disease. Their ancestors came from eastern Europe, and they make up the majority of the Jewish population in the United States today. It has been estimated that there are six million possible carriers of the gene in this country alone. Although the number is large, it should be possible to test all those of child-bearing age.

The occurrence of the disease in an isolated population is ideal for a concerted program of heterozygote detection. The sophisticated and centralized nature of the population is helpful, as is the availability of a simple, accurate, and inexpensive blood test for a carrier. For these reasons, and because intrauterine detection is available for couples who are found to be heterozygotes. Tay-Sachs disease meets the criteria for mass screening programs intended to identify carriers in a population.

A pilot screening program was established in the Baltimore-Washington area in 1971 by Dr. Michael Kaback, then assistant professor of pediatrics at Johns Hopkins. Kaback was ideally suited to launch such a program. Young and vigorous, he radiates enthusiasm. He is an excellent pediatrician, biochemist, and geneticist; and he is Jewish.

He chose the Baltimore-Washington area as the place to begin a Tay-Sachs screening program for a number of reasons. He worked there and knew the area. Its Jewish population of about a quarter of a million was large enough to make a screening program statistically meaningful, yet small enough not to overwhelm the investigators. He knew that this pilot program would be carefully studied for potential application on a broader scale. He knew it had to be executed with great skill. Logistics were of prime importance. It is one thing to test for a few heterozygotes and quite another to screen an entire population.

A first step was to involve the people themselves. Mike made a direct appeal through newspapers, the religious press, and direct mailings to the target community. He persuaded rabbis and others influential in Jewish community programs of the program's importance. This first aim was to educate as many people as possible about Tay-Sachs disease and about the purposes of a screening program. Training articulate people who could communicate with others was of fundamental importance.

In conjunction with this education program there had to be further research done to refine the identifying chemical test. Dr. Kaback and his colleagues automated the process, establishing all the necessary controls and standardizations needed to be certain the automated test would not only handle all the samples but would also provide the precision and accuracy necessary to identify all heterozygotes. Forms had to be devised so that all essential questions could be answered on paper. It was important to have written records of previous pregnancies, the presence of diabetes, and the use of oral contraceptives. Any of these variables can alter the outcome of the identifying blood test. In instances in which the blood test is adversely affected, an analysis of the leukocytes provides the required information. The leukocyte test does not have to be performed unless the blood test is positive for both partners, one of whom may be pregnant and not really a carrier of the defective gene.

The logistics of follow-up and counseling for all those positively identified as carriers had to be devised. No information, particularly genetic information, is of any use unless understood. Genetic information must be carefully and wisely interpreted.

Once the logistics were in hand, the next step was to gather the target population for actual screening. This meant attracting all potential carriers of child-bearing age—roughly, all individuals eighteen to forty-three years of age. The natural place to bring them together was the local synagogue, the center of the Jewish community. There blood could be drawn for the test and all necessary information could be gathered.

The first screening sessions drew more than thirty-five hundred people in six weeks. More than five hundred volunteers assisted in administering programs at the Beth-El synagogue in Baltimore, the Oheb Shalom synagogue in Bethesda, and the Baltimore Hebrew Congregation and the Jewish Social Service Organization in Rockville. Each person to be screened filled out a brief form, went through a line, and had a small amount of blood drawn. In order to make the program self-supporting, each individual was asked to contribute five dollars. Although the contribution was purely voluntary, more than 90 percent chose to make it. Blood samples were refrigerated and taken in batches to the laboratory for analysis. Persons with a positive reading, those who were identified as carriers of the disease, were notified within a few weeks.

The actual screening program for the Tay-Sachs gene was begun only after an extensive program of public education about the nature, occurrence, and availability of treatment for the disease. The people being tested knew what they were after from the outset. Because of this enlightened attitude, community and individual support proved magnificent.

Aware that theirs was a pioneering, almost revolutionary effort, Kaback and his group moved relatively slowly. After testing several thousand people, they paused late in 1971 to study their results. By early 1972 they had screened approximately seven thousand Jewish people. Over two hundred carriers were identified. Eleven couples in which both members were heterozygotes were found before they had borne any children with Tay-Sachs disease.

Three hundred people can now be screened in the laboratory each day. Many have been convinced that mass screening for the disease will work on a much larger scale. Plans for similar programs are being made or are under way in New York, Chicago, Philadelphia, Los Angeles, and Toronto.

In New York City the Jewish community is vast. A program that will screen every person of reproductive age is formidable. The target population includes more than a million people. Community organizations and physicians provide the natural resources to tackle so huge a project. An encouraging factor is the absence of a scientific or medical barrier to mass screening. One might think that the testing of millions of persons for a recessive gene would run into insurmountable complications. It certainly invades an individual's privacy to a degree. The stakes are high and seem worth the price. Dr. Kaback did his homework well.

The lessons now being learned from Tay-Sachs screening programs will be applied to screening for the carriers of other harmful recessive genes. Once the initial development and refinement of screening programs are completed, there is the prospect of having such tests routinely performed, possibly before marriage. Each couple of Ashkenazic descent might have a Tay-Sachs blood test, much as the Wassermann test is now done. There are obvious hazards with this approach. Prospective marriages have been broken off by less distressing news. Yet it is obviously better to know one is a carrier before a Tay-Sachs child is born so that potential pregnancies may be monitored to ensure the birth of normal children.

Mass screening for the carriers of genetic disease is a brief story thus far. New methods for detection, new modes of treatment, and other research advances guarantee that the story will become even more impressive.

Although carrier detection through mass screening programs is of immense benefit to society as a whole, it can be used to solve genetic problems on an individual basis. Dr. John O'Brien, who discovered the biochemical defect in Tay-Sachs disease, has told us about a schoolteacher who consulted him because she had heard of his work and knew that a sister had died of Tay-Sachs disease. She was worried about whether or not she was a carrier. Since she was three months pregnant, her concern was well grounded. In previous years a counselor would have told her that her chances for having the heterozygous genotype would be two in three. Dr. O'Brien performed the leukocyte test, which indicated that she was, in fact, a carrier. The next step was to test her husband for the defective gene. He proved not to be a carrier. She could then be assured that their child would not have the disease. Genetic counseling in this case could be individualized and very supportive. Their baby was normal.

13. Population Genetics

In considering programs for the detection of heterozygous carriers and ways to control a disease throughout a population, we come to grips with the subject of population genetics.

The study of genes in populations has long fascinated geneticists. It has led them to exotic places among primitive peoples. It has led to a careful tracking down and examination of our more complex, highly outbred, and dispersed populations. Many books have been written about the subject. They are hard to follow because the field is steeped in mathematics. A population geneticist is virtually wedded to his calculator. By the time he writes about his subject he has usually made extensive use of a complex computer. Some of the general principles of population genetics can be understood without recourse to sophisticated computations or higher mathematics.

The Hardy-Weinberg principle provides the cornerstone for any consideration of the distribution of genes throughout a population. G. H. Hardy was a mathematician at Cambridge University in England around the turn of the century. Wilhelm Weinberg was a physician in Stuttgart, Germany. In 1908 both men simultaneously developed an idea that was to become a guiding principle in the study of population genetics. Original stimulus for their work came from consideration of human inheritance patterns. Both men were pondering the distribution of single gene traits among human populations. Once Mendel's concepts of dominant and recessive factors had been grasped, early geneticists wondered why a dominant trait should not increase in frequency until it ultimately replaced the recessive. If the gene for brachydactyly, or short, broad fingers, is dominant, why don't people all have short, broad fingers? Or why doesn't everyone have Huntington's chorea?

Hardy and Weinberg found that the key concepts were those of gene frequency and equilibrium, or balance, among genes in a population. They were able to explain the persistence of a recessive allele in a gene pool in terms of its frequency. It is known that if a homozygous dominant parent (AA) marries a homozygous recessive (aa), all the offspring in the next generation will express the dominant trait. The recessive allele has not disappeared from the gene pool.

It is present in exactly the same proportions as it was in the parental genotypes in which 50 percent of the genes were the dominant allele (A), and 50 percent were the recessive (a). In the offspring of this mating the alleles have simply been rearranged. Each individual carries one dominant and one recessive gene, producing the typical heterozygote (Aa) and exactly maintaining the fifty-fifty ratio or frequency between the two alleles. In this fashion the relative frequency of each allele is preserved in equilibrium. Populations in nature tend to maintain this continuous balance between gene frequencies for a particular trait from generation to generation. The constancy of the proportional occurrence among alleles was initially demonstrated by Hardy and Weinberg. Their findings have been subsequently confirmed by many other population geneticists.

Knowledge of gene frequencies is of great importance to the geneticist. To determine the relative frequency of the alternative alleles for brown (B) and blue (b) eye color in a population of 500 people, the geneticist would begin by counting the apparent, or phenotypic, frequency of the trait. The survey might reveal that 455 members or 91 percent of the population had brown eyes and 45 or 9 percent had blue eyes. Among the 455 individuals with brown eyes, some would be homozygous (BB) and some heterozygous (Bb). Observation will not reveal which of the two genotypes is present in the individual with brown eyes. Since the recessive phenotype for blue eyes can be produced by only one genotype, each of the 45 individuals with blue eyes must be the product of two recessive alleles (bb). Since a blue-eyed individual occurs only when a recessive allele in a gamete from one parent is matched by a recessive allele in a gamete from the second parent, the occurrence of a blue-eyed individual is the result of two independent chance events. Since the product of these two events, a blue-eyed individual, happens in 9 percent of this population, the probability or frequency of each individual event, the frequency of gametes with the recessive allele (b) is equal to the square root of the product. In this population, since 9% = 0.09, then its square root, $\sqrt{0.09}$, is 0.3 or 30%. This is the frequency of the recessive allele in the population.

The geneticist then knows that 30 percent or 300 of the thousand genes for eye color in this population of 500 individuals are the recessive allele (b). Since there is but one alternative allele (B), there must be 700 dominant alleles in this population's gene pool for eye color. So the gene frequency is 70% = 0.7. The frequency of the two alleles B + b, 0.7 + 0.3, must add up to the total, or one. With this information the geneticist can determine what proportion of the brown-eyed individuals are homozygous and what proportion are heterozygous carriers. Since the occurrence of the homozygous dominant individual (BB) requires that two gametes, each bearing a dominant allele, be joined at fertilization, the predictable frequency with which this chance event occurs is the product of the probabilities of each gamete bearing a dominant allele, or

$(0.7)(0.7) = 0.49$. The geneticist now knows that among the 500 individuals in this population, 49 percent, or 245 individuals, are homozygous for the dominant allele. Since 9 percent of the remaining individuals are homozygous recessive, 42 percent of the population, or 210 people, are heterozygous.

This method for determining the gene frequency of dominant and recessive alleles was initially developed by Hardy and Weinberg. They stated this principle in general mathematical form. If any dominant allele is called (p) and any recessive allele is called (q), the sum of the gene frequencies in a population is $p + q = 1$. Since the birth of homozygous dominant individuals results from the chance mating of two dominant alleles, each with a frequency of (p), the product (p^2) represents the predictable occurrence of this genotype. Because the heterozygote bears both a dominant (p) and a recessive (q) allele, the probability of such a mating is (pq). Because a dominant or a recessive allele can be provided by either heterozygote parent, the actual probability is the sum of (pq) + (qp), or 2pq. Since the birth of homozygous recessive individuals results from the chance mating of two recessive alleles, each with a frequency of (q), the product (q^2) represents the probable occurrence of the recessive genotype. Thus, the mathematical distribution for the three possible genotypes in a population can be generally stated as follows:

$$p + q = 1 \qquad p = \text{frequency of the dominant gene}$$
$$p^2 + 2pq + q^2 = 1 \qquad q = \text{frequency of the recessive gene}$$

This mathematical statement is a familiar one from high school algebra.

Application of the Hardy-Weinberg principle to human disease is of great importance to medical geneticists. Knowledge of the gene frequencies helps them to assess the potential impact on the population of an abnormal gene. A particular inherited autosomal recessive (aa, or q^2) may be observed to occur once in every 10,000 births. This is the frequency of albinism. The ratio of 1 in 10,000 represents the relative number of times when two recessive alleles (aa) will meet in a zygote. This provides the (q^2) value for the disease. The frequency of the recessive gene (q) in the population is the square root of 1/10,000, or 1/100. One in every 100 genes (1% = 0.01) in the population is the abnormal gene for albinism. The frequency of the dominant allele (p) is equal to $1 - q$, or $1 - 0.01$, or 0.99. Ninety-nine out of every 100 genes in the gene pool of the population is the normal dominant allele. Computation of the percentage of carriers follows the determination of 2pq, which is about 1 in 50. This explains the relative frequency of albino individuals. These kinds of computations are essential in determining the potential effects of every abnormal gene, like the one for albinism, on a population including the predicted incidence of affected individuals, the numbers of carriers expected to be found in mass screening programs, and so on.

The accuracy of the Hardy-Weinberg principle assumes that gene frequencies within populations remain stable from generation to generation. This kind of equilibrium is generally the rule, but it is not absolute. As an environment changes, the survival value associated with a particular gene may change. If a given food source has been widely available, possessing a gene that controls production of an enzyme that digests this food has obvious survival value. If this food source were eliminated from the environment, possession of the gene for this digestive enzyme would lose its value. If an alternative allele had existed in the gene pool that produced an enzyme ineffective for the digestion of the original food source, inheritance of the homozygous condition for this second gene would have probably proved lethal. The allele would be maintained in this gene pool, however, by heterozygous carriers who also possessed the dominant, effective gene. If the alternative allele produced an enzyme effective in the digestion of a different, less accessible food, it could exist in the population in both the heterozygous and homozygous recessive genotypes.

If, indeed, the original food source were withdrawn from the environment, homozygous dominant individuals possessing two genes for the same digestive enzyme for the food source might not survive to produce offspring. The gene frequency for this dominant allele might diminish. If the recessive allele were effective for the digestion of the second food source, this gene should become the dominant allele in the population and its frequency would be expected to increase dramatically. Individuals possessing it would naturally survive in competition and produce offspring. Those individuals possessing the original dominant gene in the heterozygous condition could survive and produce offspring if their second allele were effective in digesting the second food source. This genotype provides an example of hybrid vigor in which the heterozygote is preadapted to potential environmental change. An alteration in the environment that eliminated a food source could lead to the natural selection for survival and reproduction of individuals with a previously less advantageous allele.

The environment can dramatically change the survival value of given genes and their frequency within the population. The value of inherited variations or alleles is determined by the environment. This explains the genetic basis of evolution, the origins and survival of species. If the recessive allele did not prove effective in the digestion of alternative food sources, neither allele in the population's gene pool would have any survival value, and the population, possibly a whole species, could become extinct.

Because particular populations of a given species become isolated from one another over periods of time, different selective factors may alter gene frequencies among distinct subgroups of interbreeding populations of a species. The relative proportions of dominant and recessive alleles in the limited gene pool of a population may differ so greatly from the species as a whole that separate varieties, strains, or races may develop. The observation that gene frequencies remain constant assumes that mating within a species is a random process, with every possible combination of alleles having an equal probability.

Among human populations many factors limit the potential randomness of mating. These limiting factors may be cultural or geographic. People tend to marry others who are a lot like themselves physically, culturally, and racially. The practice of selective, or assortative, mating has produced many subpopulations within the species of man. The gene pools for these isolated subgroups may reflect gene frequencies different from the species as a whole. Because of the conscious or unconscious factors that dictate the selection of a mate, it is not surprising that various groups exhibit features characteristic of their gene pool. That certain abnormal genes have a far higher frequency in some populations characterized by assortative mating helps account for the high incidence of cystic fibrosis among Caucasians, sickle cell anemia among blacks, Tay-Sachs disease among Ashkenazim, and thalassemia among certain Mediterranean peoples.

The tendency for abnormal gene frequencies to occur among limited populations is called *random genetic drift*. The term was coined by the population geneticist Sewall Wright. This phenomenon occurs in small populations or isolates that have formed for religious, social, or geographic reasons. These isolates are relatively rare today, but in the not so distant past, before efficient means of transportation and communication, most human populations lived in small, widely separated groups. In such small populations the frequency of one gene may by chance rise to a very high level. In a small religious isolate in Pennsylvania known as the Dunkers, the proportions of the blood groups A, B, and O were found to be very different from those of parent populations in Germany. Among Blackfoot Indians the blood group A is present in 80 percent of all individuals, while only 2 percent of Ute Indians are of blood group A. These differences are probably a result of genetic drift toward unusual gene frequencies.

The founder effect is similar in its action to genetic drift. It is based on random or chance occurrences. The original colonization of an unpopulated area by a small number of couples could by chance include one or more founding individuals with genes differing significantly from the parent population. These founders then populate the area with descendants reflecting the variant gene frequencies.

One of the most important modifiers of gene frequency within any population is mutation. Mutation involves a change in the DNA of the gene, usually in the arrangement or number of nucleotides. It may convert a dominant allele into a recessive, or it may create an entirely new allele at the same chromosomal locus. The appearance of a mutation changes the frequency of a gene in subsequent generations very slightly. The reason it is important in the genetics of populations is that it provides a basis for choice through natural or artificial selection of one or another genetic constitution that might have advantages for survival of the species. This is the way that evolution works.

Mutation is a relatively rare event. A majority of really severe dominant diseases that are present from infancy result from the spontaneous appearance of a new mutation, or change in the DNA. If we know the number of instances in which a disease occurs sporadically in a population and the total number of births, we then know the mutation rate, at least for that gene. It was found that achondroplasia occurred eight times in a series of ninety-four thousand births in Copenhagen. This provides a frequency for the mutation of once in approximately twelve thousand births. Each live birth resulted from the fusion of two gametes, one from the mother and one from the father. A mutation could have occurred in either. Since this is the case, we must multiply the number of live births by two to determine the rate of mutation producing the abnormal gene. The rate of mutation for achondroplasia in Copenhagen was one in twenty-four thousand. Most estimates of mutation rates in general are of the order of one in every hundred thousand.

Genetic counseling could have an effect on the occurrence of dominant disease through new mutation. The data available indicate that one risks new mutation as an older father. The ages of fathers of sporadic cases of achondroplastic dwarfs produced by spontaneous mutations are significantly higher than the average for the general population. This is true for other dominant disorders as well.

The male produces many gametes, or sperm, through meiosis, in contrast with the female, who produces relatively few eggs. Although the female produces her gametes early in life, the male continues producing sperm cells year after year. The possibility of a copying error in the replication of DNA in his gametes becomes increasingly likely with each subsequent meiosis. These errors in DNA synthesis lead to mutation.

The clear implication is that it is wise to have your children when you are young. Advanced age in the mother leads to a greater incidence of chromosomal nondisjunction producing the Down syndrome and other chromosomal abnormalities. Advanced age in the father leads to elevated rate of mutation and the spontaneous appearance of new dominant diseases.

Mutation may be produced artificially. When Müller first induced mutations in fruit flies, the results led to valuable research. It is known that chemicals can produce mutation. These agents include the nitrogen mustards that were first developed as war gases and have more recently been employed to treat certain forms of cancer. It is probable that other mutagenic, or mutation-causing, chemicals will be found. Some chemicals that are in our environment today or will be added to it tomorrow may be discovered to be mutagenic. The most frequent mutagen is physical. It is ionizing radiation that may come from X rays, radioactive isotopes, and the by-products of nuclear reactions. It is important that we maintain an awareness of the genetic risks involved through exposure to these radiations. Although there are other more compelling arguments against nuclear warfare, the risk of inducing mutations and its long-term genetic consequences should provide sufficient argument against the testing of nuclear weapons. The same potential may be relevant to the widespread dependence of civilian populations on nuclear power. Avoidance of X-ray exposure in gonadal areas, particularly the elimination of the concentrated exposures to fluoroscopy in people who are still of child-bearing age, makes excellent genetic sense.

The operation of natural selection following mutation is easy to follow in principle. The elimination of a deleterious gene produced through mutation usually takes place within a generation. Often the disorder produced by the mutation is so severe that the homozygote dies before reaching the reproductive age. This type of influence does not greatly affect the frequency of a gene in a population. The (q^2) for most recessive diseases is quite small. For the albino, who does reproduce, it is one in ten thousand, while 2pq, the incidence of carriers, is one in fifty. If selection operated on the heterozygote, it would have a greater impact on the balance. The best example of this principle is found in sickle cell anemia.

Sickle cell anemia is not a rare recessive disease. In black populations it is produced by a common recessive allele. It is a disease that kills a major portion of its victims before they reproduce. Geneticists have been able to determine why sickle cell anemia is so common in American blacks and among the Africans from whom these people trace their ancestry.

Scientists started with the knowledge that the home of sickle cell anemia is in tropical Africa, south of the Sahara. It is found in a broad belt across the center of the continent. In Africa virtually no homozygous patients with sickle cell anemia reach adulthood. The incidence of carriers of the abnormal gene in some tribes is as high as 40 percent. The incidence in West Africa, the area from which the ancestors of most black Americans were brought to this continent, is 20 to 25 percent. It has been estimated that some forty million black Africans have the sickle cell trait, that one million have the disease, and that eighty thousand of them die yearly of the disease.

No gene could achieve such an incidence or high frequency if its harmful nature were not somehow balanced by some survival value for those who carried it. If all sickle cell patients die early, before they reproduce, the sickling gene is constantly being eliminated from the gene pool. The gene would soon fade away unless there were compensating features that counterbalance the damage it does.

James Neel discussed the implications of this situation in 1953. He pointed out that there were two possible explanations. One was a very high mutation rate for the sickling gene. This would require a mutation rate three thousand times that ordinarily found in man. Studies in Africa found no evidence for this possibility. The other explanation was that of a balanced polymorphism in which the heterozygote for hemoglobins A and S enjoys some advantage not shared by normal homozygotes for hemoglobin A.

A British scientist, Lord Brain, has been credited with the first suggestion of what that hypothetical benefit might be. He pointed out that the areas in which the frequency of the sickle cell gene was highest coincided with the areas in which malaria was most common. A. C. Allison found evidence that the sickle cell trait provides its carriers with an increased resistance to malaria. Carriers of the sickle cell trait were found to have fewer parasites of the deadly falciparum variety of malaria in their blood during the crucial period of infancy. Sickle cell carriers had a lower childhood mortality rate than noncarriers. In one study only one person with sickle cell trait in a group of one hundred patients in five African cities succumbed to malaria. Based on calculated frequencies for the defective gene, there should have been twenty-three sickle cell carriers in the group. Of real importance is the fact that no case of fatal cerebral malaria has been observed in a child bearing the sickle cell trait.

It is generally accepted that the sickle cell trait somehow interferes with malarial infection. The protective mechanism probably involves the natural consumption of sickled cells and their malarial parasites in the spleen. Sickled red blood cells are destroyed in the spleen much more rapidly than are normal cells. Since malarial parasites reside in red blood cells, they could be eliminated from the body. This phenomenon of balance, in which homozygous recessive individuals (SS) with sickle cell anemia die young while carriers with only one recessive allele are provided with a life-extending resistance to selective factors in the environment, is known as balanced polymorphism. In fact, this is the first and best example of the operation of balanced polymorphism in natural selection at work in the human species. A genetic equilibrium has been reached in which the gene achieves a frequency at which the lives it saves by providing resistance to malaria are balanced by the lives lost to sickle cell disease. The fact that one of ten black Americans carries the gene indicates that the recessive gene frequency is dropping in this country from the level found in West Africa. This is probably because the sickle cell trait provides no selective advantage in the malaria-free environment of North America.

Anthropological studies of human hemoglobins have given further insights into the mechanisms of population genetics. Hemoglobin C, discovered in American Negroes, is thought to have come, as did hemoglobin S, from West Africa. It is not frequently encountered there. About 10 percent of the people in Accra, Ghana, have hemoglobin C. To the east in Zaire, it is nonexistent. The gene frequency is low in Liberia to the west and in Nigeria to the east. But to the north in Ghana as much as one-fifth of the population has the gene for hemoglobin C. Neel has observed, "Never in the history of genetics . . . have geneticists been quite so close to having a ringside seat at the origin and dissemination of a new gene." The reasons for the spread of the hemoglobin C gene are not known.

It is puzzling that the gene for cystic fibrosis continues to exist with a high rate of frequency. The disease itself is almost invariably fatal at an early age. It is assumed that there must be some benefit in the carrier genotype that balances the deaths caused in the homozygous recessive condition. Among heterozygotes there may be some kind of advantage like that enjoyed by carriers in the sickle cell disease. This could involve a selective edge in the reproductive process. If carriers are more likely to marry or more likely to have children, they may have a selective advantage that preserves the gene in Caucasian gene pools.

Some of the reasons for a selective advantage associated with a given gene are not too complicated. Color blindness is fairly frequent in human populations. It has been reasoned that in an early society in which survival depended on skill in hunting, a color-blind hunter might have been less confused by nature's protective coloration than a normal counterpart who missed his prey because of the camouflaging colors. This might or might not have been the case, but myopia, or nearsightedness, certainly would have proved a disadvantage to the hunter. As society became gradually more complex and sophisticated, a nearsighted person, unable to hunt, might have turned toward more scholarly pursuits. This propensity might have provided a selective advantage to this individual and his offspring. An alternative idea is that if most of those with better vision were out hunting, a nearsighted fellow around home with a lot of women might have ended up responsible for more offspring.

A clear example of this type of selective influence has been observed in the occurrence of albinism among a number of North American Indian populations. The gene is quite frequent in some tribes. The explanation seems to involve more than a relative capacity to hunt. The albino has very sensitive skin and very sensitive eyes. He cannot hunt in the open. He cannot farm. This may have created a situation in which women and albinos were isolated together. Apparently one thing led to another, and the gene for albinism spread effectively.

14. Multifactorial Problems: Subtle Patterns of Inheritance

Medical genetics came of age when exact numbers were substituted for imprecise estimates. By applying Mendelian rules to human genetics, by pinpointing the specific cause of a genetic disease and its pattern of inheritance, whether autosomal recessive, autosomal dominant, or X-linked, a physician can tell parents exactly what odds they face in pregnancy.

This approach has proved effective in the diagnosis and treatment or prevention of many inherited disorders. Some diseases that seem to be genetic in origin do not follow the rules. These are often conditions that occur with considerable frequency among individual families without following prescribed inheritance patterns. They constitute some of the most common problems encountered by medical geneticists and their patients. In most of these disorders an exact cause for the condition is unknown. Often it appears that a combination of genetic and environmental factors is responsible. The patterns of inheritance that emerge in charting a pedigree turn out to be irregular. Predicting the risk of occurrence in any given pregnancy becomes difficult. The nature and severity of the disease may vary greatly. This may mean that what seems like one disease among various individuals may be quite a number of different diseases, each with its own cause or causes. The workings of genetics in these conditions are subtle.

These conditions are generally described as *multifactorial*. The word means that several factors act jointly to cause the disorder. There are a number of possibilities that may fit this general category. Each of them may be operative in different instances. A typical familial multifactorial disease is thought to result from an interaction of genetic and environmental factors. Among environmental factors some of the most important are those present in the uterus before a baby is born. Although a disorder may be described as multifactorial if it involves no more than two separate causative conditions, some multifactorial disorders seem to involve the interaction of quite a large number of factors, both genetic and environmental. Other multifactorial conditions may be described as polygenic. These conditions result from the interaction of a number of genes rather than from the single-gene defects previously considered. In these instances the problems may be multifactorial, but all the factors are genetic. Another possibility is that the symptoms of a polygenic condition may mimic those caused by a single-gene defect. In such situations it may be as difficult to diagnose the exact cause of the disease as it is to determine the genotype of brown-eyed individuals (BB or Bb). The way to come to grips with these problems is to study affected individuals and their families, applying statistical analysis to the data found. Some very useful facts have been discovered in this way.

Multifactorial conditions include some well-known, frequently encountered conditions as well as some relatively obscure abnormalities. One of the most prominent is cleft lip and the cleft palate that may or may not accompany it. Clubfoot is another, as are spina bifida and anencephaly, defects of the spinal cord and brain. Pyloric stenosis, a narrowing of the digestive tract, is a common cause of vomiting and intestinal obstruction in the early weeks of life. Congenital dislocation of the hip also falls into this multifactorial category. Some geneticists would also list rheumatoid arthritis. Heart disease and cancer may belong on the list. Diabetes is certainly among multifactorial diseases.

This is a gray area of genetic disease. A subtle pattern of environmental and genetic factors blends to influence the incidence of abnormalities. So it is with most normal traits. Think of height, weight, or intelligence. All are determined by a subtle interplay of heredity and the environment.

There is an enormous range of height among different individuals. At some of the extremes genetic influences are easy to detect. Patients with the Turner syndrome, in which there is only one X chromosome, are extremely short. XYY males are usually quite tall. Thus, chromosomal factors may influence height. Single genes also influence longitudinal growth. Most causes of extreme shortness, or dwarfism, are genetic in origin. Conditions that produce exaggerated growth such as that found in gigantism may be genetic in origin. Within the much larger population who are judged to be "normal" in height, there is a considerable range in variation. There are families in which everyone is tall and families in which everyone is short. Assortative, or selective, mating of marriage partners with similar characteristics compounds these genetic tendencies over many generations.

Often there are changes in stature that do not have a genetic origin. In recent generations both sons and daughters have tended to be taller than their fathers and mothers. The American soldier in George Washington's time was considerably smaller than men in uniform today. The most dramatic of these secular changes has been seen in people from Japan. In California and in Hawaii second-generation Japanese are often as tall as their Anglo-Saxon schoolmates. It has generally been assumed that the major factor in this steady increase in height with each generation is nutritional. Nutrition certainly plays a part, but the truth is we do not really know why there has been such a dramatic change in stature. It is clear that the reasons will be found to be multifactorial.

The many factors involved in establishing intelligence and intellectual performance are even harder to evaluate. At the extremes it is easier to see the effects of genetic influence. They must be present in all of us. The question of intelligence has become increasingly controversial as certain scientists have attempted to explain it in terms of ethnic theories. In any population there is an enormous variation in intellect. Careful studies have indicated that both environment and heredity are involved. It is a multifactorial phenomenon.

One must look closely at the multifactorial genetic diseases to detect the interaction of genes and the environment. It is possible to see concentrated occurrence in families, not with the precise mode of inheritance associated with single dominant or recessive alleles, but in discernible patterns nevertheless. In cleft lip and palate a family in which there has been one affected child has a 4 percent chance of bearing another. This is not a large risk compared to the 25 percent risk of recurrence for an autosomal recessive gene or the 50 percent risk for an autosomal dominant. But it is a statistically significant increase over the risk in the general population. In families in which two individuals have been affected, there is a 10 percent incidence of the abnormality in subsequent pregnancies. If one identical twin has a cleft, there is a 40 percent chance the other twin will have one. This risk factor is four hundred times that in the population as a whole.

This is the kind of pattern observed in other multifactorial diseases. Odds are higher in a family in which there has been an affected child than in other families. It is also true that the risk for subsequent children rises with the number of individuals in that family who have already been affected.

These are the factors that genetic counselors take into account in advising families with a history of multifactorial diseases. They are called empiric risk factors. They have been identified through direct observation, or empirically, from studies of large numbers of patients in large numbers of families. An understanding of these risks and their magnitude can be very helpful in deciding what to do in planning a family.

Dr. C. O. Carter, director of the British Medical Research Council's Clinical Genetics Unit, has made a careful study of multifactorial diseases. He believes that this pattern of inheritance reflects the existence of what he calls *risk genes*. For a given condition there may be one or more risk genes. These may produce dominant or recessive genetic conditions. Most people will bear only a few of a sizable number of possible risk genes for any given multifactorial disease. A few people will have enough of the risk genes for a condition to be pushed over the "risk threshold" and have the disease.

What about the offspring of parents with multifactorial diseases? Why are not more children of such individuals affected as are their parents? Since each child inherits a unique combination of chromosomes from each of two parents, children may receive fewer risk genes from the affected parent than non-risk genes from the other parent and thus be free from potential inherited disease.

Another factor is the environment, particularly the intrauterine environment. Specific conditions in the womb may make one pregnancy very different from any previous or future pregnancies.

The influence of the environment on the expression of genes can be observed in congenital dislocation of the hip. This disorder is at least five times more common among girls than boys. The reason is not known, but there is evidence that female hormones, including those secreted by a woman during pregnancy, can act to loosen the ligaments that bind the bones of the leg to the female hip. During pregnancy this loosening is part of the natural preparation for childbirth and would be expected to make passage of a baby through the birth canal easier. Male animals do not respond in this fashion to the female hormones, so this effect is sexually specific. If the fetal female ligaments respond in the same way to the female hormones as do those of the mother, there would be a significant chance for dislocation of the hip. Genetic disease in which the basic problem is laxity and looseness of connective tissue is often accompanied by the dislocation of hips and other joints.

An environmental influence that promotes dislocation of the hip is breech birth, in which a baby makes its entry into the world feet or bottom first rather than the normal head first. In a study conducted in 1952, 16 percent of babies with congenital dislocation of the hip were found to have had breech deliveries. Only about 3 percent of babies in the general population are born in the breech position. There may be other causative factors for the dislocation, involving the shape of the socket into which the end of the femur, or thigh bone, is inserted.

An interesting environmental factor has been clarified through cross-cultural studies of early infant rearing. Some American Indian populations and the Lapps of Finland were found to have a high incidence of congenital hip dislocation. These groups are racially quite distant and their gene pools may be thought to share relatively few genes. What they do share is the practice of swaddling infants, wrapping them tightly as papooses. This minimizes movement. It also brings the hips into a position that promotes dislocation. In cultures that allow an infant considerable freedom of movement, there is a far lower incidence of dislocation. This is particularly true in populations in which the infant is carried almost continuously in a sling on the back of the mother. The rider's hips spread widely as the legs tend to encircle the mother. This is precisely the therapeutic position used by orthopedists to correct a hip dislocation when it does occur.

Convincing statistical evidence has been assembled by Dr. Carter and others. The concept of multifactorial genetic disease and its causation by a combination of genetic and environmental factors is widely accepted. Among the multifactorial disorders there is an appreciable risk for recurrence of the disease among first-degree, or closest, relatives of an affected individual. In the case of cleft lip, predicted recurrence of the condition is 4 percent for siblings. Other first-degree relatives include parents and children. The figure among them should again be 4 percent. Among second-degree relatives, such as aunts, uncles, nephews, and nieces, this figure is sharply reduced. In the case of cleft lip, the risk of recurrence in second-degree relatives is less than one percent. The risk drops even faster with less closely related individuals. Among relatives such as second cousins there is not a significant difference in risk from that of the general population. The incidence of congenital dislocation of the hip among females in the general population is one in five hundred. Second-degree relatives have a risk factor that is three times this normal value, while first-degree relatives have a risk factor that is twenty-five times the general rate. Pyloric stenosis, which is more common in males, generally occurs at a rate of one in two hundred births. The risk in second-degree relatives is five times greater and in first-degree relatives is ten times greater.

These numbers are very useful in counseling families in which multifactorial disease has occurred. Other general principles may also be useful. In any one affected family the severity of a multifactorial condition varies more among affected individuals than with diseases caused by single-gene defects. This variation is to be expected since affected individuals do not share all the same causative or contributing factors with others. The risk to relatives of individuals with a severe case of the disorder is greater than the risk to relatives of a mild case. It probably takes more factors or more penetrant factors to produce a severe disease than a milder one. In a family with a child who has a cleft on only one side of his lip, the risk of having a cleft in subsequent siblings is one in forty. In a family in which a child has clefts on both sides of the lip and of the palate, the risk of recurrence is about three in fifty. Where an abnormality is associated with gender, as in congenital dislocation of the hip, the risk to relatives varies according to the sex of the involved family member. In pyloric stenosis, which is much more common among males, the children of females who have had this disease are three times more likely to develop pyloric stenosis than the children of males who have had the disease. For the disorder to appear in the female, who is usually protected, there have to be more potent factors or a smaller number of favorable factors for the disease to be expressed. Transmission of these penetrant factors produces greater risk among her relatives.

In counseling, the general rules are probably more important than the exact numbers. It is not really important to most families whether they have a risk factor of 2, 4, or 6 percent. It is more important to distinguish this order of magnitude from those of less than one percent and from the Mendelian 25 or 50 percent.

In each instance of multifactorial disease the risk factors have to be specifically determined for each separate disease. For some they are not yet known with any precision. For some the inheritance pattern is confusing. Diabetes is to some extent genetic in origin. Its expression, in certain varieties of the disease, is to a degree controlled by environmental factors. Some middle-aged people can be free of disease by proper regulation of their diet. What is called diabetes may be a number of different diseases, all producing similar symptoms. Therefore, assessment for modes of transmission is difficult. In some isolated population groups, particularly some American Indians, diabetes is common and seems to follow a Mendelian, single-gene pattern of inheritance. It certainly does not follow these principles in most populations. The kind of early-onset diabetes that starts in childhood or before the age of thirty appears to be a very different disease from the late-onset disease that first appears in middle age. The early-onset type requires insulin treatment and is always more severe. It is a much rarer disease than the late-onset type. Its incidence is about two per thousand. The increased risk to siblings of this disease is about twenty-four times that of the late-onset diabetes.

Since some of the multifactorial diseases are common, we might consider a number of them individually.

Cleft lip: In approximately one of every thousand pregnancies in the United States, something goes wrong in the development of facial structures. Normal features develop when two sheets of tissue fuse to form the upper lip and palate. When they fail to join, a central gap is left above the chin and in the roof of the mouth. Sometimes only the lip is cleft; sometimes only the palate. Both the lip and the palate are cleft in nearly half of these cases.

The various factors that cause cleft lip and palate are largely unknown. There are genetic factors, but the limitation of genetic causes is indicated by the fact that in identical twins one infant may have the cleft while the other is normal. This is true even though both twins have precisely the same genes. In experimental animals clefts have been induced by drugs, radiation, and deficiencies of certain vitamins. The conditions required to produce clefts in these animals do not appear to be applicable to the human anomaly.

A special relationship may exist between cleft palate and cortisone. This steroid hormone and related molecules induce clefts of the palate without similar cleavage of the lip among various strains of mice. This lesion is a rather unusual occurrence among mice, as it is in man. Generally, a lip defect occurs in conjunction with a palate defect. Cortisone is clearly an environmental factor that may produce cleft palate in mice.

There is also a genetic factor. Some strains of mice are almost completely resistant to the environmental effect of cortisone, while in at least one genetic strain treatment of the pregnant mother leads to cleft palates in nearly 100 percent of the offspring. Extrapolation of this experience to people is not clear-cut, but there have been reports in the medical literature of human infants with clefts of the palate following a mother's treatment with one of these steroids during pregnancy. There have also been many pregnant women treated with cortisone whose infants did not develop clefts. Causation seems to be multifactorial. People may be like mice in this respect. They may have to be genetically predisposed to the effects of cortisone in order to produce offspring with the malformation.

It is true that some clefts occur as part of well-recognized syndromes. Some of these are caused by dominant or recessive genes. Some are of chromosomal origin. Other conditions are polygenic.

Clefts of the lip and of the palate can be repaired surgically. The ultimate result is often quite attractive. One of the biggest problems is in accepting a baby's appearance until the lip is structurally and cosmetically corrected. Surgical treatment to close the lip can sometimes be done within weeks of birth. The palatal defect cannot be closed until there has been some growth, usually for at least a year. Speech therapy is often necessary.

Clefts are thought to cause problems with feeding. They almost never do. The usual infant can suck well without any special nipples. When sucking is a problem, babies can quickly be taught to cupfeed using a medicine glass or shot glass.

Infants and children with cleft palates are unusually susceptible to middle ear infections. This knowledge can lead to early diagnosis and the early institution of treatment in order to prevent hearing loss. As many as 20 percent of children affected with cleft lip or palate have other birth defects that may take the form of major malformations. These children should be carefully examined to be certain there is not a major remediable defect.

Cleft palate occurring by itself is twice as common in white infants as in blacks and affects 50 percent more girls than boys. Cleft lip, with or without cleft palate, is twice as common in boys as in girls. Parents who have had a child with a cleft lip run a 4 percent risk of bearing another affected child in a subsequent pregnancy; when cleft palate occurs alone, the abnormality has a recurrence risk of one in fifteen for subsequent pregnancies.

Clubfoot: The formal name for this condition is talipes, derived from the Latin words for ankle (*talus*) and foot (*pes*). The affected foot is twisted so that the affected person appears to walk on the ankle. The most common form is *talipes equinovarus*, in which the foot is twisted inward with the toes bent down. There are other variations: *talipes calcaneo-valgus*, in which the foot is bent outward with the toes turned upward, and *talipes equinovalgus*, with the foot bent inward and twisted.

Clubfoot is a fairly common anomaly. *Talipes equinovarus* is twice as common in boys as in girls, an imbalance not found in other forms of clubfoot. It was once thought that clubfoot was purely environmental, that twisting of the baby's foot occurred because of a malposition of the fetus within the uterus. It now seems clear that genetic factors are involved. Identical twins are ten times more likely to have the abnormality than are nonidentical, fraternal twins. Both kinds of twins share the same uterine environment, but only identical twins have the same genotype. A family with one child affected by clubfoot has a much higher chance of having another in a future pregnancy. The risk of recurrence varies between 2 and 8 percent for these families.

Treatment can be highly effective. For most patients therapy consists of bandaging the foot or placing it in a cast in order to bend it toward the normal position. Treatment should begin early, often before the newborn leaves the hospital. It is often successful enough to permit the child to take his or her first step with a normal foot. In more severe instances surgery can be performed to correct the deformity. While periodic checkups must go on for years to ensure that the treatment is succeeding and to guard against relapses, the prognosis for most children with clubfoot is very positive.

Spina bifida and anencephaly: These conditions represent defects in the central nervous system, the spinal cord and brain, in which the normal closure of developing tissue does not occur. They are abnormalities of fetal development. Spina bifida often leads to hydrocephalus, but this is a secondary defect caused by the problem in the lower spine.

The same genetic factors appear to be involved in both spina bifida and anencephaly. Parents who have a child with either condition have a 5 percent risk for recurrence in each future pregnancy. A family in which a child has anencephaly has a one in twenty chance of bearing a subsequent child with spina bifida.

Anencephaly is a disease in which an infant is born without the major part of its brain. Skull, skin, and hair are missing. Every structure above the eyebrows is usually absent, and the top of the head is open. Survival is impossible. These infants live at most for a few days. Anencephaly occurs in one of every thousand births. It is three times more common in girls than in boys.

Spina bifida results from the failure of developing vertebral bone, muscle, and skin to fuse properly. This leaves a hole or cleft in the back, usually in the lower spine, and permits the meningeal membranes, which cover and protect the spinal cord, and the spinal cord itself to protrude from the body. This condition is known as meningocoele when only the membranes protrude and meningomyelocoele when the spinal cord also protrudes. In most cases some of the individual nerves or whole portions of the spinal cord are involved in the defect. There is always cerebrospinal fluid in the protruding membranous sac. It is thin-walled and easily breaks, producing leakage of the spinal fluid. When a leak occurs, it is easy for infection to enter and produce meningitis, an inflammation of the meningeal membranes. The prognosis in this condition is usually not favorable.

When the spinal column is intact, surgery to eliminate a meningocoele may produce excellent results. If the spinal cord has been disturbed, many of the nerves in the affected area suffer irreversible damage. A child with this problem may never gain control over bladder or bowels and may never be able to move the lower extremities. Infection is a constant danger. Hydrocephalus, or an enlarged head due to fluid retention, may occur, even after an apparently uneventful closure of a simple meningocoele. This complication adds another dimension to the potential degree of brain damage.

At one time nearly all children with meningomyelocoele died at an early age. Neurosurgeons can successfully keep many of these children alive. It is a difficult life for a majority of these children and their families. They require continuous long-term help from an army of medical specialists: urologists, neurosurgeons, orthopedic surgeons, physical therapists, and others. With all of this care, many patients never walk normally.

The link between anencephaly and meningomyelocoele has been mentioned. Occurrence of one of these defects in a family signals a 5 percent risk of recurrence of one or the other defect in later pregnancies. If such a defect occurs in two children in a family, the risk for a future defect is doubled.

In 1972 Dr. James H. Renwick, a geneticist at the London School of Hygiene and Tropical Medicine, proposed that spina bifida and anencephaly, which are common in parts of Britain, could be caused by the eating of blighted potatoes early in pregnancy. Dr. Renwick came to this conclusion from the study of epidemiological statistics showing a relationship between the incidence of potato blight and the incidence of these birth defects. In considering the United States, he observed that these defects occurred more commonly in Maine than in Idaho. Maine potatoes are more likely to be blighted than Idaho potatoes. The damage, he postulated, was done not by the blight but by natural antibiotics produced in these potatoes to fight the fungus causing the blight. The theory received support from Dr. E. E. Poswillo of London, who was able to produce birth defects of the central nervous system in laboratory animals by feeding them blighted potatoes. Skepticism about the theory is widespread. There will undoubtedly be further data on the subject. Meanwhile it would do no harm if pregnant women avoided potatoes in the early months of gestation.

Pyloric stenosis: A newborn baby appears perfectly normal at birth and goes home from the hospital at the usual time. After a few weeks he begins to vomit frequently and with increasing forcefulness. Following feedings he may vomit projectilely, spraying the food over some distance. In a short time he may become very skinny, scrawny, and generally undernourished. The alert pediatrician will suspect that he has pyloric stenosis. This is a multifactorial abnormality that occurs once in about three hundred births. It is five times more common in boys than in girls.

The basic defect is an overly thick muscle around the pylorus, which is the area that leads from the stomach into the small intestine. When the abnormal muscle contracts, virtually nothing can pass from the stomach into the small intestine. Peristalsis, which usually moves the food out of the stomach, is reversed and produces vomiting. The remedy is a relatively simple operation. The muscle is sliced longitudinally and permitted to lie open. Surgery is almost always successful. The chief danger of this condition is that its existence might not be recognized in time. Dehydration or secondary infection can be lethal in early infancy.

Sex differences influence the statistics of recurrence in pyloric stenosis. There is one chance in ten of a recurrence in a future pregnancy if an affected girl is born, but only one in fifty if the affected child is male. A father who had the condition as a baby may have one chance in twenty that a child of his will have pyloric stenosis. For a mother who had the disease, the risk in early pregnancy is one in eight.

Congenital dislocation of the hip: The sex ratio for this condition is unbalanced in the opposite direction from that of pyloric stenosis. There are five, perhaps as many as ten, cases in girls for every one in a boy. Dislocation of the hip is a descriptive term for a condition in which the hip is not necessarily separated from its socket but may be weakly or poorly articulated with it. The fit of the leg into its socket in the pelvis is not good. Often the socket is inordinately shallow.

If the condition is recognized early and treated before weight bearing and walking begins, the prognosis for correction is excellent. If therapy is not accomplished, permanent disability may ensue. Treatment is aimed at achieving a proper and permanent alignment of the leg and hip socket. This may require a splint or plaster cast. Surgery is rarely necessary. It is required only when the condition has been neglected.

An attempt to introduce precision into the estimation of recurrence risks for multifactorial traits has been made at the Department of Human Genetics at the Western General Hospital in Edinburgh. Geneticists there have developed a computer program for estimating the risk in any given family. The program, called RISKMF (Risk, MultiFactorial), gives the computer all of the basic information about the type of disease, the predicted risk of recurrence in the general population, the family's history, the degree of severity of the condition in a previous pregnancy, and so on. The computer then produces a precise estimate for the family's risk of recurrence. This can prove very helpful. It is only as accurate as the information that is fed into the computer.

In a family at risk for anencephaly or meningomyelocoele, prenatal diagnosis rather late in pregnancy might be possible. Ultrasound techniques should indicate the existence of an anencephalic head and might detect a large sac forming over a spina bifida. Amniography should potentially outline the shape of either defect. Prenatal diagnosis is not now commonly available for multifactorial diseases.

The interaction of genetics and environment in the multifactorial diseases is fascinating. Giving advice to worried parents who are concerned about one of these multifactorial conditions is complicated. There is a lot of information that must be known precisely and understood thoroughly. Risk changes with both the sex of a previously affected infant and the severity of the condition in that infant. Prior occurrence of the condition not only in the immediate family but among relatives may play a part in determining occurrence in future pregnancies. The incidence of the condition in the general population must be kept in mind. All of these facts must be balanced in order to provide a realistic estimate of risk. It is tough for parents to evaluate a statement that they have "one chance in ten, or fifteen, or twenty of having a child with disease in a future pregnancy." The magnitude of the defect is relevant. Each family must assess its potential risk for an affected child and make its own decisions. Genetic counseling for the multifactorial traits calls for rare and valuable commodities: good judgment and a feeling for humanity.

15. The Environment and Birth Defects

For all its beauties, the world is not always a friendly place for members of the human race. The cause of a birth defect may be something familiar in the world around us. Even when man lived in a much more natural state, he was exposed to environmental and developmental hazards such as the radiation from cosmic rays that continuously bombard the earth, from radioactive elements in rocks, and from viruses that seem always to have been with us.

Our civilization has made an excellent start toward the reduction of birth defects caused by viruses, but it has added some new dangers. People are now exposed to more harmful radiations, primarily from medical X rays, but also from nuclear power plants, fallout, and other complex sources of radioactivity. A new kind of danger comes from exposing a developing fetus to drugs and other chemicals during pregnancy.

Can anyone forget the tragic effects of thalidomide that so dramatized the danger of drugs to the sensitive process of early prenatal development? Late in 1960 pediatricians in Europe began reporting an epidemic-like incidence of what had previously been an unusually rare birth defect. Phocomelia is a word derived from the Greek. It means seal-like limbs. Hundreds of children all over Europe were being born with stubby, useless, phocomelic arms or legs or both. These malformations were caused by developmental failure of the long bones in the limbs. Many of the affected children exhibited other abnormalities, including malformations of the heart and intestines. The tragically disfiguring, flipperlike limbs were a constant hallmark from child to child. Retarded development was only physical. These children were of normal intelligence.

In 1961 a German geneticist, Dr. Widekund Lenz, found the explanation for this epidemic. In a beautiful bit of medical detective work he discovered that the tragedy was caused by a drug that had been consumed early in pregnancy. This compound had come into wide use as a sleeping pill. Early research on adults had indicated that it was harmless. It was quite effective in inducing a refreshing sleep without a hangover. It was marketed freely in drugstores throughout Europe. No prescription was required. The drug had many names in many countries. It is now universally known by its chemical name: thalidomide.

In those days it was not necessary to test a drug in children, gestational animals, or pregnant women before releasing it widely for public consumption. Americans were fortunate in not having an epidemic of tragic proportions. Dr. Frances O. Kelsey of the Food and Drug Administration saved this country from thalidomide. She did it because of some reports from Europe about the occurrence of neural complications observed in some adults taking the drug. The symptoms that led to Dr. Kelsey's concern were relatively minor: experiences of numbness, tingling, and a slight deterioration of the muscles at the base of the thumb. Dr. Kelsey almost single-handedly held up permission to market the drug. Lack of similar caution in Europe and Australia led to the births of more than seventy-five hundred children with the thalidomide syndrome. It was unquestionably the greatest disaster of its sort in history.

Thalidomide is an unusually potent cause of birth defects. Lenz found that even a small dose of the drug at the critical time could cause an almost 100 percent incidence of phocomelic malformations. If the drug was taken by a pregnant woman between thirty-four and forty-five days after the last menstrual period, interference with normal developmental processes in the fetus was bound to occur. The incidence of malformations was 35 percent if the drug was taken at any time during the first three months of pregnancy. This is a time when the fetal organ systems, particularly the limb buds, are growing rapidly. Because thalidomide is more dangerous for humans than for animals, testing for the drug's safety is difficult. Humans are at least sixty times more sensitive to thalidomide than mice, one hundred times more sensitive than rats, two hundred times more sensitive than dogs, and seven hundred times more sensitive than hamsters. Tests with a safety factor of ten, that is, in which animals get a dose ten times higher than the maximum human dosage, would completely miss the dangers of thalidomide. At the time thalidomide was introduced, no country was testing the effects of a drug on pregnant animals. Now such testing has been made mandatory in the United States and many other countries. Testing laboratory animals for negative effects does not, however, guarantee safety of a drug for the human fetus.

The thalidomide episode was tragic enough with the heartache and suffering it caused among affected children and their families. What made it more frightening was the glimpse it gave of how man-made dangers can influence human development. It has provoked thought about dangers to the genetic integrity of man. A change in a gene, as opposed to changes in fetal development, could be hidden for generations before emerging. Thalidomide was identified as a hazard because the defects it caused were unusual and striking and because there was little delay between cause and effect. What of a drug or other chemical that caused more subtle damage, possibly a one percent increase in the incidence of some defective chromosome? What of a drug that caused recessive mutations, so that damage was felt in future generations? It would not be easy to detect.

Questions concerning the potential impact of man-made technology on genetic heritage began to be asked with increasing frequency in the mid-1960s. They are still being asked today. After a decade there are still more questions than answers, but the groundwork has been laid for getting those answers. There are ways to study environmental causes of birth defects, and studies along these lines are in progress.

Scientists and physicians in this field are concerned with three different types of problem. One is almost entirely natural, the genesis of birth defects by viruses. One is almost entirely artificial, the production of prenatal disease by drugs and other chemicals. The third involves exposure to radiation.

There is a vocabulary that expresses the different kings of damage that can be done by these agents. It is useful to know that language. *Teratogenesis* implies the production of defects in a fetus as it grows and develops in the uterus. Thalidomide is a teratogen. It causes birth defects when taken during pregnancy. *Mutagenesis* means damage to the genetic material. Anything that causes damage to the genetic message encoded in chromosomal DNA is a mutagen. If genetic damage is done to the sex cells, ova or sperm, an inherited disease induced by the mutagen may be transmitted to subsequent generations. If damage is done to the somatic cells, which are all cells of the body except for sex cells, the effects will be expressed in that individual but will not be transmitted to future generations. *Carcinogenesis* is a related term and implies the causation of cancer. Any agent that can change normal cells into malignant cells is a carcinogen. Among chemicals, carcinogens, mutagens, and teratogens are related. Sometimes the same chemical can cause each kind of damage, dependent only on the type of cell that is exposed to it. Radiation certainly can induce birth defects, mutations, and cancer.

Some forms of cancer are genetically determined. These types are few and occur rarely. There is no clear evidence that any of these genetic cancers has anything to do with carcinogenic induction. The action of teratogens is generally nongenetic. The types of defects that result from the action of a teratogen on the fetus are very similar to disorders that are genetically determined. It is important in these drug-induced situations to determine that the problem is nongenetic and will not be transmitted to future generations, thus posing no risk to future children of the affected parents. It is not always easy to draw the line between purely environmental and purely genetic causes of disease. Sometimes a genetically determined state can alter a person's response to a drug or other environmental influence. Both genetics and the environment are often required to produce a problem. There are a number of examples of this type of interaction. Although none has been demonstrated to cause defects in the developing fetus, it seems likely that there are examples and that they will one day be discovered.

The interaction of heredity and environment is most clearly observed in the field now called ***pharmacogenetics***. This discipline involves a union of pharmacology, or the study of drugs, and genetics. A person with a pharmacogenetic abnormality is perfectly normal and healthy under usual circumstances. However, he has an inherited defect in an enzyme that is not ordinarily required to play an important role in metabolism. A newly introduced chemical, a drug that requires this enzyme in order to be satisfactorily metabolized, may turn out to be toxic, or its effects may last for a long time.

There are examples of this in clinical medicine, and in time there will probably be more. A typical example is sensitivity to succinylcholine, which is used by anesthetists. It is a muscle relaxant that is useful in causing laryngeal or vocal cord relaxation in order to permit the insertion of a tube into the trachea. This is necessary for most general anesthesia. In most people the drug produces a rather complete muscular relaxation for a short time. Because the drug acts rapidly, a doctor can insert the tube quickly. The effects of the drug are expected to disappear long before a patient awakens from general anesthesia, no matter how short an operation. The reason for this quick response is an enzyme known as pseudocholinesterase, which splits the succinyl and choline parts of the molecule, inactivating the drug.

Some people do not have this enzyme, or they do not have an enzyme that works at all well. When they are given succinylcholine, the relaxant effect may last for hours or days. The anesthesiologist usually learns this when he stops administering general anesthesia. He expects his patient to wake and be normal. The patient does wake up, but that is all. He cannot move a muscle. More important, he cannot breathe. The experience is frightening and potentially fatal. The paralytic effect does disappear in time, but in the interim the patient must be maintained by using a respirator.

The genetics of the pseudocholinesterase system have been carefully analyzed. The enzyme is encoded as an autosomal recessive gene. A number of different allelic genes is capable, when present in the homozygous genotype, of producing this abnormal response to the drug. Heterozygote detection can be done by studying the enzyme's activity in the blood. Homozygous sensitivity occurs in about one in two thousand people. This is probably frequent enough to justify routine testing prior to surgery. The reaction is of such severity that it would be preferable to avoid it rather than to rely on treatment.

There are other examples of pharmacogenetic differences among people. Some patients treated with isoniazid (INH) for tuberculosis metabolize the drug so inefficiently that toxicity is common and smaller doses should be used. This is a genetically determined reaction. Some people can taste the molecule phenylthiocarbamide (PTC). Others cannot. This tasting capacity or its absence is determined genetically. The most common pharmacogenetic problem results from a deficiency of the enzyme glucose-6-phosphate dehydrogenase. There are a number of different genetically determined variations in the enzyme. A patient with one of these defects is perfectly normal under most conditions. When given certain drugs, such as sulfonamides, antimalarials, nitrofurans, or vitamin K preparations, he promptly develops a hemolytic anemia. The rate of red blood cell destruction is so rapid that hemoglobin appears in the urine.

Glucose-6-phosphate dehydrogenase (G6PD) is an important enzyme in the carbohydrate metabolism of the red cell. It is encoded by genes on the X chromosome. G6PD deficiency is inherited as an X-linked recessive condition. It is common among American Negroes, occurring in about 10 percent of this population. Among males the incidence of occurrence is 14 percent. Among females the incidence is 2 percent. Some affected females are rare homozygous recessives, since they possess two X chromosomes with the disease allele. The disease gene may be considered fairly common. Some females with the condition are heterozygotes in whom the vast majority of inactivated X chromosomes, or Barr bodies, bear the normal gene. Among them the majority of cells are governed by the X chromosome for the recessive condition in accordance with the Lyon Hypothesis. Heterozygotes for this gene can be detected by analyzing the relative activity of the G6PD enzyme in the blood. Defects in this enzyme are also common in Mediterranean populations. These people have a different faulty G6PD than the one found in black populations. This defect and a propensity for eating raw fava beans lead to serious hemolytic reactions in these people.

Geneticists have estimated that about 20 percent of birth defects have a Mendelian gene origin. About 10 percent are chromosomal and 20 percent have purely environmental causes. This leaves about 50 percent that are thought to result from an interaction between environmental and genetic factors. It is obviously just as desirable to prevent a birth defect caused by a teratogen as it is to prevent a birth defect of purely genetic origin. However, a mutagen that produces a change in a gene is of greater danger to the species because it is transmitted to future generations and becomes part of the genetic load, or the burden of genetic defects in the human gene pool.

The job of protecting the public against mutagens and teratogens is not easy. Until quite recently the inventors and developers of synthetic chemicals used in industry and medicine had not thought much about the possibility that such molecules could cause mutations or birth defects. They focused on the positive effects they were seeking, the cure of a disease or the resolution of some medical, environmental, or industrial problem. The thalidomide episode provides a good illustration of this pragmatism. Some five hundred thousand to six hundred thousand synthetic chemicals are currently used in industrial processes. The number keeps increasing. Virtually none of these compounds has been tested for its potential as a mutagen or teratogen. More have been tested for carcinogenic potential, partly because testing for carcinogenesis is easier. Laboratory animals are exposed to the chemical agent and examined for cancer.

Cigarette smoking is the clearest example of an environmental carcinogen in our society. Animals readily develop malignancies when tars collected from cigarette smoke are painted on the skin or introduced into their bodies. Animals have been taught to smoke cigarettes. They develop lung cancers, and so do people. Smoking cigarettes does considerable damage to the body beyond causing malignancy. It has particular effects on the heart and the coronary arteries. It is one of the major mysteries of our time, with all the information available, that people continue to smoke.

Testing for teratogens is more difficult. The chemical agent must be administered to a suitable number of pregnant animals, and then the fetuses must be examined for the presence of congenital anomalies. There are considerable variations in the sensitivity of different species to different chemical agents. Compounds like thalidomide may be teratogenic in man and harmless in pregnant experimental animals. Drugs that are teratogenic in animals have been used in people for years and are clearly not teratogenic for humans. It works both ways. Since the thalidomide tragedy, test methods for teratogenesis have been sharpened.

Mutagens are the most difficult to detect. The scientist is looking for effects on future generations. Long-term studies are expensive and take some time. Scientists have turned to organisms that reproduce quickly and in large numbers in order to develop relatively inexpensive, rapid, yet reliable tests for mutation. Marvin Legator of Brown University has developed tests of this sort. He has examined the effects of a chemical agent on the bacteria within a test animal. There are billions of these microorganisms within any animal. They may pass through thousands of reproductive generations during one life cycle of the host organism. Thus, it is possible to detect signs of mutations in the large numbers of these bacteria more easily than by studying just a few of the host animals. Another form of testing calls for introduction of a suspected mutagen into male animals. Mating these males with several different females produces a significant number of offspring appropriate for the study of mutagens.

People are becoming increasingly concerned about the possibility of these dangers. The pendulum of public opinion is swinging in the direction of stronger controls with less margin for error. The world has entered a period in which the dangers of science and technology are receiving considerable attention. Man is becoming more suspicious of his own man-made hazards.

An example of this developing societal concern is observable in the approach to radiation and the regulation of its usage. The risks have been clear since the days when X rays were first introduced into medical practice. Many early radiologists developed cancers, and even today leukemia is much more common among radiologists than among other medical specialists. Society allowed radiation to be used for purposes that were really frivolous. Fluoroscopes were once found in neighborhood shoe stores. Parents could flip a switch and look at the bone structure of their children's feet while exposing them to dangerous X-ray radiation. These machines were cheaply constructed and had minimal shielding. There were no trained operators. This casual use of X rays is now illegal because the dangers of such radiations are more widely recognized. Anyone who can remember the days when shoe clerks allowed a curious child to operate a fluoroscope can see the contrast in current practice. A dentist using diagnostic X rays will drape a patient with a lead apron and carefully step out of the room before turning on the machine.

The genetic cost of exposure to radiation is now appreciated. There has been much public controversy about the dangers from the fallout of radioactive elements from nuclear weapons tests as well as debate over radiation from nuclear power plants. Under the pressure of public and scientific opinion, officials charged with establishing limits for allowable usage of radiation have steadily decreased those limits.

Radiation has always been part of the earth's environment, long before man made X rays or atom bombs. A unit used to measure radiation exposure is the rem. Natural background sources, such as cosmic rays and radioactive elements in the earth's crust, provide an average exposure of one-tenth of a rem, or 100 millirem, per person per year. The Federal Radiation Council several years ago set the allowable exposure standard from nonmedical sources of radiation at 5 rem for the thirty-year period during which reproduction occurs. That allows an average of 170 millirem per year, which is not much higher than the 100 rem per year that are unavoidable.

In 1972 the National Academy of Sciences National Research Council Advisory Committee on the Biological Effects of Ionizing Radiation evaluated the limit and concluded that it was too high. The committee was quite precise in describing its concept of the cost of exposure to radiation:

> It is calculated that the effect of 170 millirem per year (or 5 rem per 30-year reproductive generation) would cause in the first generation between 100 and 1,800 cases of serious, dominant or X-linked diseases and defects per year (assuming 3.6 million births annually in the United States). This is an incidence of 0.05 percent. At equilibrium (approached after several generations) these numbers would be about five-fold larger. Added to these would be a smaller number caused by chromosomal defects and recessive diseases.

To that toll the committee added an estimate of "congenital abnormalities and constitutional diseases which are partly genetic." The increase in these caused by the 170-millirem annual exposure would bring the total incidence of man-induced cases to between eleven hundred and twenty-seven thousand per year after several generations. There was one final word:

> The most tangible measure of total genetic damage is probably "ill-health" which includes but is not limited to the above categories. It is thought that between 5% and 50% of ill-health is proportional to the mutation rate. Using a value of 20% and a doubling dose of 20 rem, we can calculate that 5 rem per generation would eventually lead to an increase of 5% in the ill-health of the population.

The committee was careful to point out that the genetic toll would be in addition to the immediate cancer risks of increased radiation exposure. The 5-rem limit, said the committee, would cause about six thousand extra cancer deaths annually, an increase of 2 percent in the spontaneous cancer death rate. The committee recommended new limits that would permit "far lower average exposures and genetic and somatic risk than permitted by the current Radiation Protection Guide." The committee set no exact number, but it was talking about a drastic reduction in the 170-millirem-per-year limit.

There is still the possibility of genetic damage from other sources of radiation. The 100-millirem background exposure is unchangeable. Then there is medical radiation, which at the time the committee reported was controlled neither by regulation nor by law. Exposure to medical radiation varies greatly from person to person. All the committee could do was to outline some steps for reducing unnecessary exposure: restrict the use of radiation for "public health survey purposes," meaning chest X rays used to detect tuberculosis or lung cancer; license medical radiation equipment; and certify operating personnel. Medical people who work around radiation equipment should have the benefit of shielding for their testes and ovaries.

This report was prepared in 1972, forty-six years after Hermann J. Müller demonstrated that X rays greatly increased the incidence of mutations in fruit flies. The benefits of radiation and of allowing slightly increased radiation exposure for such enterprises as nuclear energy are great. Man-made sources of radiation have proved difficult to control. The argument that "a little more radiation won't cause *that* much trouble," first heard during the nuclear fallout controversy of the 1950s, is still attractive to many people. The National Academy of Sciences Committee Report follows the pattern that the more people seem to know about radiation and its effects, the more concerned they are about minimizing human exposure.

Radiation hazards have been made worse by the efforts of man. On the other hand, viral teratogens are natural hazards that have been made significantly less hazardous by the efforts of man, and more positive progress in this direction can be expected in the future.

The most notable success in reducing birth defects was the development of a vaccine against rubella, the disease known as German measles. Pregnant women and the fetuses they bear encounter many different viruses. The federal government's Collaborative Perinatal Research Study, which made detailed observations of some thirty thousand women, found that sixteen hundred of them had viral infections other than the common cold during pregnancy. Most of the sixteen hundred women had just one infection, but some contracted two viral infections, and others had more than three viral infections. Pregnant women, like the rest of us, may get influenza, mumps, infectious mononucleosis, measles, and any of the other viral infections to which they are not immune.

An agent is a teratogen when it produces anomalous development, like the limb malformations seen in thalidomide babies. A virus that infects a baby in the uterus may cause serious, even lethal disease without producing anomalies, and that is just as bad. An example is the herpes virus. Herpes viruses may cause cold sores or sores in the genital area. Some infants may acquire the virus through the placenta, while others are infected during the process of birth. The illness usually appears during the first or second week of life. There may be fever or other signs of infection, often tiny blisters on the skin. This virus may involve the liver, the lungs, or the brain when it infects a tiny baby. Most cases are fatal. New drugs being developed to treat viral infections seem to have an effect on this virus in young infants.

Another viral agent that is closer to being considered a teratogen is cytomegalovirus. It is so named because the infection produces abnormally large cells, particularly in tissue culture. This virus is particularly insidious because infection with cytomegalovirus does not produce a rash, fever, or any other symptom of infection in the mother. Like thalidomide, it is harmless to the normal adult. The effects of the virus on a newborn infant can be devastating. They include microcephaly, an unusually small head, reflecting a small brain that will be accompanied by severe retardation if the infant survives the acute infection. Many do not survive. The generalized infection produces jaundice, liver failure, and multiple hemorrhages in the skin and elsewhere. It may be possible to develop a treatment for this virus that will be lifesaving for an infant who contracts the infection late in pregnancy. Hopeless damage will have been done by birth if the fetus has been infected during the critical stages of brain development within the first three months of intrauterine life. It will be necessary to develop a vaccine against cytomegalovirus to prevent its effects at this period of gestation. None is yet available.

It is a different story with rubella, the major viral teratogen. Parents call it German measles. Its symptoms resemble those of measles, but it is a much milder disease. In fact, one of the problems is that many different viruses and probably other organisms cause a brief rash resembling rubella. Many women reaching the childbearing period do not really know whether or not they have had the disease.

Rubella causes a devastating array of related birth defects. There is a vaccine available against this virus. The development of that vaccine is one of the shining medical success stories of recent years. If the vaccine is used as it should be, and the signs are encouraging, historians will soon relegate this disease to the past. The time between its identification as a teratogen to its conquest through vaccination encompasses a comparatively brief span of little more than thirty years.

There were several heroes in the story. The first was Dr. Norman Gregg, an Australian ophthalmologist who noticed in 1941 that he was treating an unusually large number of newborn babies with cataracts. In one of the most remarkable efforts of medical detective work on record, Gregg reviewed medical reports from the previous year and found that there had been an epidemic of rubella in Australia. When he checked further, he found that every mother of a child with cataracts had contracted rubella early in pregnancy. He correctly concluded that the rubella had caused the cataracts. These babies showed other birth defects as well. Gregg concluded that the entire malformation syndrome was caused by intrauterine infection with rubella virus.

Gregg's shrewdness is worth considering. As an adult disease, rubella is noteworthy for its mildness. A low-grade fever, a slight rash, a few days of weakness, and it is gone. To connect this seemingly innocuous disease, treated mostly in children, with the enormous damage done to a fetus during pregnancy was a remarkable feat of insight.

Dr. Gregg's finding was vigorously pursued even during the war years. Many different investigators were soon able to provide confirmation of his original observations. At first it seemed that any woman who contracted rubella during pregnancy would bear a child with birth defects. That turned out to be an exaggeration because the investigators were starting with affected children and working backward. When they started with infected mothers and worked forward, they found a picture that was less bleak. If infection occurs in the first month of pregnancy, about half the children will have abnormalities. About one in five babies will be born with defects if the mother is infected during the second month, and perhaps one in ten if the infection occurs in the next three months. After that the danger is considerably diminished.

Two factors are involved in establishing these odds. The first is whether the rubella virus crosses the placenta to reach the fetus. If it does not, damage will not occur. The second is the rate and stage of development of the fetus when the viral infection occurs. Damage is greatest early in pregnancy when most organs are being initially formed. The extent of infection in the fetus also determines the degree of damage.

Defects caused by rubella virus are heartbreaking. Affected infants have cataracts. They may be blind or may develop glaucoma. Deafness may be total or partial. Most of the affected babies have congenital heart abnormalities, many of them quite severe. They may be microcephalic. They may have very tiny heads and severe mental retardation. Some infants may die early from their defects. More live but are so severely handicapped that they end up in state institutions for the retarded.

Rubella epidemics seem to occur in cycles of from six to nine years. An epidemic is followed by six to nine years of relatively low incidence, after which there is another epidemic, and the cycle is repeated. An epidemic occurred in the United States in 1958. Another, the worst in years, swept across the nation in 1963–64, causing an estimated ten million rubella infections. Estimates of the damage done by that epidemic range from fifteen thousand to twenty thousand infants born with birth defects, and some eight thousand to thirty thousand fetal deaths.

When that epidemic struck, researchers already were at work on a vaccine against the disease. But they were not ready. The hope was that they would be for the next epidemic. Rubella virus had been isolated in several laboratories in 1961. After that, it took some years to develop methods for growing large amounts of virus in tissue culture. Once fairly large samples of the rubella virus were available, efforts could be made to produce a vaccine.

There are two general ways to make a vaccine against a virus. One is to use chemicals to kill the virus, which is then injected into the body. This was the principle of the Salk vaccine against poliomyelitis. Although incapable of causing disease, the protein coat of a killed virus often stimulates the body's immune system to produce antibodies that will prevent the disease. A second method is to manipulate the virus itself, breeding it generation after generation to produce a strain of virus that is too weak to cause a disease but strong enough to induce antibody formation in the host. These antibodies do not distinguish between strains of the virus, and thus protect the individual against all infectious strains. This was the principle of the Sabin vaccine against poliomyelitis. Virologists worked toward a weakened or attenuated live virus vaccine against rubella because live vaccines have been thought to provide longer and more complete protection than do killed vaccines. The goal was to protect women against rubella throughout their reproductive years.

By late 1965 Drs. Harry M. Meyer, Jr., and Paul D. Parkman of the National Institutes of Health isolated a live rubella virus and were testing it under carefully controlled conditions. The vaccine was licensed for general use in 1969. Millions have since been vaccinated against rubella. If the vaccine is used as it should be, birth defects caused by rubella should vanish as surely as the crippled limbs of poliomyelitis.

The rubella vaccine story is one of the most heartening achievements of medical science in our time. The 1963–64 epidemic filled schools for deaf and handicapped children. The human cost was fantastic. The financial cost of treating children with rubella in 1963–64 was enormous. Dr. Louis Z. Cooper of New York University's Rubella Birth Defect Evaluation Center estimated this expense at more than two billion dollars. On the basis of past history, the next rubella epidemic should have occurred toward the end of the 1960s or in the early 1970s. There is no sign of it thus far. Let us hope this means it is gone for good as an epidemic disease.

The elimination of birth defects caused by rubella is somewhat more complicated. Some thought is required to make the most effective use of rubella vaccine. It was designed to protect pregnant women and their fetuses. However, it cannot be given to a pregnant woman. Even though the virus is attenuated, there is considerable risk that the vaccine itself might be harmful to the fetus. Public health officials in the United States began the rubella vaccination campaign with explicit cautions against vaccinating any woman who was likely to become pregnant about the time of the vaccination. Instead, children were given the vaccine. Because almost all cases occur in children, preventing the disease in children should stop the infection from spreading to adults.

In Europe public health officials used a different strategy. They used the vaccine on mature women first, taking care to warn the vaccinated women against becoming pregnant for at least three months after immunization. Now that this initial group has been vaccinated, both Europe and the United States have essentially the same program: to vaccinate all children. The vaccine was given to women who did not have antibodies against rubella, while making sure that the vaccine was not given to a pregnant woman. Some 85 percent of adult women do have a natural protection or immunity because they had the disease in childhood. Many physicians will give the vaccine to a woman without antibodies immediately after childbirth, when the chances of another pregnancy are smallest and when parents are most receptive to information about risk in pregnancy.

Other viral infections early in gestation may also cause fetal infections. Still others may even cause birth defects, but there is not enough evidence available to incriminate any of them. Physicians are cautious about any disturbance of the body's normal functioning during the early, critical days of pregnancy when the fetus is so vulnerable to harm.

An infectious agent that produces a chronic infection and permanent damage in the fetus is the parasite *Toxoplasma gondii*. It causes a disease called toxoplasmosis. Toxoplasmosis infection in the adult is usually a minor proposition. Most people do not even know they are infected.

Toxoplasma is harbored by many animals. If the meat from those animals is not thoroughly cooked, the parasites may survive and infect humans. Contracted during pregnancy, the disease can cause microcephaly, calcifications in the brain, eye problems, and mental retardation. It has been estimated that one of every four thousand children born in the United States is affected by the parasite.

The villains in this story are raw meat and cats. Although undercooked meat is an overlooked danger for those who like their steaks and hamburgers rare, the warning that pregnant women should avoid eating raw meat is easily understood. The danger from cats needs explanation. *Toxoplasma* cysts form in the digestive system of cats. After excretion these cysts can be infective for as long as a year. Distressing though it may be to cat lovers, pregnant women should stay away from cats. It is not wise to introduce a cat into the house in which there is a pregnant woman. The cat may have the parasite. If there is already a cat, the pregnant woman should not empty the cat's litter box because the cysts may be present in high concentration. She should avoid digging in a garden where the cat's feces may be buried, and even avoid petting or holding strange cats when visiting other homes. The odds against infection from any one encounter with a cat are small, but why take chances when so much is at stake?

That question is an excellent one with which to introduce the subject of chemical mutagens and teratogens. In this field almost all the dangers are man-made. Until recently hazards from chemicals to the unborn were unknown, while the benefits of chemicals for society were obvious. Chemicals have a large effect on the way we live. Chemistry gives us the drugs that have cured important diseases, such as pneumonia and typhoid fever. Chemicals are the anesthetics that permit surgery. Chemicals preserve our foods and change our moods. Chemicals change old materials and provide new ones. There are hundreds of thousands of chemicals, most of them synthetic. They are part of our environment and they touch every aspect of our lives. It is probably true that most of them do not harm us in any way. However, thalidomide started geneticists thinking. We have begun to formalize our protections against teratogenic drugs and their effects on the fetus. We have really only begun to worry about the effects of chemicals on the genetics of man.

The LSD story illustrates the difficulties of investigating this type of problem. In the mid-1960s a young American drug culture was exploring the hallucinogenic properties of lysergic acid diethylamide, LSD. It is a pretty frightening drug for many reasons other than the genetic. Evidence is that its popularity has waned considerably. A few abnormal children were born to women who had taken LSD during pregnancy. It appears now that the two events may have been unrelated, but geneticists began to examine the chromosomes of people who had taken LSD. Chromosomal abnormalities were found that were similar to those observed following exposure to radiation or known mutagens. Cells from those who consumed LSD revealed many broken, distorted, and fragmented chromosomes. In 1969 Dr. Kurt Hirschhorn of New York's Mount Sinai School of Medicine declared that LSD "can produce profound chromosomal damage in humans." It does so in some 75 percent of persons who use it. He spoke on the basis of studies that he, Dr. Maimon M. Cohen of the State University of New York at Buffalo, Dr. William A. Frosch of New York University School of Medicine, and others had carried out. In addition to chromosomal abnormalities in the cells of persons who had taken LSD, these scientists also found abnormalities in cell cultures treated with LSD. The literature warned that the use of LSD could cause birth defects.

That contention was quickly questioned by other scientists. They had two criticisms. The first was that LSD could not clearly be isolated as a cause of any one condition found in drug users. Because most users of LSD had also used a variety of other mood-changing drugs, it was unclear which teratogen might have produced the noted damage. A drug sold on the street as LSD might well contain an entirely different drug. The second criticism was of the cell culture experiments, in which the concentrations of LSD used to treat the cells were far greater than would be expected in the bodies of LSD users. In 1971 a group of investigators headed by Dr. Norman I. Dishotsky of the Mendocino State Hospital in California declared without reservation that "pure LSD ingested in moderate doses does not damage chromosomes *in vivo*, does not cause detectable genetic damage, and is not a teratogen or carcinogen in man."

Few geneticists today are prepared to talk in conclusive scientific terms about LSD. In a study reported in 1972 by Drs. Cecil B. Jacobson and Cheston M. Berlin of Washington, D.C., 148 pregnancies were studied in 140 women who acknowledged using LSD just before or during pregnancy. There were 53 therapeutic abortions, 12 spontaneous abortions, and 83 live births. Of the babies born alive, 8 had major birth defects. Of 14 embryos from therapeutic abortions that were examined, 4 had gross defects. Many of the women were unable to conceive again during the eighteen-month period of the study. Conclusive evidence against LSD? Hardly. Drs. Jacobson and Berlin pointed out that many of the women in the study had used other illegal drugs, many were poorly nourished, and many had infectious diseases, all of which clouded the picture. But there was an enormous fetal wastage in this group of women. Either LSD or something else about their life-style was bad for human reproduction.

The final chapter for LSD has not yet been written. Someone who may sometime have taken LSD should not be unduly frightened. Certainly it is inadvisable for a person to take LSD, particularly anyone who is pregnant.

The difficulties in reaching definite conclusions about LSD, in which some really distinctive abnormalities have been seen, illustrate the problem of coming to any conclusions about other drugs. The list of drugs that are known to cause birth defects is relatively short. Hormones given during pregnancy have resulted in the birth of female children with external genitalia resembling those of a male infant. This masculinization occurs when women are given male hormones, but the danger is so obvious that very few women have been so treated. Some female hormones that have been used in women to prevent miscarriages have a chemical structure that also permits them to act as male hormones. Drugs given to control the maternal thyroid can interfere with the thyroid in the developing fetus and produce an enlarged goiter. Iodides given to asthmatics can do the same. The antibiotic tetracycline, given late in pregnancy, can cause permanent discoloration of the teeth.

One of the most unusual and disturbing discoveries about drugs during pregnancy was made in 1972, when physicians in Boston found that several young women who developed cancer of the vagina shared a common history. All of their mothers had been given a synthetic hormone, diethylstilbestrol (DES), during pregnancy to prevent spontaneous abortion. More than one hundred cases have been recorded in which the administration of DES to a pregnant woman has been followed, nearly two decades later, by vaginal cancer in a daughter. The fact that an effect of a drug can remain hidden for so long is worrisome. Many obstetricians and others advise that no drug be given during pregnancy unless it is used to treat an illness that poses a clear danger to health.

It may be an achievable goal to keep drugs away from pregnant women, but keeping all chemicals away is impossible. Anyone eating a normal American diet is exposed to perhaps three thousand different chemicals that are used as food additives—preservatives, emulsifiers, artificial colors, and stabilizers. All the substances used to give food the qualities needed for the modern supermarket are chemicals, and they stay in the food. Many of these chemicals have never been tested for mutagenicity or teratogenicity. It was only in 1972 that the Food and Drug Administration began a safety review of these compounds.

Less certain is the possible genetic threat posed by the thousands of chemicals used for all of the varied purposes of our modern society. Gasoline itself is a chemical, as are the herbicides and pesticides used in gardens; so are the chemicals in plastics. Occasionally, one of these compounds comes to the public attention when new information emerges, but even trained scientists are often at odds about the significance of such information. The fact that huge sums of money may ride on the interpretation is of no help.

The nation's detergent manufacturers, seeking to replace the phosphates that so distress ecologists by causing excess growth of algae in lakes and streams, settled on a substitute called nitrilotriacetic acid (NTA). Millions of dollars were spent based on that decision. Scientists found that NTA could increase the toxicity of some metals and thereby cause fetal abnormalities in mice and rats. The government "suggested" that the manufacturers reconsider their choice of NTA. Millions of dollars went down the drain. The case against NTA is far from proved. When potential risk is so enormous, there can be no choice.

Why take chances when the cost of a mistake is so high? The expense of caring for one severely malformed child has been estimated at $250,000. From an economic standpoint alone, preventive genetic medicine makes undeniable sense. In terms of human suffering the potential savings from attempts to prevent malformations are incalculable.

What steps can be taken to determine whether a given chemical causes birth defects or genetic injury? An extensive program of testing in animals is one approach. A registry for birth defects or some other central mechanism for surveying human populations might be another.

Dr. James V. Neel has proposed an advanced system for monitoring mutation rates in man. Blood samples could be taken annually from approximately 365,000 newborns. This represents about one in every ten new Americans. The samples could be analyzed to detect variants in twenty different blood serum proteins and red cell enzymes. The cost per analysis, using automated equipment, would be about ten dollars a sample. This would mean a total annual cost of less than four million. Dr. Neel believes such a system could detect a 50 percent increase in the mutation rate. The generally accepted figure is that twenty mutations occur in every 100,000 births. Dr. Neel thinks his system could detect an increase to thirty mutations per 100,000 births, thus providing the continuing genetic record that would monitor destructive changes in our environment.

Environmental agents pose a difficult problem, and imaginative solutions are required. It is important that something be done about them for the sake of the long-term genetic health of the human race. Dr. James Crow of the University of Wisconsin has estimated that a single mutation, once it occurs, remains in the genetic material for forty generations. Humans are, Dr. Crow says, "producing an increasing burden of mutational damage with each succeeding generation, since each generation adds its own mutations to those handed down from the past." The challenge of preserving our genetic heritage is one of the most important we face.

16. Treatment of Genetic Disease: The PKU Story and Its Role in the Genesis of Screening Programs

Treatment of genetic disease is in its infancy. Although major emphasis has been placed on prevention, real progress has been made in developing approaches to the treatment of inherited disorders.

There are a number of treatment categories, each specific for the management of particular kinds of genetic conditions. The first involves the addition of a protein that is missing or ineffective as a result of the action of an abnormal gene. A second, called product-replacement therapy, supplies the affected individual with the otherwise missing molecules that are usually products of an abnormal enzyme. A third therapy is to avoid certain drugs or foods because the enzyme for their proper metabolism is lacking. A fourth provides large amounts of a coenzyme, often a vitamin, to stimulate an imperfect enzyme to appropriate activity. A fifth provides a missing gene. A sixth prevents accumulation of abnormal molecules in the body. These molecules are responsible for the clinical manifestations of some genetic diseases. Drugs can be used that promote the excretion of an abnormal molecule or prevent its formation. In some cases this can be accomplished through careful nutrition. A special diet can be formulated that limits the intake of a molecule that cannot be metabolized. These therapeutic methods provide striking examples of the fact that genetic diseases are often treatable.

The idea of treatment by supplying a missing protein is familiar. It is the technique used in the management of diabetes. This method has been successfully employed over many years. In most diabetics, particularly those with the severe disease that begins in childhood, the difficulty in sugar metabolism results from a failure in the production and release of the hormone insulin from specialized cells in the pancreas. Commercial insulin is extracted from the pancreatic tissues of cattle or pigs and supplied in purified form to the diabetic patient. This therapy is not easy for the patient, who must inject himself with a supply of the hormone each day of his life. The treatment can be inconvenient, annoying, or even painful. Its discovery was a medical miracle. Previously patients with this form of diabetes invariably died.

Some diabetic patients produce antibodies that act against injected foreign insulin. This immune reaction is not surprising since the molecule, a kind of protein, comes from other animals with a somewhat different parent gene for insulin. It is difficult for these patients to achieve the desired metabolic sugar balance. The immune reaction is not a major, or too common, problem because insulin is a rather small polypeptide molecule. If injection were tried with a large protein, such as an enzyme, an individual would react so violently that the foreign enzyme would be rendered ineffective. Serious, potentially fatal allergic reactions could begin. This kind of allergic reaction to an injected foreign protein is called anaphylaxis. It is so serious that such an approach is not currently feasible in the treatment of diseases like Tay-Sachs in which an essential enzyme is either defective or entirely missing. It does work if only a few injections are required, but then never again. The enzyme asparaginase, which is now prepared in large quantities from bacteria, is useful in the initial treatment of children with leukemia. It is used with the greatest attention to possible anaphylaxis. The treatment cannot be repeated. In genetic deficiency diseases the need is for a molecule that can be provided indefinitely without immune rejection. An obvious solution is to prepare the missing protein from human sources. This does not completely avoid the possibility of anaphylaxis since each person's DNA is unique, but it usually prevents severe reactions from occurring. One of the best examples of this approach to treatment is the use of human growth hormone in pituitary dwarfism.

Most children grow like weeds. They do not have to think about it or work at it. It just happens. When growth is retarded and a child is short, he and his parents do worry about it. Shakespeare devoted some thought to this problem in *Richard III*. In this play the young Duke of York comments on the differences between his own growth rate and that of his sibling:

> *Small herbs have grace, great weeds grow apace.*
> *And since, methinks, I would not grow so fast,*
> *Because sweet flowers are slow, and weeds make haste.*

In most instances there is nothing to fear when a child grows slowly. It may take a visit to a physician with some special knowledge of endocrinology to be certain.

Occasionally a child doesn't grow because his pituitary gland does not synthesize enough growth hormone. The pituitary is a tiny gland at the base of the brain. It produces a number of protein hormones that regulate the action of other glands, such as the thyroid, adrenal, and gonadal glands. It also produces the hormone that has a primary responsibility for growth in childhood. Children lacking this hormone may grow normally for about a year. After that they tend to grow very poorly. Without some outside help they reach adulthood much reduced in height.

Help is now available. Through a tremendous national effort, pathologists are collecting and preserving human pituitaries, which are one of the most useful by-products of autopsies. The post mortem pituitaries are shipped to chemists expert in the complicated business of extraction and purification of the small amounts of growth hormone. It takes many pituitary glands to yield enough hormone to treat a single child. Because the body synthesizes and releases growth hormone on a regular basis, the molecule is not stored, and concentrations at any given time tend to be small. For these reasons the national supply of growth hormone must be carefully rationed. It can be supplied to physicians who have the laboratory and clinical expertise to make a precise diagnosis of growth hormone deficiency and to manage its treatment.

Once embarked on a treatment program, one of these diminutive patients grows rapidly. The beauty of this approach is that not much hormone is required. It does not have to be given forever. The objective is to achieve a normal height. After it is attained, the individual no longer needs the molecule. Growth hormone has now been synthesized artificially. It is still too difficult to reproduce the pituitary's efficiency, but the treatment is a model for the ultimate provision of important protein molecules when they are missing. The present-day management of growth hormone deficiency makes an affected person normal. Without it an individual would be a dwarf.

Treatment of a genetic disease by providing a molecule whose production is blocked by a faulty enzyme may be called product-replacement therapy. Its effective use can be illustrated by an example from endocrinology, the science of hormones. An autosomal recessive abnormality determines the enzymatic defect leading to the disease known as the adrenogenital syndrome. In this condition the steroid hormone cortisol cannot be synthesized by the adrenal gland. This is an important hormone. In its absence patients may suddenly go into shock and die, particularly if the associated salt-retaining hormone cannot be made.

Cortisol normally exerts a feedback control on the production of another hormone from the pituitary. As the concentration of cortisol increases, the production of the pituitary hormone, adrenocorticotropic hormone (ACTH), decreases. In the absence of cortisol the pituitary produces large amounts of ACTH. Excess ACTH causes the adrenal glands to enlarge, and all the hormones they normally synthesize are produced in excess, that is, all the hormones except cortisol. Among those hormones excessively produced by the adrenal glands are androgens, the male hormones. Their presence in large concentrations accelerates growth. There is a rapid skeletal maturation. Bones fuse early. Although the patient as a young child is much taller than other children of his age, he ends up as a rather short adult. Boys with this condition experience rapid sexual development and enter puberty precociously. Affected girls are masculinized. Since this process begins before birth, a girl may be so affected that it is difficult or impossible to determine whether she is a boy or a girl. A doctor would immediately know that something was wrong with the genital organs.

Effective treatment of the disease requires the addition of the missing steroid hormone, cortisol, or the related steroid, cortisone. This treatment reverses the excessive growth rate in males and the masculinization process in females. Although it takes careful management and close chemical monitoring of the treatment program, therapy is extraordinarily effective. Like the diabetic, the affected individual must take the medication every day of his or her life. Injection is not required, as these steroids can be taken by mouth. There are not yet many examples of this kind of product-replacement therapy. There will be more.

The use of drugs that prevent the accumulation of a metabolic product leading to clinical disease is best exemplified in the treatment of gout. It is important to remember that the clinical problems of this disease all result from the prolonged accumulation of high concentrations of uric acid in body fluids. The therapeutic aim is to rid the body of the excessive uric acid. This is a long-term aim. If gout is treated only when the joints ache, there can be no progress. The uric acid levels must be reduced and kept reduced.

There are two ways to do this. The most appropriate is determined by the nature of the condition. If an individual has normal or low levels of uric acid in the urine, the easiest method for eliminating what has been stored within the body tissue is to increase excretion rates of the toxic molecule into the urine. This can be achieved with probenecid (benemid), a drug that influences the kidney's handling of a number of organic molecules. By inhibiting the normal reabsorption of uric acid in the kidney, probenecid promotes its excretion in the urine. This method will not work in patients who produce excessive urate and have elevated levels of uric acid in the urine as well as in the blood. Probenecid is dangerous for these people. They can be effectively treated with allopurinol. Allopurinol is a chemical whose structure was designed to resemble hypoxanthine's. It inhibits the action of the enzyme xanthine oxidase. This enzyme produces uric acid from hypoxanthine and xanthine. Allopurinol is a remarkable drug. It readily lowers the amounts of uric acid in both blood and urine. It puts patients on their feet. People who were bedridden can now go dancing.

It is impressive to realize that there are so many kinds of possible treatments for inherited disorders. Each is applicable to a number of specific conditions. In thinking about genetic disease, people commonly throw up their hands and say, "If it's genetic, there is nothing that can be done." Nothing could be further from the truth. It is true that most of these treatment methods are new. They represent the fruits of recent research. Much of it had its origin in the phenylketonuria or PKU story, which provides us with a model for the development of techniques to identify, diagnose, and treat genetic disorders.

Phenylketonuria was discovered in 1934 when a Norwegian mother brought her two mentally retarded children to Dr. Ashborn Følling. She was impressed with their peculiar musty odor and felt that its explanation might provide a key to the disease. Dr. Følling accepted the idea that an unusual odor might mean that something was biochemically wrong. He began testing the children for the possibility of an abnormal body chemistry. He found that their urine turned a rich green color on the addition of ferric chloride. Normal urine is not affected by this chemical. The green color is caused by the presence of large amounts of a molecule known as phenylpyruvic acid. Its presence in the urine is abnormal. Spurred by his discovery, Dr. Følling began to test other retarded children. Surveying some hundreds of institutionalized individuals, he found a total of ten whose urine contained phenylpyruvic acid.

With these clues, Følling and other physicians began to examine further the condition, whose name is phenylketonuria or PKU. It is so called because phenylpyruvic acid is one of a number of different kinds of molecules known as ketones. It was soon established that PKU is an inherited disease. It is transmitted by a single autosomal recessive gene. Scientists have identified the specific molecular result of the abnormal gene. There is a deficiency of the enzyme phenylalanine hydroxylase. This enzyme is found only in the liver. It ordinarily metabolizes phenylalanine to tyrosine, another amino acid.

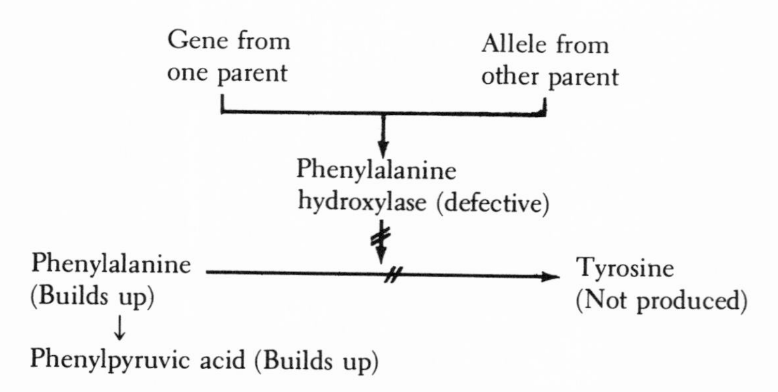

When this enzyme does not function properly, phenylalanine builds up in body fluids. In an attempt to rid itself of phenylalanine when its main metabolic pathway is blocked, the body converts the excess molecules into associated chemicals, such as phenylpyruvic acid, phenyllactic acid, and phenylacetic acid. All of these molecules, sometimes referred to as metabolites, as well as phenylalanine itself, are found in large concentrations in the blood, spinal fluid, and urine of a child with PKU. For reasons that are still unknown, high levels of phenylalanine and these related metabolites prevent brain cells from developing normally. The result is severe mental retardation. The average I.Q. of children with PKU is well under fifty.

Knowledge of the abnormal biochemistry associated with this condition led to the idea that if the accumulation of these compounds in the body fluids could be prevented, infants with PKU might develop normally. It worked. Scientists found that the mental retardation that usually characterizes PKU can be avoided by feeding affected infants a special diet that is sharply reduced in its phenylalanine content. It is important to recognize that this amino acid cannot be eliminated entirely from the diet because it is essential to life. The proper PKU diet contains just enough phenylalanine to support growth and no more. The diet must be instituted as early as possible. The brain is a rapidly developing organ in the young infant. Damage to brain cells can never be repaired. The aim is prevention before serious damage has occurred.

At first the only way to accomplish this aim was to work with families in which a child had already been diagnosed as having PKU. In those families tests of phenylalanine concentrations were initiated with the birth of the next child. As soon as a baby was found to have PKU, treatment was started. With this kind of very early therapy, spectacular results were obtained. In families in which previous children were really hopelessly retarded, the subsequent and treated infants were growing up normally. They had normal I.Q.s. These results represented a major breakthrough in the treatment of genetic disease. It is one that has provided hope for the treatment of other forms of mental retardation and of genetic disease in general.

The numbers of patients who could be treated in this way were not large. Eligible individuals had to be siblings of known patients. The population base for detection was increased by careful screening for PKU in populations of retarded children found in clinics and institutions for the handicapped. The numbers remained disappointingly small even though treatment was now possible. This was frustrating. Early treatment meant early detection, but there was no really satisfactory method for identifying children with PKU in the first days of life. Some doctors began using ferric chloride screening tests on urine. In the "diaper test" a strip of material impregnated with ferric chloride is exposed to the wet urine-containing diaper. If phenylpyruvic acid is present, the strip will turn rich green. Experience has shown that the diaper test misses many patients with PKU. Phenylpyruvic acid is chemically unstable and readily disappears from the urine. Babies under one month of age, the ideal time for testing, can have a high phenylalanine level and a negative urine test. The vast majority of newborn infants were not even getting this test. Patients with PKU were often undetected until it was too late to prevent severe mental retardation.

The therapeutic ideal is to identify the disease before neurological damage is done. To accomplish this objective there would have to be screening programs for the study of apparently normal infants in order to detect the first signs of this treatable disease.

The idea of screening is simple and sensible. The mechanics are more complex. An obvious first problem is the development of a suitable test with which to detect the disease. A less obvious problem is applying the test to the children who need it. A relatively low incidence of most genetic diseases means large numbers of people must be screened to find just a few cases of any given disease. Any widely used test must be inexpensive, easy to administer, and unusually accurate. Once the identifying test is performed, the problem of subsequent management arises. There must be a meticulous system for the rapid pursuit of each positive test for the disease so that a definite diagnosis, or its exclusion, can be made. Facilities for initiation and follow-through on a treatment program must be available. Screening is not as easy as it sounds.

A start has been made as the era of mass screening for genetic disease is upon us. The beginning, made with PKU, has encountered a few difficulties, but that is to be expected from a first effort. The steps taken provide help for an unprecedented number of patients. Valuable lessons have been learned for the future.

If any one moment can be identified as the start of the era of mass genetic screening, it was late in 1961 when Dr. Robert Guthrie of Buffalo, New York, wrote a brief letter to the *Journal of the American Medical Association* reporting that he had developed a test for detecting PKU in newborn infants. The test is ingenious and inexpensive. It can be applied almost immediately after birth with almost perfect accuracy and at low cost. The Guthrie test sounds complicated. It has two basic ingredients: a colony of bacteria that requires phenylalanine for growth, and a chemical, beta-2-thienylalanine, that competes with the phenylalanine molecule so that the bacterial colonies do not grow. The concentration of the inhibitor is so adjusted that with the amounts of phenylalanine found in normal blood, organisms will not grow. The bacteria will thrive when higher concentrations of phenylalanine, such as those found in PKU, are present.

The Guthrie test is administered in the following fashion. A few days after birth, usually on the last day of hospitalization, a few drops of blood are obtained from an infant's heel. These are absorbed on a sheet of filter paper. The paper is sent to the laboratory, where the identifying bacterial test is performed. A round disk is punched out of the filter paper. A number of these disks are put into sterile plates containing the bacteria, nutrients, and the beta-2-thienylalanine.

If the blood is normal, no growth occurs. The inhibiting molecule keeps the bacteria from multiplying. If a child has PKU, the high levels of phenylalanine in its blood will neutralize the inhibitor and allow the bacteria to grow. The technician simply waits eighteen hours and checks for bacterial growth. In this way hundreds of samples can be processed at once. The technical skills required are minimal. The test is so definitive that it is very difficult to miss a patient with PKU.

Guthrie was soon to gain backing for a large-scale application of his identifying test. With support from the United States Children's Bureau, more than four hundred thousand newborn infants were screened in a study that was concluded in 1964. Of these about 275 were found to have positive Guthrie tests for PKU. A more detailed quantitative follow-up test showed that 37 of the positives were in fact true cases of PKU. This number is what would be expected from an effective screening. While the number of false positive tests was high, there were no false negatives. No child affected with PKU had been missed by the Guthrie test. The consequences of overlooking a single case would be tragic. It would be better to perform follow-up tests on 100 children too many than to miss a single child with PKU.

The results of the trial were so impressive that its momentum swept the nation. A drive to make PKU screening compulsory was begun in 1964. By 1967 forty-six states required PKU testing by law. Many hospitals in the other states were performing the Guthrie test voluntarily. Today it is estimated that 90 percent of all newborns in the United States are tested for PKU. The laws are permissive rather than mandatory in some states. The record of performance in those states is not as good as it is in the others. Results in Massachusetts and California, where strict legislation was established almost from the outset, have been examined. They provide an enviable model for the rest of the country and the world. It is clear that PKU can be detected early. An effective program can prevent the retardation that would otherwise result from the disorder.

There have been some problems with the broad-scale screening programs. A number of false negative tests have been uncovered. Screening programs have provided evidence that PKU is a more complex disorder than initially thought. More than one kind of PKU has been recognized. It requires sophisticated techniques for screening, diagnosis, and treatment.

A fundamental question concerns the levels of concentration at which a Guthrie test is declared positive, indicating that a child may have PKU. The unit of concentration is the milligram percent, commonly abbreviated mg% or mg percent. This is a scientific shorthand for the number of milligrams of a substance found in 100 milliliters or cubic centimeters of a fluid, such as a baby's blood. It is a measure of relative concentration. The results of the screening test are expressed in terms such as 20 mg percent, meaning that 20 milligrams of phenylalanine are present in each 100 milliliters of blood.

At 6 mg percent or above for phenylalanine concentration, the Guthrie test has been classified as positive, and the child is suspected of having PKU. With concentrations below 6 mg percent, the test has been considered negative, and PKU ruled out. In Guthrie's own laboratory the critical concentration is now placed at 4 mg percent.

Phenylalanine levels ordinarily rise after birth to an abnormal concentration, and in different babies they may rise at different rates. Screening programs test newborn babies while in hospital nurseries. In this country babies normally go home one to three days after birth. A recent study by Dr. Tony Holtzman of Johns Hopkins showed that during this three-day period as many as a quarter of the babies with PKU could be missed because the critical concentration of phenylalanine had not reached its maximum. After three days few babies with PKU have concentrations under 12 mg percent. These observations could account for the large differences in incidence reported in some areas. There is a thirtyfold difference in the incidence of detected PKU between Maryland and Buffalo, New York. Throughout the United States the overall incidence is 6.6 per one hundred thousand. In some areas the incidence of positive screening tests ranges from 5 to 151 per one hundred thousand.

An interesting set of observations has emerged. It is now apparent that the levels of phenylalanine in girls with PKU rise much more slowly after birth than in boys. It is much easier to miss a positive diagnosis for the disease in screening females. In one series of twenty false negative tests in patients who ultimately turned out to have PKU, thirteen were girls. Screening programs have been reporting more males than females with PKU. These findings provide strong arguments for follow-up testing in babies in whom early test results are negative. This is particularly true for girls.

The sensitivity of testing in different laboratories is variable. Quality control has not been nationally standardized and no one monitors most laboratories for quality. Dr. Guthrie has argued strongly for regionalization of testing, with large numbers of tests funneling through a small number of closely monitored laboratories. This would permit the use of automated methods leading to savings in time and money. It would allow for a close check on quality and sensitivity. Regionalization would help morale among laboratory technicians. Until the screening load reaches fifty thousand to one hundred thousand tests per year, not many positive tests can be expected. Without the reinforcement provided by the detection of positive tests for the disorder, it is difficult for the technician to remain critically alert and enthusiastic. It is also hard to keep the machinery for follow-up, notification, and management properly coordinated. Regionalization of laboratories is apparently working well in some states and in most European countries. This is the exception. The rule in the United States seems to be fragmentation, particularly where private facilities are employed. An example of decentralization is found in California, where more than two hundred different laboratories do screening for PKU at a charge of from one to fifteen dollars per test. In large regional laboratories the cost per test has been estimated at fifty cents.

After the detection of a positive Guthrie test, a venous blood sample is obtained from the baby. This sample is sent to a laboratory equipped for the quantitative chemical assay or analysis for phenylalanine. We routinely test for both phenylalanine and tyrosine molecules. In an infant with PKU, phenylalanine concentration is very high and the tyrosine concentration, its normal product, is very low. The most common false positive tests are found in patients who are simply immature and have high levels of many amino acids for a while. In these infants the tyrosine level is always much higher than the phenylalanine. This simple assay settles the question of most false positive tests. For the others, those with high phenylalanine concentrations and normal or low tyrosine concentrations, the infant in question should be admitted to a hospital and studied under conditions that precisely control phenylalanine intake. In most babies with typical or classical PKU, the blood concentration of phenylalanine becomes quite elevated on a normal diet. By the time of hospitalization these concentrations are well above 20 mg percent, usually over 30 mg percent, and often over 50 mg percent. This is impressive when compared with a normal adult concentration of under 1 mg percent. Phenylpyruvic acid and the other metabolites are found in urine of patients with PKU. We have never known an exception. It is important to test for these by-product molecules to establish a definitive diagnosis of PKU. This kind of extensive biochemical analysis accurately distinguishes patients with PKU from others picked up by the screen who do not have the disorder.

It is important to begin proper dietary treatment as soon as possible. This is not easy. It requires careful and frequent monitoring of the exact concentration of phenylalanine in the blood. The amounts of phenylalanine in the diet have to be individualized. Many babies are hard to feed. They vomit easily. They refuse to eat. As they get older, they may use their diet as a focus for conflict and control over their parents. A program of dietary therapy must be followed closely through some of the hardest years of childhood. Even in the most skilled hands, a successful regimen is not easy.

A number of children were found in the process of screening who had elevated levels of phenylalanine reflected in a positive Guthrie test but did not have PKU. Chemical tests confirmed the high blood levels of phenylalanine, but they were not as high as blood levels in classic PKU. These patients were not given the special PKU diet. They developed normally without mental retardation. They are considered to have "hyperphenylalaninemia without PKU" or *atypical PKU*. Most can be categorized using a new phenylalanine concentration cutoff point. A majority have phenylalanine blood levels above 6 mg percent but below 20 mg percent. It is not clear why they have such high levels of phenylalanine. They may represent a number of different genetic variations, none of them previously recognized, because they do not have symptoms of disease. They provide an extreme of normal genetic variation. Everyone is biochemically unique. Most chemical variations are so small that they do not in any way influence health. It would be unfortunate to subject a child with a normal variation for phenylalanine concentration to the same rigid diet required by the child with PKU. Some with atypical PKU may need such dietary treatment, but very few. If all children with positive Guthrie tests who do not have high tyrosine concentrations were subjected to the kind of initial program of diagnosis just described, each child's tolerance for dietary phenylalanine would be precisely known, and those who did not need control would be clearly established.

It is generally true that infants with levels greater than 6 mg percent but less than 15 mg percent do not need treatment. Those with a reading above 25 mg percent almost always have classic PKU and need the special diet. In the intermediate area, between 15 and 25 mg percent, the issue is questionable. Diagnosis and a need for treatment can be decided upon only by careful individual study.

The other issue that the atypical PKU story raised is more general. In the early days of the screening programs many people thought treatment of PKU would prove relatively simple. More patients were diagnosed, and greater numbers of doctors were suddenly confronted with a patient needing nutritional therapy. There were only a handful of people in the world who had had real experience with administering a diet to infants in which an essential amino acid was limited. Specialists in the profession have known that a certain amount of each essential amino acid is required for growth in each baby. The amounts differ slightly and have to be individualized with frequent assessment of amino acid levels in the blood. The physician must constantly monitor the rates of growth in height and weight. The amounts of phenylalanine required in patients with PKU are really not different from those of other babies. These amounts are required for the minimal synthesis of the proteins required for growth. Normal babies can metabolize amounts of phenylalanine considerably greater than those requirements, while those with PKU cannot. No baby can survive with less than the required amount of phenylalanine, even if he has PKU.

In the early years of mass screening programs and, more or less, mass treatment, some babies received too little phenylalanine. Those for whom this deficiency was most obvious were babies with atypical hyperphenylalaninemia. This kind of phenylalanine deprivation can cause stunting, microcephaly, hypoglycemia (low blood sugar), anemia, and mental retardation. At least two infant fatalities have been reported in which malnutrition with a diet low in phenylalanine was the probable cause of death. These experiences were tragic. They led some physicians and others who had welcomed the screening programs to register public opposition to the whole idea. Dr. Samuel P. Bessman, a man with impressive credentials in biochemistry and pediatric research, was particularly articulate. He attacked the idea of legislating these screening activities. There were those who wondered in public if the overall result of the programs would do more harm than good. This might be the case if atypical hyperphenylalaninemia were more common than classic PKU and if stringent dietary treatment made these atypical patients retarded when, if left alone, they would have been normal. The debate over PKU screening and treatment lasted several years. Only the remnants of that debate are still heard. The PKU picture is now clear. The problem is far more complex than thought at the start of mass screening programs. Diagnosis and treatment require sophisticated understandings. Recognition of the need for expertise is an accomplishment of the screening programs.

Once babies with elevated phenylalanine levels due to transient causes are eliminated from the numbers of positive tests by the tyrosine assay, it is clear that of the remaining positives, the vast majority have classic PKU. Both those individuals with the classic and atypical forms apparently inherit their conditions as autosomal recessive traits. Dietary therapy demands expert management to maintain carefully determined levels of phenylalanine. Such management is now established practice.

Children with PKU do not have to be kept on the special diet forever. In most cases it can be discontinued at six or seven years of age. By that time brain development is complete. The biochemical abnormality somehow affects only the developing brain. Cessation of the rigorous regimen is a good thing because it gets much harder to keep an older child away from normal food with its high concentration of phenylalanine. Sometimes it is hard for a family to abandon a strict diet it has maintained for six years. It is sometimes even hard for the doctor. These problems require understanding, and sometimes gradual change is a help. An older child occasionally feels better with less phenylalanine. Sometimes very high levels of the molecule produce irritability or itching of the skin. These problems are uncommon. To some extent this relative rarity results because most of us eat much less protein than the young infant. The untreated child or adult with PKU has a much lower phenylalanine level than the untreated infant.

PKU screening is now part of the nation's public health program. It was started in an era in which funds for medical research and public medical programs were plentiful. The recession of the early 1970s produced severe cutbacks in federal spending for such programs. Officials in government have looked carefully at the enonomics of PKU screening. In the cold light of cost-benefit analysis, the program has emerged with flying colors.

It costs about three or four dollars per child to screen for PKU. Some two hundred children with PKU are detected annually through screening. The cost nationwide for the screening is perhaps eight to ten million dollars. A single untreated child with PKU costs society at least a quarter of a million dollars in the course of his lifetime, usually in institutional care. In this way society gets back five dollars for every dollar invested in PKU detection and treatment. Another aspect of the economic question is reflected in the earning power of the normal individual who emerges in health from an effective program of screening and treatment. He or she is to be compared with the institutionalized, retarded person with untreated PKU. This kind of cold monetary reckoning is not appealing, but the value of saving two hundred children from hopeless retardation is.

Fiscal calculations are important in dealing with officials who cannot be reached in any other way. It is sometimes hard to see the savings from PKU testing. The costs of screening might stand out as a large item in a state budget that fiscal watchdogs may be tempted to eliminate. In the District of Columbia a decision was recently made to end PKU testing. In three years seventy-seven thousand newborn infants were tested for the disease without the detection of a single affected individual. In announcing its decision, the district noted that PKU screening was costing $135,000 a year and that 84 percent of the births in the district are of nonwhite babies, among whom the incidence of PKU is roughly one-sixth that among Caucasians. The District of Columbia could end its PKU screening quickly because the program was not written into law. Some have said that it is better to avoid legislating such programs because laws rob physicians of valuable flexibility. It will be hard to sell that to the parents of the next baby with PKU born in the District of Columbia.

Screening for PKU and the treatment of the disease are by no means restricted to the United States. Treatment for PKU began in England and Germany. The programs in those countries are highly sophisticated. Throughout western Europe and in Israel there are excellent programs. The screening programs in West Germany and Switzerland are similar. Screening is voluntary, but health care delivery is highly stylized, and these are highly ordered societies. In Switzerland screening for PKU has gone from 4 percent of the population of newborns in 1965 to 96 percent in 1971. In West Germany the latest estimate was 85 percent. The state pays for screening. It is simply done in every hospital. In Switzerland all the tests are performed in three laboratories, ensuring quality control. The specialized diet is provided by the government to all recognized patients. In Germany this is paid for, as is all health care, by national health insurance. The same is true in England, where screening tests and treatment expenses are borne by the national health service.

Throughout Europe the standby of the dietary treatment for infants with PKU is Albumaid, a low phenylalanine product made from human serum proteins. In this country and in England the standby is Lofenelac, a formula made from the protein in cow's milk. Dr. Horst Bickel of Heidelberg has said that in Germany he has increasingly used mixtures of amino acids rather than either of these products. This is also the case for patients being treated at University College Hospital in London. Both groups report excellent dietary efficiency, better taste, and improved patient acceptance. Another issue is the potential versatility provided by such diets. If artificial mixtures of amino acids were commonly used in the management of PKU, the cost would go down, and these mixtures could be suitably modified to provide economical treatment for other inborn errors of amino acid metabolism.

A look at screening programs in other countries reveals some interesting things. In France it is much harder to overlook a patient with PKU since babies are not usually discharged from the hospital until seven to ten days after birth. This allows plenty of time for the phenylalanine concentration to become elevated. In Israel there has been an effective screening program for many years. The results have shown that virtually all patients with PKU have been of Sephardic or Oriental origin. The frequency of the gene for PKU among the Ashkenazim, or European Jews, is extremely low. This is the population in which the gene for Tay-Sachs disease is so high. The incidence of PKU in West Germany is about one in every eight thousand births. In Switzerland, it is about one in eighteen thousand. It has been thought that these populations are so similar genetically that this difference might mean different criteria are being used by the laboratories of one country compared with those in the other. Time will certainly provide the answer. In the United States the incidence of PKU is approximately one in fifteen thousand births.

The successful treatment of PKU raises questions for the successfully treated individual. As girls mature, they face a very difficult decision about whether to bear children of their own. Some ninety-two babies have been born to mothers with PKU. In almost every case the children suffered from severe mental retardation, even though the children themselves did not have PKU. Apparently the high levels of phenylalanine in the mother's body affected the developing brain of the fetus, causing the same kind of irreversible nerve damage that infants with PKU suffer after birth. It is possible that a low phenylalanine diet during pregnancy in these women would protect their infants from retardation. This has not yet been established.

Encouraging results have been obtained by Drs. J. D. Allen and J. K. Brown in Dublin. One of their patients with PKU had borne three successive retarded children. A diet was established that effectively lowered her phenylalanine levels. This was done in the hospital. When she became pregnant again, she was hospitalized and treated through dietary means for the last five months of pregnancy. Her fourth child is of normal intelligence.

It is certain that this problem must be faced in the next few years. By the late 1970s the first of the two thousand or more treated children with PKU will be nearing the childbearing age. It will be important to explain to the females in this group the special risk they face in marriage and pregnancy. Many women do not know they are pregnant until two or three months after conception. Scientists do not know when it would be too late to start effective dietary treatment. It has been suggested that a low phenylalanine diet might be instituted in each of these young women whenever conception is possible. Sterilization and adoption are other options. All of these women should seek the guidance necessary to make the right decision.

Success in the screening and treatment of PKU leads logically to a consideration of screening for other genetic diseases. A number of metabolic diseases are possible candidates for this kind of program. They include maple syrup urine disease, homocystinuria, and galactosemia. Various decisions have been made about this issue in various states. The usual one is that it is not economically feasible to screen for these diseases because they are all rarer than PKU. There is no question that scientists could not mount the same economic argument for screening in these diseases as for PKU. However, PKU screening is already with us. Major expense is incurred in obtaining blood and getting it to a laboratory. As long as a blood sample is being drawn, it might pay to test it for as many different conditions as possible. That argument is currently being tried in Massachusetts, where the ninety-five thousand infants born annually are being screened not only for PKU but for a battery of other conditions. Each of these conditions is rare. With multiple testing a screening program usually detects about thirty infants annually with one or another of the diseases in the screen. There is disease identification in about one infant of every three thousand tested. This figure is impressively large. In Dr. Guthrie's laboratory in Buffalo a single blood sample from a newborn infant can be screened for eleven different conditions. This increases the yield of disease identification per population of infants screened.

Criteria for the selection of diseases for screening have become clear. Dr. Charles Janeway, writing in the *New England Journal of Medicine*, has outlined a list of criteria.

> The screening test must be simple, cheap, and easy to perform on small, readily collected samples; test samples must be stable during shipment to the laboratory.
>
> The screening test must be oversensitive, so that it identifies all the cases. There should be a number of false-positives, but no false-negative tests.
>
> Means must be at hand for the prompt study of all suspect cases by qualified experts, using more accurate methods that will reliably identify the true cases.
>
> There should be an effective method for treatment of the disorder, once it has been identified.

Geneticists in general would agree with these criteria, although we would hope that a rigid adherence to a requirement for treatment would not always be the rule. There are many ways in which definitive genetic information may be used to help a family and prevent disease when treatment is not available. In any case a philosophy similar to Dr. Janeway's has been outlined by the American Academy of Pediatrics and by the Maternal and Child Health

Service of the United States Department of Health, Education and Welfare, which has published an excellent booklet entitled, "Recommended Guidelines for PKU Programs for the Newborn." The latest edition is available for fifteen cents from the Superintendent of Documents, U.S. Government Printing Office, Washington, D.C. 20402. In addition to detailed guidelines, the booklet lists laboratories throughout the country that are helpful in the definitive chemical diagnosis of PKU.

Future screening for metabolic disease will involve multiple testing of a single drop of blood obtained from the newborn. One drop on filter paper can be split into many punches. There are now bacterial tests like the PKU test that will detect at least six treatable diseases. Each is much rarer than PKU, but multiple testing along with PKU screening would increase a program's yield at little expense, thus improving the benefits to cost ratio. The diseases that could be screened include maple syrup urine disease, homocystinuria, arginosuccinic aciduria, and hypothyroidism. An interesting approach now available is to test the blood sample for galactose, a sugar. This uncovers two different enzyme defect diseases that cause galactosemia. Each produces cataracts early in life. A program for detection could prove important in preventing blindness. This is now part of routine screening in Switzerland. Six laboratories in the United States are performing multiple screening tests. We can expect to see programs like this throughout the world. The dividends in prevention of genetic disease can be enormous.

17. The Future: Genetic Engineering and Other Approaches to the Treatment of Genetic Disease

The fruits of genetic research are being rapidly incorporated into the clinical practice of genetic medicine. Advances in diagnostic techniques, particularly in prenatal detection and in identification of the heterozygous carrier of an abnormal gene, are now used to prevent disease. Methods for identifying an affected patient and for understanding the nature of his disorder generally precede the development of therapeutic techniques. Yet a growing number of specific treatments for inherited conditions are now available. Although this aspect of genetics is in its infancy, there should be many meaningful developments in coming years.

Some lag between advances in research and their application to the human patient is inevitable. Appropriate time is required for testing, confirmation, and assessment of new information. Review of problems and theories currently under investigation may provide insight into the nature and direction of future clinical practice.

An area of investigation with tremendous potential for the prevention or treatment of inherited disorders is genetic engineering. This name may evoke images of *Brave New World* and *1984* among scientists and geneticists as well as the general public. Healthy skepticism is important, but it should not be translated into an unreasoned hysteria that could perpetuate needless human suffering. A rational analysis of the possibilities implicit in genetic engineering is essential. It begins with recognition that the term engineering refers to a whole class of manipulations, most of which do not involve any changes in the genetic material.

The first and simplest of these potential therapeutic techniques might be called molecular engineering. This approach concentrates on the abnormal protein or enzyme molecule that characterizes a disease. The focus among the inborn errors of metabolism is placed on the missing or defective enzyme that serves as the fundamental cause for all clinical manifestations of the disorder.

The Hunter and the Hurler syndromes are prominent examples of this kind of inherited disease. They are characterized by the widespread deposition of mucopolysaccharide molecules in body tissue. These massive deposits cause coarsening of facial features, stiffening of skeletal joints, and enlargement of the liver and the spleen. They inevitably produce severe mental retardation.

Because mucopolysaccharides are normal molecular components of metabolism, it has been suggested that their abnormal accumulation must result from failure of an enzyme to digest them into waste products suitable for elimination. The first evidence for the validity of this hypothesis was provided by the work of Dr. Elizabeth Neufeld at the National Institutes of Health.

Dr. Neufeld began with fibroblasts, or connective tissue cells, grown in culture medium. Mucopolysaccharides accumulate in these cells much as they do in the cells of an affected individual. To demonstrate this accumulation, cells may be incubated with a radioactive sulfate molecule that becomes incorporated into the mucopolysaccharide molecule. In normal cells this radioactive marker is rapidly incorporated and released. In Hunter and Hurler cells the molecule is incorporated and stored. It is not released.

In a now famous experiment Dr. Neufeld mixed normal cells in the same culture with Hurler cells. She found that both strains of cells behaved normally. The normal cells evidently supplied Hurler cells with a factor that allowed them to break down their stored mucopolysaccharides. This behavior demonstrated the possibility of curing a Hurler cell. A similar result was obtained using Hunter cells and cells from other mucopolysaccharide storage disorders. Each could be corrected by growth with normal cells.

Whole cells are not required to obtain this curative effect. The tissue culture medium in which normal cells have been grown may be added to a tissue culture of Hurler cells and correction occurs. The curative factors manufactured by normal cells are enzymes. The disease cells are cured because the enzyme provided is the one that is defective and causes the disorder. A next logical step is to find a way to apply this curative technique to affected individuals. The amount of enzyme required to cure all the cells of a patient with the Hurler syndrome would be large. Because the amount of enzyme produced by cells in culture and excreted into the nutrient medium is small, another source for this transforming factor must be found. Normal human urine contains an accessible supply of these enzymes. Dr. Neufeld is now at work developing methods for the extraction and purification of the enzyme in sufficient quantity to permit testing in humans.

A similar approach to treatment evolved in a different way. Three French investigators, M. C. Hors-Cayla, P. Maroteaux, and J. De Grouchy, reported they were able to reverse the process of abnormal mucopolysaccharide accumulation in defective fibroblasts. They achieved this result by substituting normal human blood serum for the fetal calf serum usually used in tissue culture medium. Their observations suggested that human blood may contain a supply of the necessary mucopolysaccharide digestive enzyme.

This implication was pursued by Dr. Nicola Di Ferrante and colleagues of Baylor University in Houston. They infused large amounts of human plasma into a patient with the Hurler syndrome and into one with the Hunter syndrome. They carefully studied the composition of the mucopolysaccharides of the urine before and after the infusion period. The biochemical changes were remarkable. The large molecular mucopolysaccharide molecules that characterize these diseases were being broken down into much smaller molecules that could be eliminated from the body. Visible phenotypic changes occurred in these patients. Their thick, cold skin became softer, warmer, and more elastic. Their claw-shaped hands could be extended. A hyperactive individual became quiet and more manageable. It was an exciting result.

The investigators at Baylor joined forces with those at the M. D. Anderson Hospital in Houston who had a powerful blood cell separator at their disposal. With it Dr. Di Ferrante and Drs. Alfred Knudsen and John Curtis obtained large quantities of white blood cells, principally lymphocytes, which they infused into a six-year-old boy with the Hunter syndrome. The biochemical effect was even greater than with blood plasma. Clinical changes were striking. There was a marked softening of the skin, a decrease in the size of thick skin lesions, and an increase in joint mobility. Improvement was maintained over a three-month period.

These experiments were not well controlled. First experiments seldom are. The results are consistent with theory, and they are most encouraging. At the same time it is clear that the ameliorative effects of this treatment are transient. Repeated plasma infusion, even when started very early in life, will not prevent the typical degeneration of the Hurler syndrome. Nature protects the brain against incursions of foreign proteins, even if their presence would be beneficial. Infusion techniques do not seem to permit the normal enzyme to reach all the necessary target cells or to maintain its biochemical integrity for long periods of time. They do point the way to further research and the refinement of genetic technology. Ways to keep the patient's body susceptible to these curative effects and to deliver the enzyme to the cells without continuous infusion are needed. Both techniques should be possible.

A promising approach to the problems of continuous accessibility and delivery is that of enzyme modification. The function of an enzyme is to join two smaller molecules into a larger molecule or to digest a larger molecule into two smaller molecules. A portion of the enzyme molecule, called the reactive site, is capable of interacting with specific molecules, called substrates, which are acted upon by the enzyme. The relationship between a substrate molecule and an enzyme is highly specific. This specificity is based on the physical arrangement of the atoms in both molecules, their chemical properties, and the environmental conditions in which they are found. A normal enzyme combines with the substrate, produces its effect on the substrate, and then is released without being itself permanently affected. The enzyme molecule can be used over and over again. In the case of the Hunter and the Hurler cells, specific enzymes fail to break apart specific parts of mucopolysaccharide molecules.

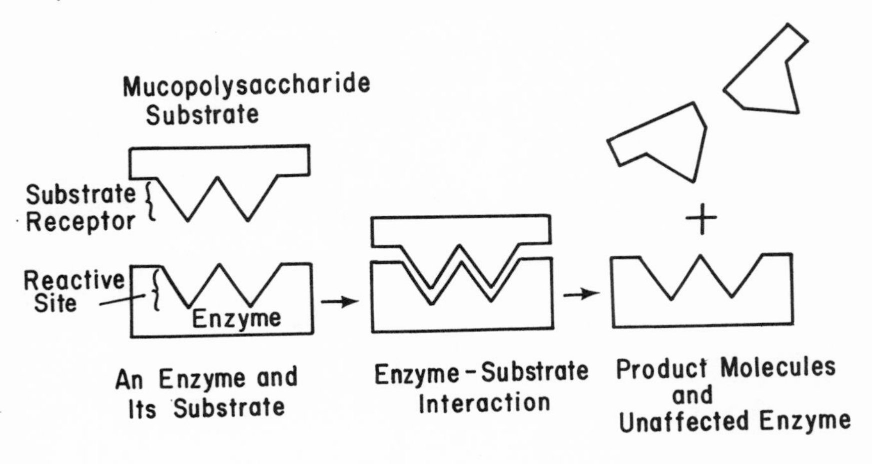

FIGURE 36. *Schematic diagram of the way an enzyme acts on a substrate.*

Most inborn errors of metabolism result not from an absence of the enzyme in question but from a change in its primary structure, probably the reactive site, which alters its activity. The aim of enzyme modification is to achieve a chemical change in the enzyme molecule, making it more effective. This might be done by reacting the enzyme with a specific substrate or unrelated molecule so that the characteristics of the enzyme are changed. An alteration of this sort in an abnormal enzyme might be enough to make it behave normally. If such a change could be produced in the test tube, there might be ways to do the same thing, or something like it, in an affected individual. Because the enzymes involved in human diseases may be unstable or so altered that a reactive site is somehow prevented from interaction with substrate, approaches to enzyme modification may one day involve a molecule so specific that, when administered by vein or mouth, it could seek out the appropriate enzyme and alter it in the patient. The result would be a drug therapy for enzyme deficiency diseases.

Although the modification of a patient's own enzyme is a therapeutic ideal, successful introduction of the normal enzyme from other sources seems more immediately feasible. Delivering a normal enzyme to appropiate sites in the body is complicated by the chemical and physical properties of these molecules. Sensitivity to heat, the surrounding chemical environment, and the action of antibodies threatens to destroy an enzyme before it reaches appropriate target cells.

Greater structural integrity has been incorporated into some enzymes by treating unstable crystalline forms with bridging, or cross-linking, agents. These create chemical bonds that link various amino acids of the protein into a fixed and rigid structure. The resulting enzyme maintains its integrity even when hit with a hammer. Modifications of albumin, a protein found in blood serum, have been made so that the molecule can be boiled for hours without changing any of its biochemical properties. The usual change in albumin with boiling is demonstrated when an egg white is cooked.

Splitting off of some functional group could change an enzyme's pattern of distribution throughout the body. Certain carbohydrate groups that are linked to proteins are responsible for differing degrees of penetration into the tissues. Natural barriers to the movement of enzymes within the body are created by a molecule's relative solubility in water or fat. An ideal structural modification of an enzyme might be to make it more soluble in both water and fat without altering its basic function. This would permit controlled penetration of differing organs, tissues, and cells. The same principle has been used in the enzymatic digestion of oil slicks in the ocean. An enzyme capable of degrading fatty substances is much more effective if it can be kept at the oil and water interface. It is possible to provide such enzymatic modification by the addition or substitution of appropriate chemical groups on the enzyme. Some such change will be necessary if normal enzyme is to be delivered to the brains of individuals like those affected with the Hunter or Hurler syndrome.

A number of approaches have been tried in which a normal but foreign enzyme protein is made available to a target substrate while protecting it from antibodies and other digestive enzymes. Among the most promising is that of Dr. T. S. Chang of McGill University. Dr. Chang is an organic chemist who has developed thin films that will form tiny spheres of controllable size under appropriate conditions. He makes microcapsules that closely resemble the human red blood cell and are of the same size. They can be made selectively permeable so that various molecules can pass in or out of them freely while others are either retained or denied entry. One might imagine enzyme molecules placed inside a number of these microcapsules and enclosed in a small plastic tube and connected to a bypass between an artery and a vein. Substrate molecules brought by the circulatory system could be continuously acted upon by the appropriate enzyme. Dr. Chang has in fact used the enzyme urease, enclosed in these spheres, to treat uremia in experimental animals. The technique has proved extraordinarily effective, and he hopes to try it soon in man.

Dr. Chang has done some experiments on human patients. He has encapsulated charcoal rather than enzyme in these microspheres. He, in effect, has created hundreds of artificial micro-kidneys, hundreds of times more efficient than any of the large devices currently in use. Patients in Montreal are now being treated for renal failure with this method.

Investigators are currently at work to develop techniques for encapsulating functional enzymes in Dr. Chang's microspheres. Their purpose is to achieve a continuous extracellular treatment of blood with the implanted enzyme. This should work for conditions like PKU in which disease results from the failure of a single enzyme at a single site in the body. Phenylalanine hydroxylase, which normally metabolizes phenylalanine, is synthesized only in the liver. Unlike many enzymes, it is not required in every body cell. Blood passing through the liver tissue is detoxified by the enzyme. The introduction of this enzyme anywhere in the body should be enough to prevent accumulation of the metabolic products of phenylalanine that cause the clinical features of the disease.

Another approach to the treatment of genetic disease falls into a category somewhere between molecular and cellular engineering. The Fabry disease provides a case in point. Patients with this disorder have skin lesions called angiokeratomas. Prominent over the hips, back, thighs, and buttocks, these lesions do not blanch, or whiten, with pressure. They have a characteristic dark red color. Among the clinical manifestations of this condition are attacks of excruciating pain. The pain, which often produces a burning sensation and usually starts in the fingers and toes, may be unrelieved even with the use of narcotics. These painful crises are self-limited. They disappear spontaneously, but they invariably recur. Patients experience repeated episodes of fever without infection or other obvious cause. Pain probably results from spasms of the small veins caused by the invasions of the vessel walls by fat molecules. Patients later develop many forms of vascular disease. They may have myocardial infarctions; these are areas of destroyed cardiac tissue which result from coronary artery blockage. Cerebral vascular thromboses, or strokes, are common in the Fabry disease even before the age of twenty-five. Affected individuals experience seizures or other signs of cerebral vascular disease, and death may result in this way. They more commonly develop progressive renal impairment and die from kidney failure.

The Fabry disease is one of the sphingolipidoses disorders whose symptoms are produced by accumulation of fatty glycolipid molecules in body tissues. Tay-Sachs disease is also a sphingolipidosis. The compound that accumulates in the Fabry disease is the so-called GL_3 lipid known as ceramide trihexoside. It contains three six-carbon, or hexose, sugar molecules chemically bonded to one another. One of these is glucose and the other two are galactose. The enzyme ceramide trihexosidase is required for the splitting off of the terminal galactose molecule to convert GL_3 to GL_2. Its synthesis is determined by genes on the X chromosome that are altered in patients with the Fabry disease.

In a first approach to therapy Drs. William Krivit of the University of Minnesota and Charles Sweeley of Michigan State University and their colleagues attempted treatment by plasma infusion. They knew that enzyme was present in the normal human plasma. They undertook to infuse two patients who had the Fabry disease with normal plasma in order to provide active enzyme for the breakdown of the accumulated GL_3 substrate. Within six hours of the infusion there was a rapid rise in the amount of enzyme detected and a continuous drop in the amount of Fabry lipid, or GL_3, in the plasma. The effect was transitory as the enzyme completely disappeared over the course of about six days. The results were sufficiently attractive to lead to an attempt to provide a more continuous source of enzyme.

A long-term supply of missing enzyme might be provided by an organ transplant containing normal cells with normal DNA and normal enzyme. This kind of therapy has been under consideration for the treatment of inborn errors of metabolism for a number of years. It is now a reality.

In the Fabry disease the argument for the renal transplantation was immediate because a number of patients suffer from potentially fatal renal insufficiency. These patients have now been treated with kidney transplantation. The normal donor organs were obtained from individuals who had met with accidental death. Prior to transplantation no enzyme could be detected in the blood of any of these patients. Over a period of years an enormous quantity of the lipid had accumulated in their blood plasma. There was a sudden and sustained development of enzyme activity following transplantation. This activity, at its peak two hundred days after kidney transplantation, represented about one-tenth the amount of activity in normal adults. In the management of patients with inborn errors of metabolism, only very small amounts of enzyme are required to get rid of the symptoms of disease. In the first month after transplantation the amount of lipid in the plasma returned to the normal range and stayed there. Prior to therapy the first patient showed no evidence of kidney function. This was measured using an intravenous pyelogram. In this process a dye that is injected into the blood is concentrated and excreted by the kidney. Since it is an opaque dye, X rays taken after injection outline the kidneys and the excretory tract. No kidneys at all were visible in the pretransplantation films. Following transplantation the donor, or third, kidney was able to concentrate the dye. Six months later both the patient's own kidneys were also able to concentrate the dye and three kidneys could be seen on the X-ray films. This was a dramatic visual demonstration of the effectiveness of treatment. Cells of the transplanted kidney had been accepted by the host and produced enough of the missing enzyme, ceramide trihexosidase, to remove the stored GL_3 molecules from the original kidneys and other organs. The severe episodes of crippling pain disappeared, and the three patients considered themselves well. This was, indeed, a remarkable result. Further examples of renal transplantation as an approach to therapy in enzymatic defects can be expected.

Cellular engineering provides a third approach to the treatment of genetic disease. Its application may begin with the story of an extremely sick infant.

Tommy had Di George's syndrome. Cataracts had been noted in both eyes at birth. At nine days of age he began to have convulsive seizures. He nearly died during the first of these. Analysis of a blood sample revealed a low concentration of calcium. Intensive study revealed that he had been born without parathyroid glands. These are tiny glands in the neck, located behind the thyroid. They control calcium balance in the body. Reflection brought to mind a syndrome described by Dr. Angelo Di George in which the thymus gland as well as the parathyroids are missing at birth. The absence of these glands is thought to result from a failure of cellular differentiation processes during embryonic development. The parathyroid problem can be clinically managed using supplements of vitamin D and calcium. Lack of a thymus during infancy can be devastating. The body's immune system, which protects an individual against invasion by viruses, bacteria, and other infectious agents, fails to develop properly. Thymectomy, or surgical removal of the thymus, in newborn animals is life-threatening. So is the Di George syndrome usually lethal in the human infant.

During the first month of life Tommy had a continuously infected, runny nose and chronic diarrhea. He had infections of the mouth and skin that resisted all attempts at treatment; he had a chronic urinary tract infection. Biopsy of a lymph node revealed a situation virtually identical to that seen in mice thymectomized shortly after birth. A white blood count revealed a very low proportion of lymphocytes. These cells provide the backbone of cellular immunity, and they are thought to have their origins in the thymus during early life.

On the basis of experiments with infant mice, it had been suggested that patients born without a thymus would make ideal candidates for immunologic reconstitution. By implanting a foreign thymus into such an infant, one might theoretically be able to provide the essential components of the immunological defense system. The efforts leading to Tommy's thymic transplantation surgery provide a dramatic example of international scientific cooperation. Dr. William Cleveland of the University of Miami, Florida, who had worked out the patient's problems to this point, communicated with Dr. H. E. M. Kay, a fetal pathologist at the Royal Marsden Hospital in London. Dr. Kay is probably the world's authority on the fetal thymus. He obtained a thirteen-week-old female fetus, dissected the thymus, and put it on board a jet bound for Miami. The package arrived in the middle of the night, and Dr. Bernard Fogel whisked it off the plane through customs and to the hospital. The operation was begun immediately by Dr. William Brown. The thymus was divided into three small pieces, and each was inserted into the belly of the large rectus muscle that runs down the center of the abdominal wall. Almost immediately there was a dramatic change in Tommy's lymphocyte count. Within eight months the architecture of the lymph nodes was perfectly normal. The patient had by this time appeared normal for a considerable period of time. Tests of cellular immunity were normal. All the chronic infections disappeared. After transplantation the patient was a very different infant. He began to grow and develop.

These observations contributed considerably to understanding of the function of the thymus in conferring immunity on an individual. Nature has provided man with complex physical and chemical defense systems against the microorganisms that produce infectious disease. Instructions for these sophisticated defense mechanisms have been naturally selected during the course of man's evolution and are an integral part of his inherited gene pool. The recognition and destruction of foreign proteins and other large organic molecules form the basis for these immune systems. Any protein synthesized by messages from DNA different from our own has a different arrangement of amino acid sequences that are recognized as "foreign." This unique system identifies the protein coat of many viruses and the cell membranes of many bacteria as alien molecules. Mechanisms for the destruction of these foreign elements through protein digestion usually follow, and in health the body effectively rejects the invasion of disease microorganisms. The same system is at work in identifying other foreign proteins. Those found in pollen, certain drugs, and other agents lead to the immune response known as an allergy. Those alien proteins found in in the cells of transplanted organs lead to the immune response known as *rejection*. Not all protein synthesized according to instructions from foreign DNA is recognized as alien. Most people are not allergic to pollen. At some point in development the body apparently learns to distinguish chemically between "acceptable" and "alien" proteins.

Drs. Max Cooper and Robert Good, then at the University of Minnesota, developed a theory to explain the body's immunological mechanisms as a dual defense system. At some point in embryonic life plasma cells, probably in the gastrointestinal lining, begin to differentiate from less-defined stem, or parent, cells. The plasma cells produce many different kinds of specific molecules, called antibodies and immunoglobulins, and they keep producing them throughout the life of the organism. The antibody molecules and immunoglobulins are carried by the circulatory system. Antibodies are capable of bonding with foreign proteins. This coupling of an antibody with an alien protein, called an antigen, usually renders the antigen ineffective. The action of the immunoglobulins, called humoral immunity, can destroy the alien antigen or make it susceptible to further attack. Humoral immunity represents one element of the dual immunological system.

Later in fetal life specialized cells differentiate from undifferentiated stem, or primordial, cells in the thymus gland. These cells apparently seed clones later located in bone marrow and lymph nodes. These cells can squeeze in and out of blood vessels, tissues, and organs with ease. Their function is to surround, digest, and absorb foreign proteins. This process is called phagocytosis. Its name is derived from the Greek word *phagein* ("to eat") and the Latin word *cyto* ("cell").

When an infant is born without a thymus gland, the development of cellular immunity is impossible. Transplantation of a fetal gland into an individual like Tommy will not result in immunologic rejection because the lymphocytes responsible for the rejection mechanism are missing. A thymic graft proves effective because it provides the lymphocytes essential for cellular immunity. The chemical nature and properties of these transplanted white blood cells are in part conveyed according to the chemical instructions of the donor's DNA. The cells are distributed widely throughout the recipient's body. For these reasons treatment of the genetic disease by thymic transplantation is considered a form of cellular engineering.

Inherited immunologic deficiency diseases are understandable on a cellular or molecular basis, much like the inborn errors of metabolism. There are at least a dozen diseases in the category, some involving cellular immunity and some involving antibody or humoral immunity or both. The next step in the story of cellular engineering was taken in 1968 with the transplantation of bone marrow into a child with deficiency in both components of his immunological system.

Dual system immunologic deficiency means that the thymus-derived, cellular immunity is missing, as is the plasma cell antibody or immunoglobulin immunity. This occurs in two types. The so-called Swiss type is inherited as an autosomal recessive condition. The other form of dual immunologic deficiency disease is sex-linked. Dr. Robert Good, who is now the director of the Sloan-Kettering Institute in New York, and his colleagues Drs. R. A. Gatti and Richard Hong, all then at the University of Minnesota, thought that this problem should logically be approached by the transplantation of a primitive, or stem, cell, which might then give rise to both lines of immunologically competent cells, plasma cells and lymphocytes. Their opportunity to test this hypothesis was offered by the referral of a five-month-old boy who had inherited the sex-linked form of the dual or combined immunological deficiency disease. In his family eleven male infants had inherited the disease. All had died within the first year of life. Other siblings who failed to inherit the condition had been born and survived. This patient, David, proved to have a low concentration of serum gamma globulin, indicating defective humoral immunity. He had numerous draining pustules in the scalp and in the right armpit. He had a pneumonia from which staphylococci were cultured. These bacteria cause an unusually destructive kind of pneumonia.

The logical way in which to obtain undifferentiated stem cells, which will give rise to populations of both lymphocytes and plasma cells, is through bone marrow transplantation. Transplants of bone marrow had previously been used occasionally in the treatment of certain kinds of anemia and leukemia. In those instances the host's immunological defense system had matured, and introduction of foreign bone marrow cells would be expected to produce a violent immunological response in which the host's white blood cells responded to the graft, or transplanted cells, as if they were antigens, and vice versa. By subjecting the host to total body X-ray treatment or chemotherapy, it had proved possible to suppress the host response so that the transplanted tissue could be accepted.

Studies of these patients made it clear that the transplantation of bone marrow is very different from transplantation of an organ like a kidney. When an organ is transplanted, the big problem is that the host's immunological system tends to respond to the foreign tissue as an antigen. This is the *host-versus-graft reaction*. When bone marrow, a lymph node, or the spleen is transplanted, the immunocompetent cells they contain act as if the host were an antigen. The new cells tend to reject the recipient in what is called a *graft-versus-host reaction*. All previously studied patients had died from this reaction.

By the time David, the baby with the immunological deficiency, was referred to Dr. Good, a number of advances had taken place in understanding transplantation immunity. One gene site, the HLA locus, controls the production of the powerful antibodies involved in immunological rejection. Multiple alleles operate at this site. If the DNA of these alleles is the same in both donor and recipient, the antigens synthesized will be histologically compatible, and both donor and host cells will accept the other's proteins without an immune response. If the alleles at this gene site are different in the donor and host, the antigens they produce will elicit an immune response.

Excellent tests for histocompatibility have been developed by Dr. Fritz Bach of the University of Wisconsin and by Dr. Paul I. Terasaki of UCLA. In inbred mice it has been found that the fatal graft-versus-host reaction was difficult, if not impossible, to produce unless the donor of the immunologically competent cells differed from the host at the critical genetic locus. This is the H_2 histocompatibility locus in mice. Matching at the HLA locus in man, like matching at the H_2 locus in mice, makes for prolonged skin and kidney graft survival. This has become the mainstay of kidney transplant programs for the treatment of renal failure. It seemed reasonable that if a good match could be obtained at the HLA locus, it might be possible to achieve immunologic reconstitution in a deficient patient without destroying the patient by the graft-versus-host reaction. One would expect very few matches of this sort in the general population, but at least 25 percent of siblings might be expected to have a satisfactory histocompatibility match.

In David's family one of the four siblings, a girl, turned out to be histologically compatible with him. Bone marrow was obtained from David's eight-year-old sister and injected into his abdominal cavity. One week after implantation he became feverish and began to vomit. Fluid infiltrations were noted in both the right and left lungs. Two days later, he was still feverish and irritable, and he had a coarse rash. The entire response was typical of the graft-versus-host reaction. A biopsy of the skin confirmed this diagnosis.

David next developed an autoimmune anemia. Autoimmunity results when the body's immunological system fails to recognize its own proteins, responding to them as if they were foreign antigens. His red blood cells were being destroyed by his own immune system. Anemia resulted. The hemoglobin concentration dropped precipitously. His doctors held their breath and waited. Within three days the rash spontaneously subsided. David's temperature returned to normal, and he again began eating well. Shortly thereafter he developed a few loose stools, and a few small ulcers were noted in the rectum. This was also characteristic of the graft-versus-host reaction, but it looked as though the reaction had been mild and the end of it was in sight. From this point forward David did quite well.

Three months later David began to develop new and serious complications. He exhibited symptoms of pancytopenia, or a deficiency of every element of normal blood and bone marrow. This included thrombocytopenia, a decrease in numbers of blood platelets involved in clotting mechanisms, and leukopenia, a decrease in numbers of white blood cells, as well as severe anemia. This was almost certainly a direct consequence of the immunologic assault of the donor lymphocytes now thriving against cells bearing host antigens, particularly the blood cells. A striking result was the almost complete cessation of red cell production in the host, followed by the abrupt disappearance of host red blood cells approximately 120 days after the onset of the graft-versus-host reaction. A second bone marrow transplantation was then performed with marrow obtained from the same sister. Sixteen days after the second transplant, dividing cells in the bone marrow were all of the female variety, or karyotype. There was a dramatic restoration of the populations of red cells, platelets, and other blood cells. Twenty-two months following transplantation, examination of David's blood revealed only cells of female origin.

This landmark approach to the management of the graft-versus-host reaction was a gutsy one. It would have been possible to control the graft-versus-host reaction with immunosuppressant drugs, but that would have destroyed the very transplant that was designed to give this boy an acquired immune defense system. Dr. Good and his colleagues banked on the validity of their studies in mice, and with full consent of the boy's parents, they chose to let this reaction run its course. This was the right decision.

David has become a true *chimera*, an individual who can tolerate two genetically different cell populations in his system. The chimera was a mythological beast that was composed of the parts of different animals. Considerably more evidence for cellular chimerism has been obtained in David, who is in no way mythological and in every way a healthy individual. He started life with red cells of blood group A, with its specific protein antigen. This situation continued after the first transplant. His donor sister was type O. Sixteen days after the second transplant, when the dividing cells of the marrow were all of the female karyotype, blood cells drawn from a peripheral vein were of both donor type O and host type A, with type A predominating. Eight months after the transplantation the peripheral red blood cells were exclusively of group O, and the patient's white blood cells were antigenically identical to those of the donor. Infusion of group A red blood cells at this time revealed a perfectly normal rate of survival. They were not rejected, as is typical if type A antigens are introduced into the typical type O bloodstream. This patient was now a true immunologic chimera, completely tolerant of both types of cells.

David and his sister, Doreen, the donor, are now both normal, healthy children. David's height and weight are average for his age. Physical characteristics are entirely normal. Psychometric evaluation by the Denver Developmental Screen has shown his social and intellectual development to be perfectly normal for his age.

This success has been followed by some others. In 1969 investigators in Holland reported the first successful marrow transplantation in a five-month-old infant with the autosomal recessive form of dual immunological deficiency. He was treated by transplantation of a fetal thymus and bone marrow cells from his seven-year-old sister.

Transplantation of marrow from a donor with different alleles at the HLA site is still quite hazardous. The major problems in such transplantation involve finding safer methods for inducing immunologic tolerance and more effective ways of modifying the graft-versus-host reaction. If the risks accompanying bone marrow transplantation can be eliminated, this form of therapy will have enormous potential in the treatment of previously incurable diseases of the blood or lymphoid tissues.

Therapeutic management using bone marrow transplantation has been employed to treat the Wiscott-Aldrich syndrome. This X-linked condition is not completely understood. It appears to be a disorder of platelet formation and immunologic development. Involved patients have severe eczema of the skin; platelet deficiency, or thrombocytopenia, characterized by black and blue bruises; and markedly increased susceptibility to infection. Affected individuals often have bloody diarrhea during the first months of life.

Platelet deficiency is associated with abnormal precursor, or undifferentiated, cells in the bone marrow. These large cells, called megakaryocytes, exist in normal numbers but have an abnormal shape. Their immunologic defect involves the macroglobulins, large immunoglobulin molecules. Blood group antigens, such as the A and B proteins, are absent. A number of these patients have developed malignancies of the lymphoid tissues. A recent major development in the management of this condition has been produced by the use of *transfer factor* in therapy.

The action of transfer factor is a fascinating and challenging immunologic phenomenon. It was discovered in 1954 by H. S. Lawrence of New York City. The transfer factor, which is soluble, is contained in the fluid extracted from ground-up, or macerated, white blood cells. Although its chemical nature is not exactly known, its active molecules are small enough to pass through the pores of a simple membrane. Their immunologic effect is remarkable. Certain individuals are hypersensitive to tuberculin. If a small amount of this material is scratched into the skin, the inflammation associated with a typical immune response will follow. This response means that the individual has been infected with the tubercle bacillus and often that he has developed some immunity to it. He is, in a sense, allergic to the presence of the antigen.

White blood cell extract from an individual with a positive tuberculin test may be transferred into an individual with a negative tuberculin test. The negative test indicates a lack of immunity. Retesting reveals that tuberculin hypersensitivity has been acquired by the individual receiving the transfer factor. Molecules in the white blood cell extract, or transfer factor, are capable of altering the nature of the immunologic system by introducing characteristics from a donor's white blood cells. Many different forms of delayed allergy or hypersensitivity have now been transferred from one individual to another in this fashion.

Molecular intervention using transfer factor in treatment of the Wiscott-Aldrich syndrome has produced dramatic results. Dr. Hugh Fudenberg and his colleagues at the University of California, San Francisco, have reported the results of transfer factor therapy in ten patients. Each treatment has been an apparent success. In a manner not clearly understood, the transfer factor extracted from normal white cells apparently corrects or compensates for the deficiency associated with the Wiscott-Aldrich syndrome.

The therapeutic effect of transfer factor may be transient. Seven months following successful therapy disease symptoms reappeared in the initial patient. He experienced infections, his spleen became enlarged, and skin tests again became negative. He was treated with another dose of transfer factor and then a third, following which, skin tests again became positive, in accordance with the skin reactivity pattern of the normal donor. His clinical condition improved markedly. For transfer factor therapy to be successful, extracts of the transfer agent from normal white blood cells must be derived from highly selected donors, matched as one would for bone marrow transplantation.

The latest frontier in the field of genetic engineering involves actual gene therapy. If a normal gene encoded in its DNA could be provided, the basic cause of inherited disease could be eliminated. The possibility of this kind of gene manipulation once seemed remote. The rates of advance in molecular biology have recently quickened; its application may be closer than we think.

Extrapolation from the successes of gene manipulation in microorganisms provides the background for this prediction. Bacterial genes, specific DNA sequences for single traits, have been isolated. The complete chemical synthesis of the gene for an important molecule has been reported. This man-made gene controls production of the transfer-RNA that carries the amino acid alanine, to the site of protein synthesis in yeast cells. The isolation of human genes has not yet been accomplished, but the possibility seems eminently reasonable. One might foresee the synthesis or possible modification of defective human genes *in vitro*, or in the test tube. Delivery of the modified DNA to appropriate cells in an affected individual could correct an inherited defect and provide a permanent cure.

The hurdles to be overcome are enormous. Enzyme or cellular replacement therapy will probably become standard practice long before gene manipulation can be undertaken. Gene therapy has practical implications. Enzyme replacement may relieve the symptoms of genetic disease; gene therapy could cure it. Imagine the difference in treatment of diabetes. Replacement therapy is what is done today. It means an injection of insulin every day of a patient's life. Successful gene therapy would mean a cure with a single injection. That is a very attractive proposition.

Two possible mechanisms of gene therapy are promising avenues for further research. One method involves the direct introduction of foreign, or exogenous, DNA into defective cells. Cells are capable of absorbing large macromolecules such as DNA without first breaking them down into smaller component molecules capable of passing through the cell membrane. In this process the cell membrane pinches inward, or invaginates, around the large molecule. The resulting bubble, or vesicle, migrates through the cytoplasm, ultimately releasing its contents into the nucleus. The process, called pinocytosis, is illustrated in Figure 37. If DNA derived from human or other sources could be delivered to the nucleus in this fashion, it would probably be absorbed into and accepted by the host containing defective DNA. Proper protein synthesis according to instructions from the new DNA should follow with subsequent remission of disease. This mechanism is called transformation.

A second mechanism for gene manipulation involves the delivery of exogenous DNA by viruses. This viral technique is often employed by nature. It may produce disease or permanently alter the genetic material, continually introducing new variations into the species. A typical virus is the simplest of organisms. It contains a single strand of DNA or RNA surrounded by a protein coat or jacket. As a parasite, it requires a host organism. Appropriate hosts include the whole range of cells from simple bacteria to man. In a typical virus infection the protein coat of the virus becomes enmeshed in the cell membrane

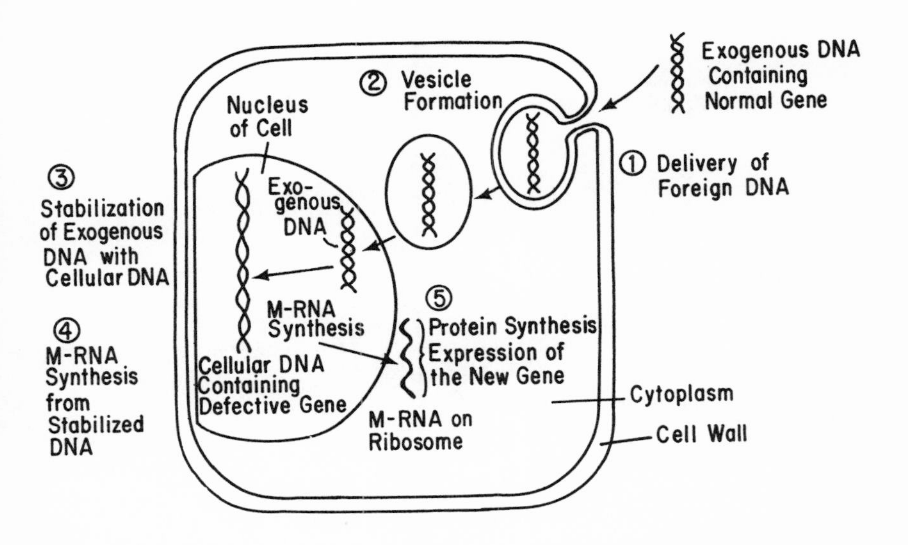

FIGURE 37. *Steps involved in the genetic engineering of a mammalian cell. The information encoded in the exogenous DNA must be taken up, integrated into the chromosome, and then expressed as a gene product. The process shown is known as a transformation, and it is caused by the exogenous DNA.*

of the host cell. Its DNA or RNA is released into the cell where it joins the host DNA. Using molecules of the host cells as raw material, the viral DNA directs its own replication and the synthesis of new protein coats. In a short period of time the host cell is converted into thousands of new viruses. The original cell membrane bursts and the viral particles are released. This is the pattern with infectious viruses that kill host cells.

In some instances the viral DNA is unable to take over the host cell's genetic machinery. Instead of new viral particles, a hybrid cell results. It bears characteristics of both the virus and the original cell, which are inherited by future generations of the cell (Figure 38).

Instances in which exogenous DNA, particularly viral DNA, becomes incorporated into the genetic material of the recipient cell are known as transductions. This kind of genetic modification has been known in bacterial cells for a number of years. The virus that hybridizes with a host cell is called a phage, or bacteriophage if the host is a bacterium. Transduction has been observed in mammalian cells. One of the most extensively studied agents is SV_{40} virus, in which the viral DNA physically integrates into the chromosomal DNA of the recipient cell during the transduction process.

The application of viral transduction to the treatment of genetic disease would involve the use of innocuous or man-made viruses. These would contain the necessary DNA sequences for synthesis of the protein that is deficient or

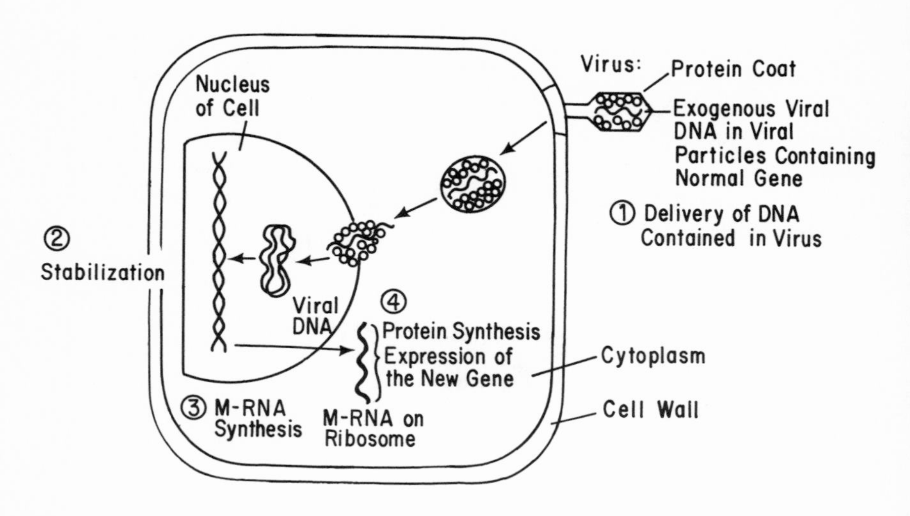

FIGURE 38. *Another approach to genetic engineering. This is called transduction and utilizes the DNA of a virus.*

defective. Once incorporated and stabilized into the host's DNA, information carried in the new gene would be transcribed into messenger RNA and conveyed to the ribosomes, or sites of protein synthesis, in the cytoplasm. Translation of the M-RNA message would result in the formation of the protein whose absence or defect had produced the disease (Figures 37 and 38).

Genetic modification of human cells according to either model, direct transformation with native DNA or transduction with viral DNA, seems theoretically possible. Alterations in genetically determined properties of the fruit fly, *Drosophila*, have been reported following the treatment of eggs with DNA extracted from other strains of *Drosophila*.

There have been a number of exciting recent experiments in which correction of genetic defects has been achieved in mammalian cells. In 1971 A. G. Schwartz, P. R. Cook, and Henry Harris of Oxford University reported the successful incorporation of chick red blood cell nuclei into the cytoplasm of mammalian cells grown in tissue culture. The host cells, cultured from mouse tissue, lacked the HGPRT enzyme, hypoxanthine-guanine-phosphoribosyl transferase, which is the enzyme missing from patients with the Lesch-Nyhan syndrome. These enzyme-deficient cells are useful for the study of hybridization with other cells or parts of cells such as the chick red blood cell nucleus. Because of their metabolic failure to activate hypoxanthine, the deficient mouse cells cannot survive alone on selective nutrient media. Those cells that survive are hybrids formed from the chick nuclei and enzyme-deficient cells.

The surviving hybrid cells synthesize the missing HGPRT enzyme according to instructions from the normal chick DNA.

When a chick red blood cell nucleus is introduced into the cytoplasm of a mouse cell, it begins to direct the synthesis of DNA and RNA according to the patterns that determine the synthesis of specific chick proteins. If the hybrid cells formed by this type of cell fusion enter into mitosis, the red blood cell nuclei are fragmented by a process called chromosome pulverization, or premature chromosome condensation, and most of the chick DNA disappears. The investigators felt that chromosome pulverization might provide a method for incorporating very small pieces of foreign genetic material, such as the gene for HGPRT synthesis, into body cells. They took nuclei from chick red blood cells from ten- to twelve-day-old embryos and fused them into the cytoplasm of the mouse cells. They then grew the cells in a selective culture medium. No cell or hybrid lacking HGPRT could survive in this medium. The great majority of cells died off. Some clones resistant to the medium appeared within a few weeks after the cell fusion. These clones were isolated and grown. They were found to contain HGPRT.

Analysis of the HGPRT molecule indicated that the enzyme in the hybrid was the chick enzyme synthesized according to the instruction from the chick DNA. An interesting feature of this experiment is that very little chick genetic material is left in these cells after mitosis. No chick chromosomes could be recognized when karyotypes were done. If the amount of chick DNA incorporated into the mouse hybrid had been large, specific antigens synthesized according to chick genes should have appeared on the surface of the hybrid cells. No such surface antigens could be detected.

This technique indicates that it is possible to incorporate fragments of genetic material into defective cells large enough to correct an enzyme defect without altering the immunologic properties of the cell and triggering an immune response. In terms of genetic disorders this suggests that cells from a patient with an enzyme deficiency disease might be corrected through *in vitro* hybridization and reintroduced into the body without immunologic rejection.

Another interesting approach to this problem of gene manipulation was also done *in vitro*. It was reported in 1971 by Carl R. Merril and colleagues in the Division of Biologic Standards of the National Institutes of Health. These investigators reasoned that the genetic code should be universal. If identical proteins are found in the cells of two different organisms, even if they belong to separate species, it is logical to assume that the DNA sequences that constitute the gene for this protein are identical. For example, a gene that codes for the same enzyme in man, mouse, and chick should contain identical DNA sequences in all three organisms.

Merril and his colleagues believed it possible to make genetic changes in mammalian cells by transduction with a specific gene from a known bacterial virus, or bacteriophage. The investigators knew that an identical defect in the metabolism of the sugar galactose could be found in the cells of some men and some bacteria. The bacterial deficiency could be corrected by transduction of the deficient bacteria with a virus called lambda phage. Fibroblasts, or connective tissue cells, from individuals with galactosemia, who have a defect in galactose metabolism, were grown in tissue culture. These cells were then subjected to transduction using lambda phage containing the appropriate nucleotide sequence for the synthesis of the missing enzyme. In time descendant generations of cells were observed to metabolize galactose properly. Evidently the DNA sequence specifying the synthesis of the missing enzyme had been incorporated from the viral DNA into that of the deficient cell. Formation of the appropriate enzyme indicated that the viral DNA message was being transcribed into messenger RNA, which directed the subsequent protein synthesis. These data suggest it might be possible to induce a correction of the affected cells *in vitro* and then transplant the corrected cells back into the patient's body. The clones of corrected cells might be expected to produce sufficient enzyme to get rid of the symptoms of disease. Even better, such a correction might be possible *in vivo*, in the living organism.

An experiment of this sort, which has been variously described as precipitous and premature, has already been carried out in man. Although the results of this research were reported in the *New York Times* on September 21, 1970, they have not yet appeared in the scientific literature. The experiment represented a collaboration between Dr. Stanfield Rogers at Oak Ridge and Dr. H. G. Turheggen, a pediatrician in Cologne, Germany. Two sisters were born in Germany with an inherited defect in the enzyme arginase. They had argininemia and accumulation of arginine in the cerebrospinal fluid. This condition has been associated with severe mental retardation. The older of the two sisters was quite retarded at the time the experiment was conceived. Dr. Rogers learned about the girls and their defect through a report in the British medical journal *Lancet*. He had been concerned for a number of years about the relationship of a virus that causes tumors in animals to findings suggesting that the virus contains the genetic code for the synthesis of arginase. Among the early evidence was an experiment by Dr. Richard Shope of the Rockefeller Institute. Dr. Shope originally discovered this virus, which produces papillomas, or tumors, in rabbits and is known as the Shope papilloma virus. He injected himself with the virus. No papillomas or other ill effects developed, but his blood arginine level decreased and stayed low for long periods of time. Later Dr. Rogers and his colleagues noted that many laboratory technicians working with the virus developed a similar depression in blood levels of arginine. He obtained evidence that the virus stimulated the production of arginase in skin cells of the rabbit.

A purified virus was injected into both girls with argininemia. Dr. Rogers has a quantity of data indicating that cells from both girls now exhibit normal arginase activity. The toxic levels of arginine in their blood have apparently been reduced to near normal concentrations because of the action of arginase. It is tempting to conclude that the injected viral DNA is directing the protein synthesis of the arginase enzyme. The younger girl is reported to be developing normally, without signs of mental retardation.

One has to retain a certain skepticism about this work until Dr. Rogers and his colleagues publish their data. They have been subjected to considerable criticism for undertaking an experiment in which live viruses were injected into people. When the research data are published, they should be reviewed scientifically and dispassionately. A technique like the one developed by Dr. Rogers could point the way to successful gene therapy in man. There are other possibilities.

The therapeutic use of a whole DNA complement, from the cells of man or other mammalian sources or from a virus, to correct a single gene defect may prove excessive. It would be considerably neater to deliver and integrate only the single required gene. There is some reason for optimism. Since bacterial genes already have been isolated, and the same seems imminent in man, it is reasonable to imagine that specific M-RNA molecules might be isolated as well. Since each M-RNA molecule is the chemical mirror image of a single DNA gene, the reverse synthesis of DNA from an M-RNA template specific for one particular protein should be possible. An enzyme known as reverse transcriptase stimulates synthesis of a precise DNA copy of an isolated M-RNA molecule. By isolating the M-RNA molecule specific for an enzyme such as arginase and subjecting it to the action of reverse transcriptase in the presence of DNA nucleotides, a normal gene for arginase could be produced. Delivery of a single DNA gene for arginase to the cells of a patient with argininemia or arginase deficiency, conceivably could cure the disease. This would eliminate the many extraneous and potentially damaging DNA sequences associated with the introduction of the whole DNA from an entire cell.

The problems of delivering and incorporating a single DNA gene could be overcome using the ability of DNA from SV_{40} virus to integrate itself with chromosomal DNA of a defective cell. With the specific gene attached, the viral DNA could then carry the biochemical information necessary for the specific gene function.

A recent and major advance is the development of what is known as recombinant DNA. Fundamental to this research were breakthroughs that provided methods for making very specific "nicks" in DNA molecules. These disrupt the DNA chain at highly specific sites. Enzymes known as restriction enzymes make these cuts at predictable spots in which a given sequence of nucleotides occurs. The enzyme recognizes the sequence as its place to make a cut. Incision in the DNA leaves sticky ends that may be annealed to other

DNAs with ligase enzymes. The result is a hybrid molecule. In this way it would be possible, and it has been done, to join a piece of mammalian DNA to DNA from a virus that is capable of getting into cells.

A concept that seems relevant to the correction of defective DNA is that of the bacterial plasmid. Plasmids are circular self-replicating bits of DNA found in microorganisms. Dr. Stanley Cohen of Stanford University described plasmids in the July 1975 issue of *Scientific American*. It is possible, using restriction enzymes, to add foreign DNA to a plasmid of the host microorganism. The hybrid will be copied *ad infinitum* within a single cell during its lifetime. This is a method for multiplying the effects of specific DNAs in one cell generation and beyond. If a human gene could be isolated and hooked to a plasmid, in no time there would be large numbers of the required gene. This technique provides a method for the selection of a specific DNA sequence. One could subdivide the genes of a cell grown in tissue culture at random using restriction enzymes and then incorporate particular human DNA fragments into a plasmid. If the plasmids were then integrated into an *E. coli* lacking the gene for the specific enzyme, growth on a selective culture medium would be limited to only those *E. coli* that had been hybridized successfully with the human DNA. Organisms that had incorporated the human gene for the enzyme into the plasmid would amplify it, transcribe it, and translate it into the enzyme required. Dr. Cohen has recently achieved such a hybridization with mouse cells and bacteria.

Much of the thought on genetic engineering has revolved about the DNA tumor viruses. The SV_{40} virus has been the favorite for study. It is possible to incorporate DNA containing very specific information into a virus that will then get into cells and express the genes encoded by the added DNA.

It can be predicted that the first human genes subjected to this kind of treatment will be the globin genes, which specify the protein portions of the hemoglobin molecule. This treatment might prove effective for sickle cell anemia or thalassemia. Many research teams have purified globin messenger RNA. This RNA may serve as an *in vitro* template for the synthesis of globin gene using reverse transcriptase. The messenger RNA might be used as a probe for the isolation of its complementary DNA from a mixture of fragments of crude, whole human DNA. The highly specific nucleotide sequence of a particular M-RNA introduced among many different DNAs might be expected to seek out and combine with only those DNAs bearing its exact complementary code. It would be theoretically possible to isolate this M-RNA/DNA combination from such a mixture. One might imagine this insertion of the specific gene into bone marrow cells of a patient with thalassemia. The infusion of these corrected cells back into the patient could end up with a cure. Something like this has been done. In December of 1975, scientists at Harvard, Drs. Argiris Efstradiadis, Fortis Kafatos, Allen Maxam, and Thomas Maniatis reported in a seminar the synthesis of rabbit globin, using reverse transcriptase to copy an isolated messenger RNA. This is very exciting business. It raises some difficult ethical questions. Even work in the laboratory on these problems could be dangerous, and scientists have begun to devote serious thought to the ethical questions raised.

Among the earliest genetic markers were genes that specified resistance to an antibiotic. It is easy to design experiments in the laboratory to test for this kind of genetic characteristic. Yet it is a bit frightening to think of *E. coli*, which are the usual inhabitants of the human large intestine and do cause some human disease, on the loose with a self-replicating gene for antibiotic resistance. If one of these infected an individual, there might be no possibility of treatment with an antibiotic. Since cancer viruses are among the tools on which to hook recombinant pieces of DNA, they might ultimately express a propensity to induce cancer. None of these viruses has ever been shown to cause cancer in people, but since they do cause cancer in animals, this is a particular source for concern.

The most worrisome possibility is that manipulations of human genes and their linkage with other genetic material might create novel rearrangement of DNA code words. Some horrendous, unpredictable outcome might be produced. The possibilities for such aberrant recombination might include the evolution of a previously unknown birth defect or the development of a new kind of virus infection that would spread like wildfire among human populations. There is no precedent for any of these concerns, but scientists are worriers, and that is good for all of us.

Dr. Paul Berg of the Stanford University Medical Center became sufficiently worried that he convinced his colleagues to call a moratorium on this kind of research in July of 1974. In February of 1975, 150 investigators involved in this research met at Asilomar, California, to discuss the problem, the potential hazards, and the potential benefits. They decided that the hazards were not, in Paul Berg's words, "entirely clear" and that the potential benefits were sizable. They developed guidelines for the optimal conduct of research on recombinant DNA and published them in the June issue of the *Proceedings of the National Academy of Sciences of the USA*. An NIH committee has since taken over the task of revising the guidelines. The current draft was hammered out at a meeting in December of 1975 in La Jolla and is to be published in 1976. The committee was chaired by Dr. DeWitt Stetten, Jr., Deputy Director of the National Institutes of Health. Dr. Stetten has said that the costs of not doing research must be weighed against the risks of performing it. He pointed out that a ban, now lifted, on using human fetal tissue halted work on a vaccine against infant diarrhea, a disease that kills many thousands of babies annually. The new guidelines will be tough but work on the manipulation of genes will go on.

It does seem likely that safeguards can be developed. One idea is to create a microorganism that self-destructs, that is incapable of life outside the special environment of the laboratory.

The guidelines developed represent a consensus about the levels of risk for the various classes of experiment. It is clear that few well-defined answers are in hand. The current agreement is to proceed with this research but with caution. The moratorium, the conference, and the guidelines developed represent the difficulties of grappling with the unknown. They also represent impressive evidence for the working of a collective scientific conscience.

These possibilities for genetic engineering raise difficult ethical problems. The scientific community is probably not yet prepared for gene therapy, either philosophically or psychologically. The ethics of genetic treatment must be worked out before the techniques are made available. It is probably true that as soon as these experiments become possible, they will be tried. It is critical that they be performed well and that the knowledge they yield be applied wisely.

There is some feeling that the first applications of this technology may be in plants, and this is a strong argument for the continuation of experimentation. There are plants which can convert nitrogen from the air into food. Such a plant needs no fertilizer. Insertion of the gene for this property into a carrot or some other vegetable could produce a food crop that fertilizes itself from the air. This could have a major impact on populations of the world in preventing starvation or famine. It will have been done through genetic engineering.

18.
Ethics in Medical Genetics

A married couple recently visited a medical geneticist. They told him they were expecting a baby. They wanted an amniocentesis because they feared that their baby might be abnormal. Amniocentesis was performed. The painstaking work of growing the fetal cells in culture was achieved. Several weeks later the geneticist was able to tell these expectant parents that there were no discernible abnormalities in the developing fetus. The baby would be a girl. Her chromosomes looked just fine. The couple then demanded an abortion. They had decided they wanted a boy.

This case may represent an extreme in the use or abuse of the services made available by medical genetics. It graphically illustrates how new scientific knowledge and techniques lead to new ethical and moral questions. In genetics many human questions are brought into a sharper focus than in other areas of clinical medicine. Geneticists and obstetricians have moved into a new frontier of medical ethics. Such seemingly benign procedures as mass screening for genetic diseases have encountered serious attack on the grounds of invasion of privacy. Prenatal detection of disease brings with it a host of ethical problems. The prospect of genetic engineering or the production of fetuses outside the human body provide the most extreme of moral dilemmas. Guidelines must be developed to deal with these problems.

Most physicians object to the performance of an abortion just because prospective parents do not like the sex of the baby. We are not used to dealing with such a frivolous approach to life. However, abortion is done every day for reasons that may be just as frivolous. The Supreme Court of the United States has ruled, in essence, that it is a woman's right not to carry a baby if she does not want it. The couple in the original example could probably get their abortion, even if the doctors at their genetics center would not do it. Because this possibility has been raised, many geneticists involved in prenatal diagnosis will not disclose the sex of a fetus. Others selectively decide when and to whom they will give this information.

The issue is not trivial. A survey recently asked, "If you could determine the sex of your infant, what choice would you make for your first infant?" An overwhelming majority wanted a male. Not too surprising? The answer is consistent with cultural patterns. When asked if the first child were a male what sex would they want for the second infant, there was again an overwhelming response in favor of the male. Put into practice, this choice would lead to a serious imbalance in society. It has been calculated that it could lead to an excess of three hundred thousand American male babies each year.

Many of these males would ultimately be unable to find female partners. The incidence of homosexuality, prostitution, and sexual crimes might increase. Men commit a disproportionate share of all crimes, particularly those of violence. Our society is already more violent than is tolerable. A society with a proponderance of males would probably be even more aggressive. Because women play a major role in the preservation of cultural aspects of American life, a shortage of females could cause many of the institutions devoted to theater, art, and music to cease to function in many communities. Some churches probably would not survive. Many surveys have indicated that women tend to vote differently from men. Selection of children on the basis of predetermined sex could influence our politics.

No one wants this kind of brave new world, but there is a real chance that we might unwittingly slide into it. Geneticists are thinking seriously about the problem. It can be solved with a modicum of care. They must exercise caution and good judgment in how the information they acquire is shared.

The prenatal diagnosis of genetic disease raises moral questions of its own. Once a diagnosis is made and a patient is known to be carrying a fetus with Tay-Sachs disease or the Down syndrome, the only alternatives are therapeutic abortion or the continuation of pregnancy with the birth of a child with a disease. One of the basic tenets of medical practice is that a physician do no harm to a patient. It is first learned in the Latin "*Primum non nocere*," which means, "First, do no harm." In prenatal diagnosis it is hard to define who is the patient. Is it the fetus or the mother? Advances in medical genetic science have forced people to consider who has the right to be born. For some, this is a tough question no matter how it is worded. For others, it is easy. With a condition as devastating as Tay-Sachs disease, there seems to be little question about any alternative other than therapeutic abortion. More difficult questions are posed by milder conditions such as galactosemia or sickle cell anemia.

Although these questions are difficult, they are relatively simple in comparison with the issues involving *in vitro* fertilization, that is, the production of fertilized human eggs in the laboratory. Genetic engineering raises the emotionally charged specter of a modern Dr. Frankenstein whose interest in achieving feats of biological manipulation overpowers any human considerations. Reality is more assuring. Scientists are vitally concerned about the application of modern biological knowledge to man. They are even more concerned about its misapplication. Involvement today with moral and ethical issues on the part of physicians is unprecedented. Their scientific journals have become a forum for intense debate. Programs and institutes are being formed in order to study, evaluate, define, and teach the ethics of both science and medicine.

At Harvard a program in ethics is jointly sponsored by the schools of law and medicine. Physicians, including prominent academicians, are using sabbaticals and fellowships to go back to school as students of this new discipline. The Institute of Society, Ethics, and the Life Sciences at Hastings-on-Hudson, New York, often called the Hastings Institute, has received considerable media attention in recent years. In 1972 it began a three-year, federally financed study of the social, legal, and ethical aspects of medical genetics. The Joseph and Rose Kennedy Institute for the Study of Human Bioethics and Reproduction has been established at Georgetown University in Washington, D.C., and the Kennedy Foundation has sponsored conferences and fellowships devoted to ethics. There is a Joint Center for the Study of Law and Human Genetics at Tufts New England Medical Center and the Boston College Law School. There are other organizations, but even this brief listing makes it clear that the medical profession recognizes that the application of genetic science to human affairs is a sensitive business. Some very basic human questions are being asked. Taboos are being forgotten. New reasoning is required, and no one is quite comfortable.

Amniocentesis and prenatal diagnosis seem to most geneticists to be a straightforward method for doing good. However, many persons, both inside the medical profession and out, are troubled by the idea of abortion. This procedure is objectionable to many Roman Catholics as a violation of a fundamental tenet of faith. Their religion equates fertilization with the beginning of a new life. Accepting these postulates as articles of faith, they view abortion as a form of murder. Some people of other religious persuasions similarly object to the death of a fetus.

It is curious to note that abortion was an accepted practice in the ancient Mediterranean communities in which Christianity began. Plato, Socrates, and Aristotle all advocated abortion as a method for preventing overpopulation. The early Judaic thinkers, expressing their ideas in the Talmud, regarded the infant as having no living soul until it left a mother's womb. Saint Augustine, who lived at the beginning of the fifth century after Christ, was the first Christian scholar to ask the critical question about when an embryo possesses a soul. Once this issue was resolved theologically, abortion potentially could be equated to the murder of a living person. The issue was not easily settled. The question was brought to Pope Innocent III in about 1200. The specific case involved a monk whose mistress had conceived a child. He was thought to have caused her to abort accidentally. The question posed to the Pope was whether the monk should be punished, not for having a mistress, but for having caused the abortion. Innocent decided that punishment was in order only if the fetus had lived long enough to have a soul. Saint Thomas Aquinas, a major Catholic theologian, explicitly defined the time for acquisition of the soul in a fetus. He asserted that this occurs when the embryo assumes a human form. An embryo does not look human until well after conception. Both Augustine and Aquinas became saints. It is interesting that neither took a position as rigid as that Catholics are now asked to live with.

Analysis of the history of the laws of societies concerning moral and ethical behavior provides perspective for the ways in which they generally reflect the thinking of men and the standard patterns of behavior in the world around them. Roman Catholic philosophy and practice accepted abortion until well into the seventeenth century.

Scientific advances led to a change in theological position. When scientists could examine embryos under the microscope, they recognized that the processes of development constituted a continuum from fertilization through delivery. There is no magic moment at which an embryo suddenly becomes something different. It is scientifically valid to consider an embryo as programmed from the moment of conception. This finding greatly influenced the position of the Church and its doctrine at a time when its authority was becoming ever more centralized. Around the turn of this century, when the science of genetics was in its infancy, decrees were issued by the Vatican that clearly defined the theological position of the Pope and Church. Abortion in any form was to be condemned.

These laws of the Roman Catholic Church reflect interpretations of scientific findings. They also reflect a particular concept of how people ought to behave. People outside the Catholic faith have expressed similar convictions. Richard Nixon in San Clemente on April 3, 1971, said, "From personal and religious beliefs, I consider abortion an unacceptable form of population control. Furthermore, unrestricted abortion policies, or abortion on demand, I cannot square with my personal belief in the sanctity of human life, including the life of the yet unborn."

The American people, as assessed in opinion polls, have a contrary view. They are overwhelmingly in favor of liberalized abortion laws. Regardless of differences in religion, a clear majority support a liberal policy toward abortion. In nationwide polls some 90 percent of Jews, 80 percent of Protestants, and 75 percent of Roman Catholics favor liberalization of existing law. This country's statutes are an outgrowth of moral and ethical attitudes. They are constantly changing, as the area of population control or family planning clearly shows. There is now a similar shift in attitudes toward abortion. The issue has not been completely resolved by the Supreme Court's recent decision, but this judicial judgment clearly reflects the thinking of an impressive majority of Americans. Those who object to abortion on moral grounds will always be able to avoid it for themselves. It does appear they will have trouble dictating the behavior of others.

Physicians, too, have been slow to accept abortion. Dr. Arthur J. Dyck raised this question in the *New England Journal of Medicine*: "Even if one wishes to leave the exact status of the fetus as a human life an open question, should it not be part of the special responsibility of the physician, as it has been traditionally, to err on the side of saving and fostering human life rather than to develop or encourage problems that selectively prevent such life?" He went on to say, "The assumption that the use and application of amniocentesis is a neutral sphere for physicians and society presupposes, that for physicians and society, abortion is not a moral issue, and that existing or future laws do or will assure that abortions are decided solely by families and physicians. To go that way is not morally neutral, and it is not life affirming."

That is one point of view. Another, voiced by Mark Lappe of the Hastings Institute, is that "bringing an individual into the world who might be expected to experience extreme physical or mental anguish as a result of potentially known genetically determined defects is to be avoided by all means possible. Insofar as a potential abnormality adds to human suffering and its elimination contributes to the avoidance of suffering, this, and only this, criterion should be the basis for counseling decisions."

In practice, medical geneticists tend to be pragmatists. They deal primarily with human suffering and consider it their responsibility to alleviate this suffering. They see firsthand how a defective child can destroy a family. Two handicapped children often prove too much to bear, even for the strongest families. This society generally recognizes that underpopulation is not a problem. Overpopulation is a problem. If we are to limit the quantity of human reproduction, it seems imperative to do something about its quality.

Practical considerations are probably more viable than abstract questions about the state of existence of the fetus. Many families seeking amniocentesis would not undertake conception if they thought there was the remotest possibility of bearing another affected child with, for example, the Lesch-Nyhan syndrome. Prenatal diagnosis gives them the opportunity to have healthy children they would otherwise never bear. It does not seriously bother most medical geneticists that it might take two monitored pregnancies to create such a normal child. In this way the practitioner is concerned not with cosmic issues but with practical ways to help the patient.

The medical geneticist is likely to turn attention toward reducing the risks of amniocentesis. Dr. Henry L. Nadler of Northwestern University School of Medicine, who has probably had more experience with amniocentesis and the prenatal diagnosis of genetic disease than anyone in the world, has emphasized the need for skill and experience. There are potential dangers to both the mother and fetus that can be minimized through careful medical attention. He has commented about the physician's responsibilities to parents who undergo these procedures: "The physician who undertakes prenatal detection of a genetic disorder must be committed to providing therapy if the results indicate an abnormality and the parents wish to terminate the pregnancy. The obstetrician need not be the person who performs the required abortion; however, he must be responsible for referring the family to a physician who will act upon their request." It is the responsibility of the physician who offers prenatal diagnosis to explain the possible outcomes and the alternatives in advance, to see that all technical details are meticulously executed, and to carry out the parents' decision faithfully, whatever that decision may be.

Questions of responsibility to society as a whole are clear from the mathematical considerations provided by the study of population genetics. Amniocentesis programs will not have an appreciable effect on the distribution of normal or abnormal genes in society. The issue confronting individual physicians is the welfare of their patients and how best to serve them.

The moral imperatives of various religions are a different matter. Codes of ethics for the use of amniocentesis and therapeutic abortion are probably not sufficiently defined to achieve common agreement. The question of therapeutic abortion plays a minor role in the overall question of abortion. In the vast majority of instances abortions are requested for reasons other than potential genetic disease. As the mores of our society with regard to abortion become more liberal, the rigid position of organized religion will probably be relaxed. The easiest place for it to soften its stand is in the area of the prenatal diagnosis and prevention of devastating disease.

Within the area of prenatal diagnosis there are difficult, specialized ethical questions. One question involves the discovery of an extra Y chromosome in a male fetus. There is a possibility that this XYY genotype is a harbinger of later antisocial behavior. Should the physician tell prospective parents that they bear an XYY fetus and recommend therapeutic abortion? Many XYY individuals appear to behave in a completely normal fashion. The degree of risk for the unborn child is uncertain. If a decision to carry out an abortion is made, the lines are at least clearly drawn.

For the physician to give parents information about the XYY syndrome without going on to abortion could be unfortunate. This question is not often apt to arise from prenatal diagnosis through amniocentesis. An XYY diagnosis is much more likely to be discovered as a consequence of routine chromosomal screening among newborn infants. Programs for this kind of survey have already been established in a number of places. If such a survey reveals a baby with trisomy 21, or the Down syndrome, the physician's responsibility is clear. If it reveals an XYY genotype, his responsibility is not at all clear.

Telling the parents about an XYY diagnosis and explaining the kinds of potential behavior are likely to cause severe difficulties for both the parents and the child. Serious questions and fears raised by such information could adversely affect the relationship between parents and child. Not telling the parents is easier, but is it ethical? It might be if the physician is in a position to maintain contact with the developing child. This choice opens the physician to a charge of withholding information, but physicians are accustomed to keeping their own counsel if that seems in the best interest of all concerned. Ultimately, the physician will have to face the question of whether the affected individual is to be told of his XYY genotype. Many geneticists would respond in many different ways to this dilemma. For any one geneticist the response would probably be different for different patients.

The ethical questions of abortion bring the entire process of reproduction into focus. The renewal of life starts with the union of the living gametes, the sperm and the ovum. Prevention of fertilization is the reproductive step at which most people feel comfortable in efforts to control population. This is true whether they are concerned with the prevention of genetic disease, the limitation of population growth, or simply the avoidance of an individual pregnancy at a particular time. It has not always been the case, but today very few people object to birth control measures that prevent the union of the gametes. Not everyone approves of oral contraceptives or other birth control devices. Most do. Abstinence, vows of chastity, monasteries, and nunneries accomplish the same thing. They all prevent life. Sober reflection has convinced most people that the creation of life must be regulated if the species is to continue to inhabit this planet. In some way or other most people who think about these things approve of the prevention of new life before it begins.

The next logical reproductive step at which judgment can be exercised concerning creation of a new life follows conception. An easy way to look at this question is to view abortion as just one more way of preventing life. It is important in the consideration of ethical issues to go one step further in this chain of reasoning. What about the baby already born? If he has a terrible disease, should he be killed? Raise this possibility and most people gasp. Although such measures were practiced by some earlier societies, even rather civilized ones, all civilized societies today clearly draw the line at infanticide.

Is this really true? Do modern societies really recoil from infanticide with invariable horror? Even this line may have become tenuous. The issue was brought before the public in 1972 at a conference organized by the Joseph P. Kennedy Jr. Foundation. It was attended by some fifteen hundred scholars, clerics, politicians, scientists and physicians at the Dwight D. Eisenhower Theater in the John F. Kennedy Center for the Performing Arts in Washington. At that conference a film was shown of the death of a baby with the Down syndrome.

The baby was born, as are many Down syndrome infants, with an obstruction in the upper intestine because the organ had not formed properly. The operation to reverse this defect is rather simple, and it would have been performed immediately if the baby had not had the Down syndrome. The parents objected to having a retarded, mongoloid child and refused permission to operate. The infant survived a fifteen-day period that created agony for the nurses and doctors accustomed to doing everything within their power to save a life. The crib was placed in a darkened room in the hospital. A sign, "Nothing by mouth," hung from one end. The baby died of dehydration.

This not an isolated episode. Similar decisions have been made by parents and often by doctors for many years. It was unique in that it was filmed, presented to the world, and discussed as an ethical issue. The death of this baby was considered in seven seminars. Most of those who commented felt a shared anguish with the parents but could not endorse their decision to will the baby's death by withholding treatment. Physicians worry that causing death by failure to provide therapy may be only a steppingstone to active euthanasia. Dr. James Gustafson of the Department of Religion at Yale asked, "Does an infant have a moral claim upon his parents?" He answered, "Yes, children do. What do we know of the infant's desire to survive? At what cost do we relieve ourselves of suffering?"

Dr. Paul Freund, professor of law at Harvard, compared parents and their children with three mountain climbers tied together. If one injures himself in such a way that the other two know their only chance for survival is to cut him free, thereby ensuring his death and their life, what should they do? Professor Freund reasoned that they should cut him free. However, he pointed out that the risk in saving an infant with the Down syndrome does not carry with it a threat to the life of either parent. Not saving the infant is as if the mountain climbers cut loose and abandoned their injured colleague to prevent themselves from getting a few bruises.

Michael Harrington, the author of *The Other America* and a participant in the conference, asked, "What if the child had been more defective?" "You mean a monster?" asked television newsman Roger Mudd. Dr. Renee Portray, an official of the National Association for the Aid of Retarded Infants at Brussels, answered, "Absolutely, let the child live. We have no way to draw the line."

Senator Edward Kennedy, president of the foundation, said, "The problems we are considering today are as profound and difficult as man has ever encountered. The path toward their solution is treacherous and uncertain. But so is the pattern of life which awaits the retarded child when he enters the world." Dr. Robert Cooke, former chairman of the Department of Pediatrics at Johns Hopkins, has described medicine as the science of care. He pointed out that the suffering people talk about in a disorder like the Down syndrome is seldom that of the child. The parents suffer, and so possibly do the physicians. "Death," wrote Dr. Cooke, "of the unoperated patient is an unacceptable means of alleviating this suffering."

Difficult ethical issues are also being raised by the beginning of mass screening programs to detect carriers of harmful genes. These programs have focused on ethnic groups in which a defective gene is concentrated, on Jews in the case of Tay-Sachs disease and on Negroes in the case of sickle cell disease. Difficulties have arisen in screening for sickle cell anemia. The medical problem of the genetic disease and its control is complicated by the social problems of black-white relationships. It is interesting that cries of genocide have been made. On the other hand, screening for the Tay-Sachs gene has been enthusiastically embraced by populations of Jews, a group that has actually experienced genocide in our time.

When the National Institutes of Health began a screening program for black employees in 1971, the whites who had planned the program were surprised to find a strong current of protest. Black employees who were the object of the program did not like the idea that it was being planned and executed by whites. There were more realistic grounds for opposition: information from the screening program was to go into personnel files, and blacks were afraid that carriers of the sickle cell gene would be labeled as poor risks for promotion. These protests were successful. Blacks took charge of the program, and the information on carriers was made confidential.

There were similar protests, on a larger scale, when compulsory sickle cell screening programs were mandated by law in several states and the District of Columbia, even though many of the laws were supported and sponsored by black legislators. The mandatory aspect of the tests and the fact that the program singled out blacks disturbed many. The Hastings Institute, reacting to those laws, said that "there is currently no public health justification for mandatory screening to prevent any genetic disease." The statement covered much more than sickle cell anemia, but the fact that the institute specializes in ethics does not necessarily qualify it as the authority on our societal ethic. Hysterical fears that have surfaced with regard to sickle cell anemia could retard the field of genetic screening at a time when it desperately needs to go forward. Privacy is touted as an important freedom, but why should people hide their heritage, especially if getting it out in the open can prevent suffering in those yet unborn?

Sometimes what seem to be freedoms are actually chains. A vivid example is provided by the gun laws in this country. There is so much freedom and privacy that people kill one another in the United States at rates approximating those of underdeveloped countries wracked by revolution. In a more civilized country like England and in a more repressive country like Spain no one can keep a gun and homicide is virtually unknown. In this country there is supposedly more freedom, but a person can walk the streets of London or Madrid at any hour of the day or night. The same is not true in New York or Washington.

The issue is a similar one in the control of genetic disease. In order for there to be progress, people are all going to have to get on to punch cards and into computers that know a lot about them and their mothers and fathers and sisters and brothers. In this way people may be a little less free. But their children, their grandchildren, and their grandchildren's children will all live freer. It may mean their lives.

The issues raised by experience with sickle cell anemia screening provide guidelines for the conduct of all testing programs for other genetic disease. Confidentiality is essential. Custodians of information about an individual's carrier status for any given abnormal gene must be selected with care. They must be relied upon not to identify anyone publicly as a carrier of a potentially harmful disease. As history has repeatedly shown, lack of confidentiality opens the door to abuses and discrimination.

The question of whether tests should be made mandatory will not be immediately resolved. Most committees, reflecting a middle-of-the-road policy, will probably advise against the legislation of testing. Experience with voluntary PKU screening is that such testing in this country is markedly inferior to mandatory testing. PKU screening is designed to identify the disease, not the gene. The only way of obtaining a 100 percent screening for a defective gene is to make screening mandatory. The important point is that effective public education should accompany any screening program. The aims of a screening program should be explained clearly to the public. Community participation must be actively and intelligently enlisted. Information about the nature and purposes of screening must be accessible to all. Diagnostic tests must be precise and accurate. They should be inexpensive and, whenever possible, automated. Most important is an efficient system for the follow-up of all positive tests for the disease or its gene. There must be ample provision not only for definitive testing but for thorough communication of the results and explanation of their implications. Privacy must be protected throughout. Only with careful attention to detail can a screening program be successful.

All of these recommendations sound obvious. Attending to the necessary details has not been so obvious. There was nothing but good will behind the campaign against sickle cell anemia. Good intentions were not enough. If prenatal diagnosis of sickle cell anemia becomes widely possible, other ethical and moral problems will follow. Should an abortion be done for a disease in which life expectancy may be as long as twenty or more years? It is harder to balance the suffering and morbidity of this disease with the right to be born. It is harder for a physician to explain the exact degree of risk to parents so that an informed decision can be made. These questions are similar to those posed by the XYY male. They will be increasingly asked as geneticists develop more and better techniques for prenatal examinations capable of detecting a greater number of inherited disorders. Ethical behavior depends on the good judgment and good will of the individual physician and parent.

If the achievements of medical genetics today raised ethical questions that are hard to answer, the moral challenge of the biomedical possibilities of tomorrow are almost impossible to grasp. One of the most frightening to many people is the technique described as cloning. Science fiction has inundated the public with the idea that it might be possible to raise large numbers of individuals who are completely identical. Cloning might be achieved by extracting cells from an individual whose characteristics appear appropriate for duplication and treating them in such a way that they develop into a complete human being identical to the one from which the original cell was obtained. Although something like it has been accomplished in frogs, the genetic technology for doing the same thing in man is a long way off. A somewhat less striking possibility would be the fertilization and growth of human embryos *in vitro*. At the proper stage in development, an embryo could be implanted into the womb. This might hold an appeal to a woman with a problem of egg development or of early implantation that causes infertility.

Dr. Robert M. Veatch, director of the medical ethics program at Columbia University's College of Physicians and Surgeons, has written:

> While all of these may seem futuristic and at the same time improbable, it is frightening to realize that they all may become technically feasible as a result of medical technology which is currently being developed for what appears to be very benevolent motives: infertility treatment, detection and correction of terrible genetic abnormalities, and, in the case of the artificial womb, extension of care for the prematurely born. The ethical implications of these currently developing technologies are truly astounding, and we had better begin to face these questions now.

One of the earliest of these controversial problems to be faced is the *in vitro* fertilization of human ova. Efforts to fertilize a human ovum in the laboratory have been in progress for some years now. The goal is to grow an embryo in culture that can then be implanted in a normal human uterus. As early as 1961 Dr. Daniele Petrucci of the University of Bologna in Italy experienced a confrontation between the moral position of society and his research. He said that he had fertilized a human egg *in vitro* and cultured the embryo for twenty-nine days, or until a heartbeat was visible. He then destroyed the developing embryo because it appeared to him to be a deformed "monstrosity." This investigator stopped further experiments on this problem after he was condemned by the Roman Catholic Church for producing a human being without "the most supreme assistances of love, nature and conscience." However, at Cambridge University in England physiologist Robert G. Edwards and other scientists have continued to work on this problem. The Cambridge researchers are thought to have mastered the technique of fertilization *in vitro*. The experiment in which the tissue culture embryo is implanted into a human uterus and brought to delivery at term has not yet been initiated, even in monkeys. To accomplish this would be a scientific tour de force. It could have very practical use in the management of human infertility. And it might not, after all, be too hard to do.

It would, of course, be terrible not to carry out such a procedure properly and to create a human who was malformed or retarded. Some ethicists seem to worry about the idea itself, even if done right. Paul Ramsey, Harrington Spear Professor of Religion at Princeton University, said of any such experiment, "Unethical medical experimentation on future human beings therefore . . . is subject to absolute moral prohibition. It clearly seems to me that *in vitro* fertilization followed by implantation is an immoral experiment on such a possible future human life." Some scientists agree. Dr. Leonard Kass, a molecular biologist, has said, "Morally it is insufficient that your motives are good, that your ends are unobjectionable, that you do the procedure 'lovingly' and even that you may be lucky in the result; you will be engaging in an unethical experiment upon a human subject."

It escapes me why the idea is inherently unethical even if it is successful. It further bothers me that scientists look at this area of research and consider a useful result "lucky." I would not want anyone to try the procedure with people until the evidence for its success in other species had been repeatedly demonstrated. The site of fertilization does not seem of great moral or ethical consequence since the fetus bearing both parents' genetic complement would develop in the genetic mother's womb.

Artificial insemination has been accepted as an answer to sterility in the male for many years. It may be employed by some who are putting sperm into banks, particularly prior to vasectomy. There does not seem to be much difference between this standard, well-accepted procedure and *in vitro* fertilization. A related problem might be that of a woman with intact ovaries who has had a hysterectomy. *In vitro* fertilization could give her a baby who was genetically hers and her husband's. It could be implanted and brought to term in a foster mother's uterus. This does not sound like an "immoral experiment."

Cloning is another issue entirely. The origins of research in this direction were with parthenogenesis, a long-known alternative to sexual reproduction. Certain egg cells, particularly those of primitive sea animals, when mechanically or chemically stimulated, will divide, form an embryo, and ultimately mature into an adult form. Something like this happens in nature with the honey bee. In this species fertilized eggs become workers and queens, while unfertilized eggs develop parthenogenetically into drones. None of these is a clone, for the unfertilized egg in the bee or in parthenogenesis experiments is haploid, bearing only one set of chromosomes. The first experiment with the cloning of animal cells was a brilliant one conceived by Professor John Gurdon, a biologist at Oxford, in England. He found that he could expose frogs to radioactivity and destroy the nucleus without damaging the cytoplasm of the egg. He then removed the nucleus from an ordinary body cell of an adult frog. This nucleus with its full set of chromosomes was inserted into the egg cell. The egg cell began to divide, producing first a tadpole, and then a fully differentiated frog. The new frog was identical to the original donor of the nucleus. Any number of new frogs could be produced in this manner, each of them identical to the donor frog.

What can be done in the frog could probably be done in man. Dr. Robert Sinsheimer of the California Institute of Technology has said that it would probably be possible to clone human organisms within ten to twenty years. This does not mean that there are no technical problems. A human ovum is very different from that of a frog. The "scenario" would almost certainly be the same as the one that Dr. Gurdon used in the frog. Once there had been division to a sixteen- or thirty-two-cell stage, implantation into a prepared uterus might be contemplated, just as in the *in vitro* fertilization studies.

Cloning offers the possibility of endlessly reproducing some set of characteristics that are prized for a particular reason. A couple who has an infant they adore may discover they are incapable of having any further children. By cloning, starting with one of the first child's cells, they could develop a twin who would be born some years after the first child. This would not be much for an ethicist or moralist to worry about. Nature previously has produced this hypothetical example of a child of the same father and mother, nurtured in the womb, delivered normally, and bearing the exact genetic material of a sibling. It should not be disturbing that the child would be identical to the previous one. People are accustomed to the idea of identical twins.

Imagine instead a decision to make a thousand copies of Henry Kissinger. By obtaining a thousand nuclei from a tissue derived from a little skin and by cloning his cells, scientists could produce a thousand or more exact copies. Although the world needs more talented people, the idea is worrisome. This is the brave new world. It is potentially closer than it seems. Thought must be given to how to control such possibilities and about who should determine whether things like cloning should be done in man. These are not easy matters. There are dangers that can be already foreseen. There are also benefits.

It is important that fears do not influence the initiation of valid research. The solution of technical problems in this area should go on. Meanwhile, there must be new structures created to ensure that the application of the fruits of research to man will be done wisely. Ethical and moral issues should be dealt with long before the technical problems are solved and the procedures are made available for human practice.

A closely related issue is genetic engineering. Changing cells and consequently human beings for the better by altering their genetic material is an idealistic goal. Failures are horrible to contemplate because an induced error in the genetic material could be transmitted for generations. Efforts to cure a genetic disease by using a virus to introduce new genetic information into the cells of a patient with a metabolic disease have already been made. The fact that they employed a virus that causes malignant disease in the rabbit raises another ethical question. The two sisters with arginase deficiency have had no carcinogenic effects from this virus. This result might have been predicted because Dr. Shope had previously injected himself with the virus without ill effect. However, malignancy may take time to develop. Any effort at genetic therapy that employs a cancer-producing virus is inherently worrisome. These agents must not be used in man until every possible safeguard has been brought to bear upon the problem.

Experiments in genetic engineering will undoubtedly be performed again. Criteria are being developed that should serve as guidelines for this work. Diseases in which the affected individual has an abnormal enzyme that must be encoded by an abnormal gene are the ideal substrate. There should be ample prior experience with the disease so that its natural history is well known, as well as the efficacy of current therapies. The quality of the product used to introduce the normal gene should be as specific as possible. A single gene would be ideal. Extensive studies should be conducted in animals to ensure against dangers such as the induction of cancer and other undesirable genetic alterations. The proper mode of therapy should be tested on cells from the patient grown in culture. The stakes are high. There are approximately four million diabetics in the United States. If a way could be found to treat them with DNA containing the gene for insulin, it could make a significant difference in their health and quality of life. It is important to develop the most stringent guidelines in order that no harm be done. At the same time it is important that fears of a brave new world not inhibit the progress of research.

"Even if biochemists achieve a capacity for genetic engineering, it is unlikely that their tools will match the tools that are already available," said Philip H. Abelson, editor of *Science*. "For example, artificial insemination is widely used to improve livestock. If some future ruling clique decided to engage in human genetic improvement, they would be more likely to adopt this technique and to employ their own semen than to use material concocted in the laboratory. Talk of the dire social implications of laboratory-related genetic engineering is premature and unrealistic. It disturbs the public unnecessarily and could lead to harmful restrictions on all scientific research."

Although it is essential that research continue, its translation to human therapeutics should be made slowly and thoughtfully. Dr. John W. Littlefield of the Harvard Medical School and Maurice S. Fox of the Massachusetts Institute of Technology expressed this need for caution: "We are still primarily in a descriptive phase in our understanding of human genetics, with little, if any, idea of how to intervene safely at any level. Let us not do to ourselves what we have done to our environment. Let us now seek public support for research toward a better understanding of normal and abnormal human biology, rather than promise quick glamorous cures."

Pleas for caution may seem contradictory. Some are based on the contention that scientists have great power at their disposal; others on the contention that scientists know too little to act. There is no real contradiction. Biologists today have the power to do more than ever, yet not enough power to do what they want to do. When they achieve all they hope, the vistas for good and for evil will be boundless. The need for ethical and moral controls will be most urgent. The bases for these controls are being established now in the dialogues among scientists, physicians, and persons outside the biomedical community.

Dr. James D. Watson of Harvard has been outspoken in his belief that these moral issues should not be left to scientists alone but should be examined in searching fashion by society as a whole. Senator Walter F. Mondale has proposed the establishment of a National Advisory Commission on Health, Science, and Society that would be specifically charged with the ethical, social, and legal implications of advances in biomedical technology. The future always arrives faster than predicted. It is in the years directly ahead, in which the first small steps are taken, that scientists and others will have a chance to develop the ways to meet the ethical challenge. It is important to be sure that man controls science. It is equally important to be sure that science does not control man.

19. Genetic Counseling: Who Are the Counselors? How Do They Work? Where Do You Go for Help?

Over the years a number of different kinds of people have become genetic counselors. As awareness of the need for genetic counseling has developed, people of more varied background and training have been attracted to the profession. Some of the first counselors were people with a Ph.D. degree in genetics. More recently physicians have become involved. Most of them are pediatricians or specialists in internal medicine. Some are neurologists, obstetricians, or ophthalmologists. Others are now specializing solely in genetics. A few dentists have done excellent work in clinical genetics. Colleges have begun to grant degrees to students who have completed undergraduate programs in genetics and genetic counseling. The important qualification of these individuals is their special preparation for actual counseling. In some genetic centers nurses and social workers participate in counseling activities. The most effective deployment of this varied manpower is a coordinated team in which skills from various disciplines complement one another. A physician is an essential member of the team.

The first requirement for effective counseling is to make an accurate, definitive diagnosis. Many clinical conditions closely resemble one another. Frequently similar phenotypic expressions have very different genetic causes, require different treatments, and have entirely different modes of transmission.

My recent experience with a genetically determined disease illustrates the importance of this principle. A baby boy was born in a local hospital. His appearance was unusual. He had tiny limbs and his head seemed too large for his body. When measured, his head was found to be of appropriate size. Because the rest of his body was too small, his head seemed relatively enlarged. This baby was clearly destined to be a dwarf. X rays were taken of his bones. There were marked skeletal changes indicating the problem involved the formation of cartilage at the ends of growing bones. While the doctors were pondering his appearance and the abnormalities of his X rays, the baby's paternal uncle, his father's brother, came to visit. He was a dwarf.

Virtually any disease is easier to recognize when it has achieved full phenotypic expression in an adult. The baby's uncle was clearly an achondroplastic dwarf. His was the classic form of short-limbed dwarfism that results from a defect in cartilaginous bony growth. A diagnosis of achondroplasia was made in the baby.

At this point the baby's doctors requested a genetic consultation from me. They had assumed that the mother, though perfectly normal in appearance, carried a gene for achondroplasia, as did the father, since his brother had the disease. This would fit the pattern of an autosomal recessive genotype that requires the inheritance of an abnormal recessive gene from each parent. I could tell them without seeing the baby that achondroplasia does not work that way. This disease results from the presence of a single dominant gene. It is fully penetrant. Transmission of achondroplasia requires a parent with the disease. Although cases arise from mutation, if the condition is inherited, it must be transmitted from an individual with the disease to his or her offspring. As a medical geneticist, I looked at the uncle. He definitely had achondroplasia. I looked at the father. He definitely was normal. I looked at the baby. He did look achondroplastic.

I seemed to have a problem on my hands. The obvious solution to the problem was that the baby's father in name was not really the father. Instead, the uncle was the father. Why else would he have been visiting the mother and baby in the first days after birth? It looked as though a family crisis was about to occur. The staff began to dream up ways of obtaining blood from the mother, the father, and the uncle in order to compare their blood types with that of the baby, thereby checking alternative possibilities for paternity.

They did not have to draw their samples. The answer was provided by careful examination of the X rays. The baby did not have achondroplasia. He had a rare and entirely different disorder known as spondyloepiphyseal dysplasia. This is a disorder of cartilage like achondroplasia but is readily distinguishable to a skilled diagnostician who knows the X-ray appearance of both conditions. This disorder is also caused by a dominant gene.

I was able to tell the family and the medical staff that this baby had a problem that arose through mutation. They could be given a picture of what he would look like in time. He would be dwarfed but ultimately very different in appearance from his uncle. The lesson is a good one. Genetics can be quite confusing if the right diagnosis is lacking. The wrong information can be much worse than no information at all. It can be very destructive.

Making a correct diagnosis is not always easy in patients with genetic disease. This is particularly true for individuals with rare malformations. Extensive experience with unusual disorders is required. The physician-geneticist is essential to any counseling team. Before counseling begins, there must be a careful clinical examination. The synthesis of the findings can be tough.

Genetic disease can involve all of the different parts and systems of the body. For this reason, the geneticist must be like a general practitioner. The physician-geneticist must also have a broad experience with unusual disorders that most general practitioners never see in a lifetime of practice. It requires a delicate balance of skills and experience.

The importance of recognizing the phenotype with real precision cannot be overemphasized. This means coming to the right diagnosis, which is critical to any kind of clinical medicine. The subtle shadings among patients with genetic disease require particular refinements. In one family it became gradually apparent that there was an inherited problem of mucopolysaccharide storage. As so often happens with late-onset diseases, the parents had three children before they realized anything was wrong with their first child. His features grew coarse. He developed bony abnormalities and a broad, clawlike deformity of the hand. Mental function began to decline. By the time he was diagnosed as having a storage disease, it was clear that his two younger brothers also had the disease.

This was a tragedy. It was compounded by the fact that the mother found herself pregnant for a fourth time. She took her children to a center where a diagnosis of the Hurler syndrome was made. This is an autosomal recessive disorder. An amniocentesis was arranged for the mother. When the fetal cells grew, it was evident that the fetus was a girl. The cells were studied for a form of staining that occurs characteristically in mucopolysaccharide storage disorders. Although this diagnostic method was beginning to be found unreliable, it was decided that since there were three involved children an abortion should be performed if the fetus could not be definitely diagnosed as normal. This is a rather common attitude among families with more than one child affected with a disease as serious as the Hurler syndrome. A therapeutic abortion was performed.

More recently this family came to San Diego. The boys were examined by Dr. John O'Brien. It was immediately obvious to him that they did not have the Hurler disorder. Their eyes were perfectly clear, which would not be the case if the boys had the Hurler syndrome. What they had was the Hunter syndrome. This disease is inherited as an X-linked condition. It occurs only in boys.

This mother became pregnant again. Amniocentesis was performed, and again the fetus was shown to be a girl. Dr. O'Brien reassured the parents that this baby could not possibly have the Hunter syndrome. Pregnancy was brought to term, and now this family has a normal, healthy little girl.

Many genetic conditions can now be diagnosed only by very specific, rather complicated laboratory procedures. Medical geneticists must have access to these procedures. It is ideal if they can call upon cytogenetic and biochemical assistance in their own laboratories or institutions. It is critical that they know what is available and where to go for it. Some procedures are done in only one or two institutions in the world. The truth is that these tests actually are available to everyone who needs them. Contact with the place carrying out these highly specialized tests can be made by any knowledgeable counseling team. Enlightened referral is terribly important. This in itself requires that the counselor be aware of recent advances and be knowledgeable about who is doing what and where. For the patient or the family, particularly those with a rare condition, the problem is to make contact with someone who can get them into this diagnostic and treatment system.

It may seem that medical geneticists function in ways that, except for the areas of special clinical experience, are not very different from those of any medical specialists. There is a real difference. It is found in the way medical geneticists look at a problem. They are concerned not simply with the diagnosis and treatment of an affected individual but with the implications for the children of future generations. They are concerned with other children of the parents, for offspring of the patient, and for relatives of every degree of affinity.

The importance of the physician-geneticist or the physician in the counseling process is apparent. How about the others in the counseling team? There is a need for everyone. Once a diagnosis is made and a genetic plan is established, the actual counseling should be done by the person who can do it best. Physicians have no corner on the market. The ability to interpret medical and genetic information is sometimes best left to people other than physicians. In a large team many different people may be involved in the actual counseling process. It is important that the genetic counselor understand all the facts, be able to answer questions thoroughly, and have an interest in the sensitivities of the communication process itself.

The most common question asked of the genetic counselor is "Will it happen again?" It is asked by the parents of a child with a genetic disease, a malformation, or a birth defect. Answers to this question depend on many factors.

In one of the most common situations the geneticist finds that the condition in the child is not of genetic origin. A number of nongenetic conditions may at first seem to be inherited. The malformed infant of a mother who had rubella, or German measles, during pregnancy may have a syndrome of mental retardation, cataracts, and congenital heart disease. Infants of mothers who took thalidomide during pregnancy had severe malformations of the limbs. If the counselor can determine that the infant's disease is not genetic, then he or she can be completely reassuring about future children.

Even when a condition is genetically determined, it does not necessarily mean that another child born to such parents is likely to bear the same defect. Many of the more common disorders, such as hare lip and cleft palate, which may be polygenic or multifactorial in inheritance, have very low risks of recurrence in a subsequent sibling. Many of them have risks ranging from 3 to 5 percent. Some are of the order of 1 percent.

If the diagnosis in a child is clear-cut and the child has a rare abnormal recessive disease with a risk for recurrence of 25 percent, each time the parents reproduce, the chance of offspring having the disease is one in four. This is a sizable risk. It means that the couple could have four children and each of them could be affected. They could also have four offspring who could all be normal. Both possibilities are consistent with a one-in-four risk in a sample of small size. In disease with this degree of risk at least one child is likely to inherit the disease condition.

Many parents confronted with a risk of this magnitude and a really severe disorder would elect not to reproduce further. What are the alternatives if they want more children? Adoption is the easiest. Artificial insemination is possible. The situation in which hereditary risk factors become apparent after marriage can easily lead to divorce. A serious disease in a child can bring a family together. It can just as often destroy it. This is as far as the genetic counselor can go in dealing with the usual autosomal recessive disease. The counselor can calculate the odds and carefully explain their implications. The decision is for the family to make.

Medical geneticists are often consulted by the sibling of a person with a genetic disease. Consultation might be with a man who has a brother with galactosemia and who has gotten married and come with his wife to ask about the advisability of having children. If all the counselor knew about him was what is known about most autosomal recessive conditions, counseling would work out as follows. The possibility he is a carrier is two in three. In an autosomal recessive mating there are four genotypic possibilities: one homozygous affected (aa), two heterozygous carriers (Aa), and one homozygous normal (AA). The first of these possibilities could be excluded for this individual because he is phenotypically normal. That leaves two other possibilities, two of which are for heterozygosity and one for homozygous normality. The gene frequency for galactosemia in the general population is about one in three hundred. If these two people were both heterozygotes, the odds of their having an affected child would be one in four. Putting this information together, the odds of an affected child in this union would be about one in eighteen hundred ($2/3 \times 1/300 \times 1/4$). That is a small risk, and most genetic counselors would be reassuring in such a situation, particularly since among the general population the risk for having some kind of genetic disease or malformation is about one in thirty.

Medical geneticists, however, can be more accurate in the case of galactosemia. The presence or absence of a particular enzyme in the blood will indicate whether or not a person is a carrier of the disease. A blood sample would be obtained from the man who sought counseling. It would be analyzed for the presence of the enzyme. If it turned out to be normal, the man could be reassured that he could not transmit his sibling's disease. If he were a carrier, his wife's blood would be tested. The chances are that she would be normal, and again the counselor would be reassuring. This couple would be told they should have no worries about galactosemia. If by rare chance she should also prove a carrier, they would be told about amniocentesis and prenatal diagnosis. If they wanted to have children, they would be advised to monitor each pregnancy by amniocentesis. In the case of a subsequent positive intrauterine diagnosis for this disease, they might choose to take their pregnancy to term. It would then be essential that the baby never ingest milk or milk products.

Genetic counselors can often perform an enormous service to their patients by filling the role of sympathetic physician, armed with precise information about genetic transmission. Couples may have had bitter personal experiences. They may have fears that they were somehow singled out for misfortune, or they may feel guilt that in some way they caused their child's handicap. These feelings may make it difficult for them to discuss their problems. It is important that they do discuss them. The role of the genetic counselor in the psychological support of the family is something that should not be underestimated. Serious disease brings misery and suffering. Genetically determined disease brings added burdens of guilt, taint, mystery, and repetition. A skilled and knowledgeable counselor can be the emotional mainstay for a family. It is important to evaluate the concerns of the family. They may be the same as those of the physician. They may be quite different.

The genetic counselor should provide the family with information about treatment. This might include some discussion of what treatments have been shown not to work. Once the diagnosis is really established, it is possible to have a meaningful discussion of the prognosis: what the future will bring and how optimal development can be promoted. In some conditions it is of interest to discuss the current direction of research. This might provide some hope in what may seem an otherwise hopeless situation. It provides an argument for staying abreast of current developments in research. Some parents of children with genetic disorders can find useful outlets working with volunteer agencies to promote advances in care and research.

Beverly Sills has been the chairman of the Mothers March for the National Foundation–March of Dimes. She is one of the opera stars of the century, with brilliant successes at La Scala, the Met, the Teatro Colón, and many others. She and her husband learned after their daughter was twenty months old that the girl had a profound deafness. Approximately six weeks later they were told their son was retarded and epileptic. Her first reaction was "Why me?" She then rephrased it, "Why them?" At first she and her husband sought advice in many medical centers. The question she kept asking the doctors was "Why?" The answer was always "I don't know." Her conviction in devoting her energies to the program of a voluntary health agency was that with support and with research more doctors will be able to answer the question "Why?" Better still, for more conditions they will be able to say, "Go ahead and have children. Our tests indicate they are going to be healthy." Genetic counseling has reached that stage for some conditions. For other conditions this advice may be a long way off.

There are many places to go for genetic counseling. The first place is to the family doctor, who may be able to solve the problem or may be able to make a referral to the best place for a particular problem. Physicians increasingly recognize the importance of referral to specialized genetic counseling centers.

Most medical centers and university teaching hospitals now have facilities for genetic diagnosis and counseling or can make an appropriate referral. Some of these institutions accept patients only if referred by a physician or other medical institution. Many now accept patients directly. In some areas, as in San Diego, the university's medical center sets up satellite clinics in local communities. Specialists from the center come to these clinics on a regular basis to see patients and families close to where they live. These services are sometimes available through the local department of health.

The National Genetics Foundation coordinates a network of forty-four institutions in the United States and Canada that provide the most sophisticated genetic counseling and access to the kinds of specialized testing discussed throughout this book. Entry into the network may be obtained by writing or calling the Foundation, 250 West 57th Street, New York, New York 10019. The telephone number is (212) 265-3166.

The National Foundation–March of Dimes maintains information on the availability of genetic services in an "International Directory of Genetic Services." It is available free on request to physicians and other medical professionals from the Professional Education Department, National Foundation–March of Dimes, P.O. Box 2000, White Plains, New York 10602.

The National Institute of General Medical Sciences (NIGMS) has a Genetic Centers program. This program funds highly complex research in genetics in a small number of institutions throughout the United States. A critical concentration of investigators and other specialists in genetics has been assembled in each center. They all offer genetic services as well as pursue research. Information on these centers and their locations may be obtained by writing to NIGMS, National Institutes of Health, Bethesda, Maryland 20014.

Similarly, the National Institute of Child Health and Human Development (NICHD) supports mental retardation centers. These are in most instances physical facilities. In each there is a program for research into the causes of mental retardation. In most of the centers clinical services for the retarded and their families are available. Information about mental retardation centers and their locations and programs may be obtained by writing NICHD, National Institutes of Health, Bethesda, Maryland 20014. The Health Services Administration (HSA) supports a number of University Affiliated Facilities devoted to a full range of services for the mentally retarded and their families. They also train health service professionals. Information about these facilities and their locations can be obtained by writing to HSA, Department of Health, Education and Welfare, Public Information Branch, Room 14A-55 Parklawn Building, 5600 Fisherslane, Rockville, Maryland 20852.

At last count there were 10 NIGMS genetics centers. The principal investigators of these centers provide communication points for those who might be interested in referrals. They are: Dr. Margery Shaw, University of Texas Graduate School of Biomedical Sciences and M. D. Anderson Hospital, Houston, Texas; Dr. J. E. Seegmiller, University of California San Diego, La Jolla, California; Dr. Arno G. Motulsky, University of Washington School of Medicine, Seattle, Washington; Dr. Charles J. Epstein, University of California San Francisco, San Francisco, California; Dr. Kurt Hirschhorn, Mount Sinai School of Medicine, City University of New York, New York, New York; Dr. Leon E. Rosenberg, Yale University School of Medicine, New Haven, Connecticut; Dr. Victor A. McKusick, The Johns Hopkins University Medical Institution, Baltimore, Maryland; Dr. Harold M. Nitowsky, Albert Einstein College of Medicine of Yeshiva University, Bronx, New York; Dr. William J. Mellman, University of Pennsylvania School of Medicine, Philadelphia, Pennsylvania; Dr. Walter Nance, Indiana University School of Medicine, Indianapolis, Indiana.

There are some other major centers in addition to this list, including that at Harvard Medical School, under Dr. Park Gerald. In the New York area there are also centers under Dr. Orlando J. Miller at Columbia University, Dr. James German of the New York Blood Center, Drs. Betty S. Danes and Alexander G. Bearn at Cornell, and Drs. Joseph Dancis and Selma Snyderman at New York University. On the West Coast there are other centers at Harbor General Hospital, Torrance, California, under Drs. Michael Kaback and David Rimoin; at Los Angeles Children's Hospital, under Dr. George Donnell; at Stanford University in Palo Alto, under Dr. Howard Cann; and at the University of Oregon Medical School in Portland, under Dr. Frederick Hecht. Major middle-western centers are those under Dr. John Opitz at the University of Wisconsin in Madison and under Dr. James Neel at the University of Michigan in Ann Arbor. The physician to communicate with for genetic services in Canada would be Dr. Charles Scriver, at McGill University in Montreal.

The following is a partial listing of genetics centers in Great Britain. In London: Clinical Genetics Unit, Institute of Child Health; P. E. Polani, Paediatric Research Unit, Guy's Hospital Medical School; James H. Renwick, London School of Hygiene and Tropical Medicine. Others include John H. Edwards, Department of Human Genetics, Maternity Hospital, Birmingham; J. Insley, Infant Development Unit, Maternity Hospital, Birmingham; Herman Lehmann, Department of Biochemistry, Medical Research Council, Cambridge; C. A. Clarke, Department of Medicine, University of Liverpool, Liverpool; A. C. Stevenson, Population Genetics Research Unit, Medical Research Council, Oxford. Also in Great Britain: Alan Emery, University Department of Human Genetics, Edinburgh, Scotland; Peter S. Harper, Department of Medicine, Section of Medical Genetics, University Hospital of Wales, Cardiff.

Families who go to any of these centers can expect that the results of all examinations and the content of counseling will be sent to their family physician or to any other physician they designate. Records are always kept. This information can be forwarded to new physicians at a later date. Follow-up is important, and new questions develop with time. I often send a letter to patients or families I counsel, outlining what has been said, so they do not have to rely on memory.

It is part of the counseling process to discuss the alternatives frankly and fully. Subjects like contraceptives and therapeutic abortion are clearly a function of genetic counseling. So is adoption. Whatever is discussed, every counselor recognizes that the ultimate decisions are those of the family. The counselor tries to help them come to the decision that is best for them.

20. Questions Often Asked

People seeking the advice of a genetic counselor have an enormous number and variety of questions. Some are unique, reflecting highly specific conditions and personal circumstances. Others are often asked. They tend to be common among people from all walks of life. A selected list of frequently asked questions is assembled here. Most have been often raised by actual people seeking genetic counsel. They by no means cover every topic.

Question: We have had a child with a genetic disease. He died very early in life. The doctors explained his was an autosomal condition and that the odds of having another child like him were one in four. Since we've already had one affected child, does this mean we can now expect to have three normal children?

Answer: Unfortunately, the answer is no. There is no such thing as memory where chance is concerned. Since you both carry an autosomal recessive gene, every child you produce has a one-in-four chance of having the same disease as your first child.

Question: What is the risk in any healthy, pregnant woman of bearing a child with a birth defect?

Answer: The risk is 3 percent or about one in thirty.

Question: My son's closest companion has sickle cell anemia. I've heard that it was passed on to him. Can my son catch it from him?

Answer: Sickle cell anemia is not contagious; it is inherited. As an autosomal recessive condition, a patient must have received a sickle cell gene from each of his parents. This is the way the disease is passed on.

Question: I've been told that I have the sickle cell trait. A doctor said something about a single dose of the disease. Could this get worse and lead to sickle cell anemia?

Answer: Can't happen. Sickle cell trait is another way of referring to the heterozygous carrier state. It means that you have one sickle cell gene and one normal gene. Only with two sickle cell genes does an individual get sickle cell anemia.

Question: My son has sickle cell trait. Should he be allowed to play football or basketball?

Answer: Yes. I discussed some of the issues of sickle cell trait and strenuous exercise in chapter 6. The best evidence is from the Olympics held in Mexico City, where nothing happened to athletes with the trait. Let your son live a completely normal life. He probably should avoid flying in unpressurized planes at altitudes above 10,000 feet. The information on the trait should be of interest to him only when he is planning his own family.

Question: My brother had cystic fibrosis. Is it likely that my children will have this disease?

Answer: No, it is not likely, but it is not out of the question either. You may be a carrier. Inasmuch as you do not have the disease and your brother did, your chances of being a carrier are two out of three. Still, in order for you to have a child with cystic fibrosis, you must marry someone who is also a carrier. Although most of the recessive genes that produce disease are rare ones, the gene for cystic fibrosis is common in Caucasian populations. So you could end up marrying a carrier. Even then, the risk would be one in four. If you put all these risk factors together, the likelihood of having children with cystic fibrosis isn't very great.

Question: Can I find out if I am a carrier of cystic fibrosis? Is there a possibility of prenatal diagnosis of this disease?

Answer: Unfortunately, there is no known way to do either of these things. It does seem likely that this situation will change with progress in research, but to date our understanding of the fundamental problem in cystic fibrosis is not sufficient to permit carrier detection or intrauterine diagnosis.

Question: How do I go about studying my family history and what should I look for?

Answer: The best way is to start with your siblings and your parents. Try to account for every birth. Draw a pedigree like those illustrated in this book. See who is alive and who is dead and, for the latter, what caused death. Are there any significant illnesses among the living? Are these diseases known to be genetic? Look them up; see if they're in this book. There are, of course, many others. Once you have had a look at the immediate family, see if you can take it back one generation. Account for the siblings and parents of your parents and for the children of these siblings. See how far back you can go.

Most of us are not sufficiently motivated to do this systematically. A shortcut is to be sure to talk to relatives. See if there are any family secrets, any skeletons in the closets, that could be genetic diseases.

If you're trying to track a particular disease that has appeared in your immediate family, the search is easier because it is targeted. Even so, it sometimes takes some detective work. Your doctor or genetic counselor can help you with this.

Question: What is the difference between genetic, hereditary, and familial disorders?

Answer: There is no difference. These terms are all synonyms in most usage. It is possible for a disease to be familial, that is, to occur in a family, in two consecutive siblings, for example, and yet not be genetic, but it is extraordinarily unlikely. I am not talking about acute contagious diseases, of course.

Question: Why do some religious or racial groups have special genetic diseases, such as sickle cell disease in blacks, Tay-Sachs disease in Jews, thalassemia in Italians and Greeks?

Answer: Segregation of genes is the rule rather than the exception. Most of the genetic diseases arose one day through mutation. It is easy to see how a mutation arising in a closely knit population, in which there is little breeding with individuals outside the group, tends to stay in that population. Thus we suspect that the Tay-Sachs mutation started among Ashkenazim in the ghettos of Europe. It essentially stayed there, as these people tended to marry and reproduce among themselves. So it is with any of the recessive diseases in any given ethnic group. Phenylketonuria is extraordinarily rare among the Jewish populations who have Tay-Sachs disease. It is instead common among the Irish. So is homocystinuria. And so it goes.

Question: What effects do drugs like marijuana and LSD or medicines like tranquilizers, antibiotics, or even aspirin have on the baby if they are taken by the mother during pregnancy?

Answer: This subject is considered more fully in chapter 15. Geneticists know that it is possible to produce congenital malformations, or birth defects, by using drugs. The best-known example is thalidomide. Many drugs, including aspirin, can be shown, under certain circumstances and in some doses, to produce anomalies in experimental animals. There is not much evidence that any of these drugs taken in normal dosages causes malformations in people. The question of LSD is still unresolved. The evidence is conflicting. The best rule is to take nothing during pregnancy that you do not absolutely have to take.

Question: Should you get your genes checked before you get married or have a baby?

Answer: There may come a time when everyone visits a geneticist before beginning a family. That's a long way off. I would advise checking under specific circumstances. If there are chromosomal abnormalities in your immediate family, especially one or more siblings with the Down syndrome, you could have a translocation chromosome. If you have a sibling with an autosomal recessive gene, it may be possible to find out if you carry the gene. If you are Jewish, it makes sense today to check for the Tay-Sachs gene. If you are black, it pays to check for sickle cell gene. There may be other situations. When in doubt, it is better to check.

Question: What happens if you marry a relative?

Answer: I've dealt with this question in some detail in chapter 5. The heart of the problem is the frequency with which people carry abnormal, rare, recessive genes. Under ordinary conditions of random mating, the chance of marrying someone else who carries one of these genes is fairly remote. But inbreeding multiplies the chances that both partners will carry the same defective genes. I have seen first-cousin marriages in which more than one unusual recessive disease affected the children. It is even possible to have more than one of these diseases in the same child.

Question: Do hereditary diseases skip generations?

Answer: Sure. This often happens in the case of an X-linked problem in which an involved father cannot transmit the disease to his sons but transmits carrier status to each of his daughters. There is nobody in that generation who has the disease. In the next generation the daughters will begin to have some affected sons. Dominant diseases may also skip a generation, or appear to, if the penetrance of the disease is variable. A person may carry the gene and even have some hidden manifestation of it without ever knowing about it.

Question: My doctor tells me that I have Waardenberg's syndrome and that it is caused by a dominant gene. It must be pretty mild in me. I have a white forelock but nothing else. I realize that some people with this syndrome may have serious deafness, but I wonder if I transmit the gene to a child will he be like me or will he have another form of this condition?

Answer: There is no predicting. In any family in which there is a dominant disease with a variable expression, there may be a whole range of variations. A parent can be very mildly affected, a child very severely, and vice versa.

Question: My father had Huntington's chorea. It began when he was thirty-two and he died at fifty-seven. I feel fine but I am only twenty-three. When will I know if I have inherited this disease?

Answer: The chances are that the disease will appear at about the same age, generation after generation, in your family. A careful neurological examination might reveal it at thirty. If you or a sibling get to be fifty without any signs of this disorder and your neurological examination is normal, the chances are that you can relax.

Question: My wife and I just had a dwarfed baby. We were told by the pediatrician that he has achondroplasia. I am thirty-eight, and my wife is thirty-six. We have three other children, and they are normal. What is the risk of our having another dwarf?

Answer: The fact that you and your wife are normal means that the dwarfed child represents a new mutation. The risk of your having another baby with this disease is negligible. However, new mutations are often associated with increased age of the father, and thirty-eight is old in this context. A subsequent child could have a different dominant mutation. The dwarfed baby, of course, carries an autosomal dominant gene. This means that the risk of that child's children being dwarfs is much higher: 50 percent, or one in two.

Question: My husband and I have a child who the pediatrician told us has achondroplastic dwarfism and clubbed feet. He told us that the risk of having another child like him was negligible, but we had another, and sure enough, she has the same thing as her older brother. What went wrong?

Answer: After examining your children and their X rays, I can tell you they do not have achondroplasia. Instead they have a genetic disorder that is known as diastrophic dwarfism. This disease is transmitted as an autosomal recessive. The risk of occurrence in every new pregnancy is one in four.

Question: If my doctor doesn't seem to be sure whether or not a disease is hereditary, gives me an answer that doesn't sound right, or is evasive, where can I get more information?

Answer: I have listed some approaches to this in chapter 19. It is unfortunately true that knowledge of genetics, and especially of rare diseases, is not widespread, even among physicians. So it is really important for you to get the best help you can find. I've heard of families in which there was a rare disease, who were told, "This disease is one in a million. It can't happen again." Well, it was one in a million in that doctor's practice, but in that family it was a recessive gene, and each subsequent child had a 25 percent risk of having the disease. A family in which a parent had neurofibromatosis was told, "Your kids will never get it; it's so rare." Neurofibromatosis is a dominantly inherited disease, so the risk for each child is 50 percent. Similarly I know of families told, "Lightning doesn't strike twice in the same place." It often does strike twice, and even more often in the case of a hereditary disease.

I recently saw a five-month-old baby in consultation whose family illustrated an interesting and not too unusual genetic story. The parents had had a baby about a year and a half before I met with them. The baby seemed well at birth, but he was observed to become weak and floppy. His parents could not find a definitive diagnosis in their home town. They traveled thousands of miles to a medical center where the baby was studied carefully. Electrical tests of the muscle and even a biopsy were performed, but the results were inconclusive. The parents were advised that no precise diagnosis could be made but that the baby was very sick. It was suggested that they try to have another child as soon as possible. When they got home, the baby began to have problems with breathing. A few weeks later he was dead.

The parents did follow the advice, and about nine months later another boy was born. The parents noted right away that he could not lift his head when placed in the prone position on his abdomen. They besieged their pediatrician, since they were so worried about floppiness. They were reassured that they were simply overanxious because of their experience with the previous baby. They brought him twice a month for examination. After three months he still had no head control and he was formally diagnosed as abnormal. Meanwhile, his intellectual development appeared to be progressing nicely. When I saw him, it was clear that he had almost no muscle tone. He had no reflexes at all.

There were tremors of the tongue. He was a typical example of the Werdnig-Hoffman disease. Electromyography confirmed the diagnosis.

This disease is like poliomyelitis in the sense that it involves the nerves that control the muscles. But it involves all of them, and it is not due to a virus. It is genetic. The gene is an autosomal recessive one. If these parents have another pregnancy, the risk is again one in four. I certainly did not advise them to try again.

Question: Is cancer hereditary? How about leukemia?

Answer: Some forms of cancer are hereditary, but not many. Retinoblastoma, a highly malignant disease of the eye, is clearly genetic. It is transmitted as a dominant condition. Furthermore, when a parent who has a retinoblastoma in one eye has children, there is an increased likelihood that involved children will have the disease in both eyes. At the same time it is true that penetrance is highly variable in this disease, and recurrence risks are less than those predicted by Mendelian ratios.

Leukemia was once thought to be hereditary. One reason was its high incidence among individuals with the Down syndrome. It is much more likely that the patient with the Down syndrome contracts leukemia more readily than normal individuals because of a decreased resistance to disease. This may be the reason that cancers sometimes seem to have a high incidence in a family. These occurrences in family units provide evidence for an infectious, rather than genetic, origin of cancers. If this is true, genetic factors would certainly seem involved in susceptibility.

Question: Is mongolism inherited?

Answer: Geneticists prefer to call it the Down syndrome. It has been discussed in considerable detail in chapter 8. The condition results from an extra chromosome 21. This can arise in a germ cell of the mother or father or in the developing embryo. Most often it occurs in the child of an older mother. The clearest examples of inheritance of the Down syndrome occur when a parent has a translocation involving chromosome 21.

Question: A mother had a child with the Down syndrome when she was in her twenties. The baby died and chromosome studies were not done. Then she had three children who were normal. They are now about to have children of their own. Should they worry about the Down syndrome?

Answer: They should have their chromosomes studied. A family history like this one could mean that the mother had a translocation chromosome. Her normal children could also have translocations, or they could have normal chromosomes. If they also have the translocation, their children may have the Down syndrome. A simple cytogenetic study will answer all of these questions.

Question: How dangerous is it to have amniocentesis done?

Answer: Amniocentesis done early in pregnancy, as it must be for genetic diagnosis, appears to carry no risk for the mother or baby. There are some potential risks, and this issue has been subjected to a nationwide study under a contract from the National Institute for Child Health and Human Development. The answers of this exhaustive study indicate amniocentesis is a safe procedure.

Question: Should every older mother, that is, over thirty-five, have amniocentesis if she gets pregnant?

Answer: I believe she should. The risk of chromosomal abnormality in pregnancies at that age and later has been discussed in chapter 8. Of course, this implies a readiness to undergo therapeutic abortion in instances of positive diagnosis of a defective fetus. I recognize that some people's beliefs will not permit this. In those cases I would not recommend amniocentesis.

Question: How much does amniocentesis cost? How much does it cost to have a karyotype done?

Answer: The cost varies with the center and with the study to be done on the cells once they have grown in culture. For the amniocentesis itself, the usual fee ranges from $100 to $125. A karyotype of blood or of amniotic fluid cells usually costs about $100. In many centers it can be obtained for nothing because the work is supported by some publicly funded program. Today most enzyme tests for prenatal diagnosis are obtainable free or for a token fee.

Question: Does diabetes run in families?

Answer: It does, but the genetics are complicated. It is probable that many factors both genetic and nongenetic influence whether a susceptible individual will get diabetes. The incidence in any family is much less than Mendelian ratios would suggest. It is also true that the genetic factor is clearer in diabetes that begins in childhood. This is probably a different disease genetically from diabetes that begins after forty. In childhood-onset diabetes, the recurrence risk, that is, the risk of involvement of a subsequent brother or sister, is about one in twenty.

Question: I am the mother of a boy with muscular dystrophy. What does this mean about my having other children?

Answer: Muscular dystrophy is inherited. It is important to understand that there are many different forms of muscular dystrophy. The mode of inheritance may be quite different, depending on the type. Therefore, this is one of those diseases in which the genetic counselor must have the most specific of diagnostic information. The most common form of muscular dystrophy is X-linked. In this disease it is sometimes possible to tell if a mother carries the gene by testing her blood and that of her son. Diseases carried on the X chromosome have a high risk (50 percent) for involvement of subsequent sons. So it is important to be sure.

Question: My baby has congenital heart disease. The doctor diagnosed it as a transposition of the great vessels. What is the risk of my having another baby with this problem?

Answer: Congenital heart disease is usually multifactorial. Transposition of the great vessels is very rare. There is a slightly increased risk that you might have another child with the disease, but it is really very low. The overall risk of birth defect in any pregnancy in any woman is higher than that. Thus, the risk of recurrence is negligible.

Question: My father was born without one thumb, and he has a heart murmur. I just had a baby who lacks one thumb as well as one of the bones in his forearm, and he also has congenital heart disease. What are the chances of having another child like this one?

Answer: You have a genetic disease in which thumb anomalies and congenital cardiac malformations go together. It is called the Holt-Oram syndrome. This disorder is transmitted as an autosomal dominant. So the risk of recurrence is one in two, or 50 percent, in each pregnancy.

Question: I have a brother who has hemophilia. My wife and I are worried about having children. My maternal uncle has hemophilia too. What are the chances of our children having the disease?

Answer: Hemophilia is a genetic disorder that is carried on the X chromosome (chapter 10). You do not have hemophilia, and therefore you must have a normal X chromosome. There is no chance that you could transmit hemophilia to your children.

Question: My brother has hemophilia. He is the only one in the family with the disease. I have no other brothers or sisters. My husband and I want to know what might happen if we have children.

Answer: If your mother is a carrier for the hemophilia gene, your chances of also being a carrier are one in two. If you are indeed a carrier, the chances that your male children will have the disease are one in two.

Question: We had a baby with anencephaly who died a few days after birth. We would like to have other children. What is the possibility of our having another baby like this?

Answer: Defects in the closure of the nervous system are at least partly genetic. In assessing risk it is necessary to tie anencephaly with lower spinal defects, the meningomyelocoeles. A family in which there has been an anencephaly may later have a meningomyelocoele, and vice versa. Taken together, the risk of recurrence is about ten times that of incidence in the general population. Still, the risk is not high. In most parts of the world it is about 1 or 2 percent. In South Wales it is about 4 percent. After two such children with either disease are born into a family, the risk jumps from 1 to 8 percent.

In a family at risk it should be possible to diagnose anencephaly prenatally. This can be done simply, using ultrasound. It is also possible to see a defect using amniography, in which a dye is injected into the amniotic fluid in order to outline the fetus for examination by X ray. There is a possibility that the study of alpha-fetoprotein may help with this diagnosis. This protein should be present in much higher amounts in the amniotic fluid surrounding this type of fetus.

Question: We so want to have children of our own, and we do not mind risking the possibility of another anencephalic infant. But is there a possibility that we might have a baby with a milder abnormality of brain development and end up with a severely retarded child?

Answer: Anyone, of course, may have a retarded child, as the causes of mental retardation are common, but this is not one of them. There is nothing about having an anencephalic baby that should cause worry about brain development in subsequent children. Remember, though, that meningomyelocoele is common in subsequent pregnancies of a family who has had an anencephalic infant.

Question: Our first child had a cleft of the lip and palate. It has been repaired nicely, and she is a lovely child. What should we think about future children?

Answer: Clefts are partly determined by genetic factors. It is likely that there are a number of involved genes and other factors that produce the condition. If neither parent was born with a cleft, the risk of having a cleft in a subsequent sibling, after the birth of a child with a cleft of lip or palate, is 4 percent. If a parent and a child are affected, the risk for subsequent siblings is 12 percent. These figures mean that in most families in which the first cleft appears out of the blue in one offspring, the chances of having another child with a cleft are significantly greater than in the general population. But numerically the chances of this happening again are rather small.

Genetic Diseases

A Chart of Some of the More Common and Important Conditions

Name of Disease	Synonyms or Scientific Name	Mode of Transmission*	Ethnic or Other Factors of Occurrence	Prenatal Detection Possible?	Carrier Detection Possible?
Achondroplasia		D		No	No
Adrenogenital syndrome	Pseudohermaphroditism	R		No	No
Agammaglobulinemia		X		No	No
Albinism		R	Common in some isolated populations, e.g., San Blas Indians, some Indians of southwestern U.S.	No	No
Alkaptonuria		R		No	No
Anencephaly		M	South Wales	Yes	No
Argininemia		R		Yes	Yes
Argininosuccinic aciduria		R		Yes	Yes
Brachydactyly		D		No	No
Cardiac glycogenosis		R		Yes	Yes
Cataract	Many different forms, e.g., see Galactokinase deficiency	D, R, X		No	No
Chromosomal abnormalities	Trisomies; translocations; deletions	C		Yes	Sometimes
Cleft lip and/or cleft palate	Hare lip	M		No	No
Color blindness		X		No	No
Cri-du-chat syndrome	Cat cry syndrome	C		Yes	Sometimes

Cystic fibrosis	Cystic fibrosis of the pancreas	R	Caucasians (1 in 3,700)	No	No
Cystinosis	Fanconi syndrome	R		Yes	Yes
Cystinuria		R		No	Some types
Diabetes	Diabetes mellitus	M	Common in American Indians	No	No
Diastrophic dwarfism		R		No	No
Down syndrome	Trisomy 21	C		Yes	No
	Translocation 21	C		Yes	Yes
Drug-sensitive hemolytic anemia	Glucose-6-phosphate dehydrogenase deficiency	X	Blacks	Yes	Yes
Fabry disease	Angiokeratoma corporis diffusion	X		Yes	Yes
Favism	Glucose-6-phosphate dehydrogenase deficiency	X	Mediterranean peoples	Yes	Yes
Galactokinase deficiency		R		Yes	Yes
Galactosemia		R		Yes	Yes
Gangliosidosis		R		Yes	Yes
Gaucher disease		R		Yes	Yes
Gout	Many forms	R, X		No	Rarely
Hemolytic (spherocytic) anemia	Spherocytosis	D		No	No

This is of necessity a partial listing. McKusick's latest edition of *Mendelian Inheritance in Man* (Baltimore: The Johns Hopkins Press, 1975) lists some 31,500 autosomal dominant, autosomal recessive, and X-linked phenotypes.

*Mode of Transmission:
- C Chromosomal (Cytogenetic)
- D Autosomal dominant
- M Multifactorial
- R Autosomal recessive
- X X-linked

Name of Disease	Synonyms or Scientific Name	Mode of Transmission*	Ethnic or Other Factors of Occurrence	Prenatal Detection Possible?	Carrier Detection Possible?
Hemophilia	Factor VIII deficiency	X		No	Yes
Holt-Oram syndrome		D		No	No
Homocystinuria		R		Yes	Yes
Hunter syndrome	Mucopolysaccharidosis, gargoylism	X		Yes	Yes
Huntington's chorea		D		No	No
Hurler syndrome	Mucopolysaccharidosis, gargoylism	R		Yes	Yes
Hypothyroidism	Cretinism	M,R, nongenetic		No	No
Joseph Family disease	Striato-nigral degeneration	D		No	No
Klinefelter syndrome	XXY	C		Yes	Yes
Lesch-Nyhan syndrome		X		Yes	Yes
Maple syrup urine disease		R		Yes	Yes
Marfan syndrome	Arachnodactyly	D		No	No
Metachromatic leukodystrophy		R		Yes	Yes
Muscular dystrophy	Duchenne type	X		No	Sometimes
	Fascioscapulohumeral types	D, R		No	No
	Distal type	D		No	No
Neurofibromatosis	Von Recklinghausen's disease	D		No	No
Niemann-Pick disease		R		Yes	Yes
Orotic aciduria		R		Yes	Yes
Osteogenesis imperfecta congenita		D, R		No	No

Osteogenesis imperfecta congenita tarda (usual form)		D		No	No
Phenylketonuria	PKU	R		No	Often
Pituitary dwarfism	Hypopituitarism	R		No	No
Polydactyly	Many forms	D		No	No
Porphyria	Usual forms	D		No	No
Pyloric stenosis		M		No	No
Retinoblastoma		D		No	No
Rubella syndrome	Maternal German measles	Nongenetic		No	No
Sickle cell anemia		R	Blacks	Yes	Yes
Spina bifida and meningomyelocoele		M		Yes	No
Spinocerebellar degeneration	Ataxia	D		No	No
Spondyloepiphyseal dysplasia		D		No	No
Striato-nigral degeneration	Joseph Family disease	D		No	No
Tay-Sachs disease		R	Ashkenazic Jews	Yes	Yes
Thalassemia	Cooley's anemia	R	Italians and Greeks	Yes	Often
Turner syndrome	XO	C		Yes	No
Vitamin D resistant rickets	Hypophosphatemia	X		No	Yes
Waardenberg syndrome		D		No	No
Werdnig-Hoffman disease		R		No	No
Wilson disease		R		No	Sometimes
Wiscott-Aldrich syndrome		X		No	No
YY syndrome		C		Yes	No

*Mode of Transmission:
C Chromosomal (Cytogenetic)
D Autosomal dominant
M Multifactorial
R Autosomal recessive
X X-linked

Glossary of Medical and Technical Terms

Achondroplasia A form of inherited dwarfism that is transmitted as an autosomal dominant condition.

Adenine One of two purine nitrogen base molecules found in DNA and RNA.

Adrenocorticotropic hormone (ACTH) A pituitary hormone. In the adrenogenital syndrome it increases because of the absence of cortisol. This causes the adrenal glands to enlarge abnormally and produce excessive amounts of a number of hormones.

Adrenogenital syndrome An autosomal recessive condition in which the steroid hormone cortisol cannot be synthesized by the adrenal gland. Its most striking feature is masculinization of the female fetus.

Agammaglobulinemia An X-linked recessive disease in which there is an absence of gamma globulin, an immunological protein important to the body's defense against infection.

Albinism An autosomal recessive disorder characterized by a lack of pigmentation producing milk-white skin, fine white hair, and pink eyes.

Alkaptonuria A genetic condition caused by a recessive gene. Lack of the gene results in faulty metabolism of homogentisic acid in the liver. Presence of this molecule causes the urine to turn black on contact with air.

Alleles Alternative forms of a gene governing the same trait; for example, the A, B, and O blood types result from alternative genes, or alleles, for specific blood proteins.

Allopurinol A drug used to treat gout. It blocks the action of xanthine oxidase, an enzyme needed for the formation of uric acid.

Alpha-fetoprotein A normal fetal protein. It is found in concentrated forms in the amniotic fluid of a developing anencephalic fetus.

Amino acid All proteins and polypeptides are composed of amino acids. Twenty-four different kinds of amino acids in varying number and sequence make up the structure of the usual protein.

Amniocentesis A technique in which cells and fluid are extracted from the amnion surrounding the developing fetus in the uterus. The amniotic fluid contains cells that wash off the skin of the fetus. These cells can be grown in tissue culture to monitor the health of the fetus. The technique has proved safe for both mother and fetus.

Amniogram A prenatal detection technique in which a small amount of dye is injected into the uterus to reveal the outline of the developing fetus.

Amnioscope A long, slender needle that can be inserted into the uterus for the purpose of obtaining a prenatal sample of fetal blood and of visualizing the fetus.

Anaphylaxis A rapid and dramatic allergic reaction to a foreign protein that has penetrated the body's exterior defenses.

Androgens A general term for the various male hormones.

Anencephaly A multifactorial condition the cause of which is at least partially genetic. An infant with this condition is born with little or no brain or skull.

Angiokeratomas Skin lesions of a dark red color that do not whiten under pressure. They are typically found distributed over the hips and buttocks of individuals with the Fabry disease.

Antibody Any of a group of molecules in the body that act antagonistically to foreign molecules, or antigens.

Antigen Any molecule, usually a protein, that stimulates the body's immunological system to form an antibody.

Arginase The enzyme that breaks down arginine.

Arginine One of the amino acids found in body fluids. Its excessive accumulation in the body is noted in individuals with argininemia.

Argininemia An autosomal recessive disorder characterized by high levels of arginine in the blood. The disorder results from a defect in the enzyme arginase. The defect interferes with the urea cycle and causes excessive accumulation of ammonia which may lead to episodes of coma and ultimately to mental retardation.

Argininosuccinic aciduria An autosomal recessive condition that results from a defect in the enzyme argininosuccinase. This produces a disorder in the urea cycle and eventually leads to increased concentrations of ammonia and periods of coma and mental retardation.

Ascites Fluid in the abdomen.

ASG method A banding technique for the identification and characterization of chromosomes by exposing them to an acid, a salt solution, and Giemsa stain.

Asparaginase An enzyme, normally extracted from bacteria. It is used in the initial treatment of children with leukemia.

Assay The chemical analysis of a substance.

Assortative mating Selective mating in which the choice of a marriage partner is not entirely random. Selection factors may be physical, social, psychological, or geographical. The limitation of randomness or isolation of genetic subgroups tends to produce gene frequencies at variance with those of the general population. Abnormal genes tend to express themselves at a higher frequency in such subgroups.

Aster The source of a cell's spindle fibers, which, as they contract, separate two chromatids during meiotic or mitotic metaphase.

Atabrine The drug name for quinacrine, a molecule that enters into intimate association with DNA. Because of its fluorescent staining properties, it will reveal those portions of chromosomal DNA as bright fluorescent bands in the presence of ultraviolet light.

"At risk" pregnancy Any pregnancy in which there is a possibility of transmitting a genetic disease.

Autoimmune anemia Anemia produced by the body's own immunological system which fails to recognize its own blood cell proteins and responds to them as if they were foreign antigens.

Autoradiography A detection technique in which the presence of a radioactive marker is revealed by its action on photographic film, much as X rays produce pictures. In cytogenetics, radioactive thymidine is employed to identify chromosomes.

Autosomal dominant disease A disorder caused by the presence of a single autosomal dominant gene, an abnormal factor located on any chromosome other than the sex chromosomes.

Autosomal recessive disease A genetic disorder in which an abnormal recessive allele is inherited from each parent. The disorder manifests itself only when the two recessive alleles are present. It is said to be "autosomal" because the genes for these traits are carried by chromosomes other than the sex chromosomes.

Autosomal recessive gene A gene for a trait whose expression is masked, or hidden, in the presence of a dominant allele for the same trait.

Autosome Any chromosome other than the sex chromosomes.

Bacterial transduction The process in which viral DNA hybridizes with the DNA of the host bacterium.

Bacterial transformation The introduction and integration of exogenous, or foreign, DNA into the nucleus of a bacterium.

Bacteriophage A virus that parasitizes a bacterial cell.

Balanced polymorphism Phenomenon in which homozygous recessive individuals for a particular disease tend to be eliminated from a population prior to reproduction, while the heterozygous carriers of the disorder are provided with a selective advantage over those who do not possess the gene. A balanced polymorphism explains the continued frequency of the sickle cell anemia gene in African populations. Although the homozygous recessive condition tends to be lethal before twenty years of age, possession of a single sickle cell gene confers resistance to malaria.

Barr body A mass of chromatin that appears as a dark spot near the edge of the nuclei of the cells of females. It is now explained as the second X chromosome, which is inactivated early in fetal life. The presence or absence of the Barr body can be used in sex determination.

Beta-2-thienylalanine A molecule that competes with the phenylalanine molecule. It is used in the Guthrie test for phenylketonuria (PKU) to determine the amount of phenylalanine present in the blood of the newborn infant.

Biopsy A small sample of tissue removed from the body for examination.

Brachydactyly An autosomal dominant genetic condition phenotypically expressed in shortened fingers.

Breech birth Birth in which a baby makes its entry into the world feet or bottom first.

British anti-lewisite (BAL) A drug originally used as an antidote for arsenic or copper poisoning; more recently used to treat patients with the Wilson disease.

Carcinogen Any chemical or physical agent that is capable of transforming normal cells into cancerous, or malignant cells. Cigarette smoke is a human carcinogen.

Carcinogenesis A process in which normal cells are transformed into malignant cells.

Cardiac glycogenosis An autosomal recessive disorder that results in the accumulation of glycogen in heart muscle leading to heart failure.

Centromere The portion of the chromosome, usually a central constriction, at which replicated chromatids and the spindle fibers are attached.

Ceramide trihexosidase The enzyme required for conversion of the GL_3 lipid into the GL_2 lipid; absence of this enzyme results in the accumulation of the GL_3 lipid associated with the Fabry disease. The gene for this enzyme is inherited on the X chromosome.

Ceruloplasmin A normal blood protein that is thought to transport copper. *See* Wilson disease.

Chimera An individual in whom there are two genetically different cell populations.

Choreoathetosis A movement disorder that takes the form of uncontrollable spasms of the arms and legs. It is a feature of the Lesch-Nyhan syndrome.

Chromatids An original chromosome and its duplicate; both remain attached by a common centromere. Once cleavage of the centromere has occurred during metaphase, the two independent chromatids are called chromosomes.

Chromatin All of the hereditary, chromosomal material found in the nucleus of a cell.

Chromosome A threadlike body composed of linked DNA nucleotides, or genes, separated by protein segments.

Clone Two or more cells mitotically descended from a single cell. All of the cells in a clone have the same genetic material or genotype. They are exact copies of one another.

Cloning In its simplest form, the mitotic production of many cells with the same DNA. A bacterial colony or tissue culture is produced by simple cloning. In more complex form, cloning involves the production of multiceullular organs with the same genotype. This process occurs naturally in the creation of identical twins.

Colchicine A chemical obtained from the meadow saffron that arrests cell division.

Consanguinity Intermarriage within a family.

Corpus-striatum Nerve tissue deep within the brain. It is responsible for coordination and modulation of muscle movements.

Cortisone A steroid hormone that may act as an environmental stimulus in the multifactorial causation of cleft lip and palate in certain strains of mice.

Cri-du-chat syndrome From the French for the meowing cry of a cat. This is a disorder that produces severe mental retardation. It is caused by deletion of the short arm of chromosome number 5.

"Crisis" Experience of an acute attack, usually of pain. Crises with severe attacks of pains are frequent in such inherited diseases as sickle cell anemia and the Fabry disease.

Crossing-over The exchange of linked genes between two members of a chromosome pair. A piece from one chromosome is exchanged for that piece of its complementary chromosome.

Cyanate A drug that has been used in the treatment of patients with sickle cell anemia.

Cystic fibrosis An autosomal recessive disease that affects the body's exocrine glands; clinical disease is particularly evident in the pancreas and the lungs.

Cystine One of the amino acids. It is excreted in excessive quantities in patients with cystinuria.

Cystinosis An autosomal recessive disease of metabolism in which the amino acid cystine accumulates in body tissues.

Cystinuria A disorder of kidney function in which cystine is excreted in excessive amounts, and large crystals of cystine form stones in the urinary tract.

Cytogenetics The study of chromosomes.

Cytomegalovirus A viral agent that resembles a teratogen. It produces abnormally large cells. Although innocuous in adults, it can produce devastating birth defects.

Cytoplasm That part of the cell located outside the nucleus and inside the cell membrane.

Cytosine One of the two pyrimidine nitrogen base molecules in DNA and RNA.

Densitometer An instrument used in chromosomal analysis to trace the various degrees of staining from one end of the chromosome to the other.

Deoxyribonucleic acid (DNA) The basic genetic material. Its molecular structure determines the replication of the genetic code and governs the formation of proteins. X-ray crystallography has demonstrated that DNA has a helical structure comprising two complementary chains of nucleotides coiled around a common axis.

Diabetes (mellitus) A multifactorial disorder of carbohydrate metabolism characterized by inadequate secretion of insulin. This results in excessive amounts of sugar in the blood and urine.

Diastrophic dwarfism A genetic disorder caused by an autosomal recessive gene. It is characterized by dwarfism and clubbed feet.

Diethylstilbestrol (DES) A synthetic hormone that has been given during pregnancy to prevent spontaneous abortion. It is thought to act as a teratogen in that it can produce vaginal cancer in the female offspring.

Di George syndrome A disorder characterized by convulsive seizures and a low concentration of calcium as well as a profound defect in immune mechanisms. It results from the absence of both the thymus and parathyroid glands.

Diploid cell Any cell containing two full sets of chromosomes. This is the normal chromosomal condition for all human somatic, or body, cells. One full set of chromosomes has been provided by the female parent and a second full set by the male parent.

Dominance The tendency of many genes to overpower the expressive capacity of alternative genes, or DNA sequences, governing the same trait. A child inheriting a dominant gene for brown eyes and a gene for blue eyes will have brown eyes.

Dominant gene A DNA sequence whose expression prevails over those of alternative alleles for a given trait.

Down syndrome A chromosomal disorder resulting from the presence of an extra autosome, one member of chromosome pair 21. It can result from nondisjunction or translocation. The disorder was once referred to as mongolism.

Drosophila The fruit fly, an important organism used in genetic research. It is a convenient laboratory animal because of its ability to reproduce rapidly and in large numbers.

Dual system immunological deficiency The absence of both thymus-derived cellular immunity and the plasma cell antibody or immunoglobin immunity.

E. coli (Escherichia coli) A bacillus normally found in the human large intestine, where it has positive, or symbiotic, relationship with the host organism. It is an organism of considerable interest for its possible use in genetic engineering.

Electrophoresis A method for separating large molecules according to their rate of migration through a medium such as gel or wet filter paper in an electrical field.

Enzyme A protein molecule synthesized according to instructions from the DNA code. Enzymes control the rate of all metabolic processes within the body.

Expressivity The degree to which the effect of a gene is manifested within an individual. In genetic disease, two individuals may possess the same gene for a disorder but be affected to a differing degree in the severity of symptoms. This is referred to as variable expressivity.

Fabry disease An X-linked disorder which results from the absence or defect of the enzyme ceramide trihexosidase which normally breaks down a large fatty molecule. Absence of this enzyme leads to severe circulatory disorders, as excessive amounts of fatty material are deposited in the blood vessels.

Factor VIII A blood protein essential for blood clotting. Individuals with hemophilia are unable to produce this substance.

Favism An X-linked genetic disorder common among Mediterranean populations. It is caused by a deficiency of the enzyme G6PD and results in anemia due to rapid destruction of red blood cells, particularly after consuming uncooked fava beans.

Fibroblasts Connective tissue cells. They grow well in tissue culture.

Fluorescent chromosomes Chromosomes treated with quinacrine or quinacrine mustard that show brightly banded patterns indicating the location of DNA when exposed to ultraviolet light.

"Founder effect" Observed in disorders common to a particular group. First appearance of the disease can be traced to one or a handful of founder fathers and mothers carrying an unusual gene.

Galactokinase deficiency An autosomal recessive condition resulting from the absence of or defect in the galactokinase enzyme. Affected patients have cataracts.

Galactosemia An autosomal recessive disease resulting from a deficiency of the enzyme galactose-uridyltransferase. Affected patients have cataracts and severe liver disease leading to early death. Simple dietary avoidance of milk and its products is effective treatment.

Gamete The mature egg or sperm cell, which before fertilization contains 23 chromosomes, or half the genetic material of the normal diploid individual.

Gangliosidosis A disorder of the metabolism of glycolipid molecules found in the nervous system. The disease is a degenerative one similar to Tay-Sachs disease.

Gaucher disease Degenerative disease of the nervous system in which cells are loaded with cerebroside, another lipid molecule. It is an autosomal recessive condition whose symptoms include enlargement of the spleen.

Gene A portion of the DNA molecule that specifically controls the expression of a given trait. The smallest genes are specific for particular amino acids and contain only three nucleotides. The gene for a protein composed of three hundred amino acids contains nine hundred DNA nucleotides in specific sequence.

Genetic engineering A field of inquiry that concentrates on the prevention or remission of inherited disorders by manipulation of the genetic material.

Genetic load The total complement of lethal or disease genes carried by an organism or a population.

Genetic polymorphism The tendency of a protein to have varying structure and function because of small changes in structure at the gene locus. Natural selection and time influence the persistence of the various protein forms in a population.

Genotype The genetic constitution of an individual. In a diploid cell a two-factor description indicates the presence of alternative alleles for a trait, for example, AA, Aa, or aa. *See* Phenotype.

Giemsa A stain that darkens sections of chromosomes, thereby highlighting characteristic banding patterns.

Glucose-6-phosphate-dehydrogenase (G6PD) An enzyme essential to normal carbohydrate metabolism. It permits the breakdown of glucose, providing energy.

Glutamic acid An amino acid. Its presence or absence is particularly significant in the structure of normal or sickle cell hemoglobins.

GL_2 A fatty molecule that is derived from the GL_3 molecule in the presence of the enzyme ceramide trihexosidase.

GL_3 A fatty molecule containing sugar molecules. It is normally broken down into GL_2 in the presence of the enzyme ceramide trihexosidase. This enzyme is lacking in patients with the Fabry disease.

Globin gene The DNA sequence specific for the synthesis of the protein portion of the hemoglobin molecule.

GM_2-ganglioside A sphingolipid or fatty molecule that in the absence of the enzyme hexosaminidase A, accumulates in the brain and neural tissue, leading to the deterioration of the nervous system in Tay-Sachs disease.

Gout An abnormality of uric acid metabolism leading to disease in the joints and kidneys. Its mode of transmission may be X-linked or autosomal recessive.

Graft-versus-host reaction The tendency of cells in transplanted bone marrow, lymph node, or spleen to reject the host as if its cells were a massive antigen.

Guanine One of the purine nitrogen base molecules in DNA or RNA.

Guthrie test A technique which uses a bacterial culture and beta-2-thienylalanine to determine the amount of phenylalanine present in the blood of a newborn infant.

"Hairy pinnae" An unusual growth of hair from the ends of the ears. This trait is thought to be transmitted on the Y chromosome.

Haploid The cellular genetic condition in which only one set of chromosomes is present. Sperm and egg gametes are haploid cells.

Hardy-Weinberg principle A principle of gene distribution theory that assumes that populations tend to maintain a constant gene frequency between alleles for a given trait from generation to generation. Mathematically expressed, for any dominant allele, p, and any recessive allele, q, the sum of the gene frequencies in a population for a given trait is $p + q = 1$. From this relationship, the percentage of homozygous dominant individuals (q^2), heterozygous individuals ($2pq$), and homozygous recessive individuals (p^2) can be calculated.

Hematuria Blood in the urine.

Hemizygous A genotype in which an allelic gene is absent. Since a Y chromosome does not contain genes allelic to those of the X chromosome, a normal male is said to be hemizygous for X-linked traits.

Hemoglobin The pigmented, iron-containing protein of red blood cells that carries oxygen to body tissues.

Hemoglobin A The normal hemoglobin molecule.

Hemoglobin beta chain A polypeptide portion of the hemoglobin molecule. The molecule is made up of alpha and beta polypeptide chains. It is in the beta chain that the modification occurs, which results in sickle cell anemia.

Hemoglobin F Fetal hemoglobin.

Hemoglobin S The abnormal hemoglobin molecule found in sickle cell anemia. This molecule differs from normal hemoglobin A by substitution of an amino acid, valine, for another amino acid, glutamic acid, in the beta polypeptide chain.

Hemolytic anemia A disorder in which red blood cells are rapidly destroyed. Thalassemia is an example of a hemolytic anemia.

Hemophilia A disease characterized by inability of blood to coagulate. It is caused by a recessive gene located on the X chromosome.

Heterozygote A diploid genotype in which there are two different alleles. In medical genetics, the allele for normality is dominant while the alternative recessive allele is the one that in the homozygote causes a disease.

Hexosaminidase A An enzyme essential to the metabolism of GM_2-ganglioside, a specific sphingolipid molecule, in the brain and other neural tissue. It is deficient in Tay-Sachs disease.

Holt-Oram syndrome An autosomal dominant disorder causing congenital cardiac malformations and thumb anomalies.

Homocystinuria An autosomal recessive disease involving the metabolism of the amino acid homocystine.

Homogentisic acid The molecule excreted in high concentration by patients with alkaptonuria. Such individuals lack an enzyme essential to the breakdown of homogentisic acid.

Homozygote A diploid genotype in which identical alleles for a particular gene are present. Both alleles may be dominant or recessive.

Hunter syndrome An X-linked disease characterized by the accumulation of mucopolysaccharide molecules in body tissues. This produces a coarsening of facial features, enlargement of the liver and spleen, and severe mental retardation.

Huntington's disease (Huntington's chorea) A genetic disorder caused by a single autosomal dominant gene whose phenotypic expression begins in adulthood. The disorder produces a progressive deterioration of nerve cells in the brain. Among its signs are uncontrollable movements of the extremities (chorea), loss of control over speech, and psychiatric problems.

Hurler syndrome A mucopolysaccharide storage disease that is inherited as an autosomal recessive trait. Signs of the syndrome include misshapen bones, enlarged liver and spleen, mental retardation, and poor vision.

Hybrid vigor The tendency of organisms with the heterozygous genotype from different strains to better survive the environment.

Hydrocephalus Abnormality in which the head enlarges and contains excessive amounts of fluid, with or without obstruction to its flow.

Hyperphenylalaninemia The presence of high concentrations of phenylalanine in the blood. The term is usually employed for individuals who do not have PKU, but who do have high phenylalanine levels.

Hypoglycemia A low concentration of sugar in the blood.

Hypotonic solution A solution with a lower concentration of ions than that found in body tissues.

Hypoxanthine A purine molecule that is normally a precursor of adenine and guanine, the purine bases. Hypoxanthine is oxidized by the enzyme xanthine oxidase to xanthine and uric acid.

Hypoxanthine-guanine-phosphoribosyl transferase (HGPRT) An enzyme that reutilizes purines, making them available for the production of nucleic acids. A defect in HGPRT leads to the Lesch-Nyhan syndrome.

Hysterotomy A surgical procedure in which the uterus is opened and the fetus removed.

Idiogram An assembly of photographs of chromosomes that classifies them in pairs according to size.

Immunoglobulin A protein molecule, derived from plasma cells, that recognizes and binds antigens. Antibodies are immunoglobulins.

In utero From Latin, meaning "in the womb." The term generally refers to the living pregnant uterus.

In vitro From Latin, meaning "in glass." The term refers to procedures carried out on a biological system in the laboratory and away from the host organism.

In vivo From Latin, meaning "in the living." The term refers to a study done on a whole animal or on man.

Isochromosome A chromosomal alteration that results from a horizontal rather than a longitudinal division of the centromere. It produces two new chromosomes with arms of the same length and genetic content.

Isoniazid (INH) A drug used in the treatment of tuberculosis. In some patients it may produce genetically determined adverse reactions.

Joseph Family disease An autosomal dominant disorder in which nerve cells from specific areas of the brain are progressively destroyed, leading to impairment of muscle coordination, loss of speech, and finally death from pneumonia.

Karyotype An individual's chromosome complement. It may refer to photomicrographs of a patient's chromosomes classified according to size and type.

Kayser-Fleischer ring A green ring that appears in the cornea of the eye in patients with the Wilson disease. It results from excessive accumulation of copper.

Klinefelter syndrome A disorder occurring in males with abnormal numbers of sex chromosomes (XXY).

Lambda phage A virus that infects bacteria and is used in DNA transduction.

Lesch-Nyhan syndrome An X-linked recessive disorder in which there is a defect in the HGPRT enzyme. It is characterized by high concentrations of uric acid, mental retardation, neurological abnormalities, and compulsive self-mutilation.

Leukemia A cancer of the white blood cells. There are multiple and acute chronic forms.

Ligase enzyme An enzyme that promotes the binding or hybridization of different DNA fragments.

Lymphocytes White blood cells important to the body's immune defense systems.

Lyon Hypothesis Theory which describes the process by which only one X chromosome remains fully active within a cell. All other X chromosomes are rendered genetically inactive, becoming Barr bodies. In the female, the developmental decision that determines whether the maternal or paternal X is rendered inactive occurs early in embryological development.

Lysergic acid diethylamide (LSD) A drug that has marked effects on mental processes. It may act as a chromosomal mutagen, although that characteristic has not been conclusively established.

Lysine An essential amino acid. Excessive excretion of lysine is found in patients with cystinuria.

Maple syrup urine disease A hereditary disease transmitted by an autosomal recessive gene producing a metabolic disorder. Affected infants have an overwhelming illness early in life and a maple-syrup-like odor to the urine.

Marfan syndrome Hereditary disorder transmitted by an autosomal dominant gene which affects connective tissue. Patients resemble Abraham Lincoln in habitus and develop dislocation of the lenses of the eyes and heart disease.

Meconium ileus A congenital intestinal obstruction which occurs in some infants with cystic fibrosis.

Megakaryocyte The large cell in the bone marrow from which platelets are made.

Meiosis The process of cell replication that includes one chromosomal duplication and two cell divisions. In the process the chromosome number is reduced from the diploid to the haploid state. Spermatogenesis, the production of sperm, and oögenesis, the production of eggs, are both meiosis.

Meningomyelocoele A malformation, at least partially inherited, involving the spinal cord and meningeal membranes.

Messenger RNA (M-RNA) A molecule synthesized from RNA nucleotides according to instructions from DNA. The messenger molecule separates from its parent DNA and migrates into the cytoplasm, where it becomes attached to the ribosomes and forms a template for the synthesis of proteins.

Metabolite Any molecule that is a product of metabolism. Phenylpyruvic acid is a metabolite of phenylalanine.

Metachromatic leukodystrophy (MLD) A hereditary degenerative disease transmitted as an autosomal recessive. Deficiency in an enzyme leads to excessive accumulation of sulfated lipid molecules. The metachromasia is an abnormal response to staining of the tissues.

Metaphase Stage in the mitotic process at which replicated chromosomes are lined up in the equator of a cell just prior to being pulled apart by their spindle fibers.

Microcapsules Spherical thin films that can be made to resemble human red blood cells in size and shape and selective permeability.

Milligram percent A measure of relative concentration in which the number of milligrams of a substance in a hundred milliliters, or one hundred cubic centimeters, of a fluid is calculated.

Mitosis The cellular reproductive process characterized by exact chromosomal duplication followed by cell division. The chromosome number remains constant from generation to generation.

Monosomy A genotype for a diploid cell in which one member of an autosomal pair of chromosomes is missing.

Mosaicism Development of a zygote with two genetically different cell populations.

Mucopolysaccharides Large carbohydrate molecules that act as a kind of cement holding cells together in tissues.

Multifactorial disease A disorder that is thought to result from an interaction of genetic and environmental factors. Diabetes mellitus is a prominent example.

Mutagen Any agent that causes damage to the hereditary material of genes or chromosomes.

Mutagenesis The process by which a mutagen produces a mutation. Exposure to radioactive fallout may be mutagenic.

Mutation A permanent and heritable alteration in a gene.

Myocardial infarction A loss of cardiac tissue resulting from an interruption of the cirulation to the heart.

Neurofibromatosis An inherited disorder caused by a dominant gene. Its chief feature is the neurofibroma, a benign neural tumor found in subcutaneous tissues.

Neurospora crassa The pink bread mold used in research by Beadle and Tatum in defining the one gene/one enzyme hypothesis.

Niemann-Pick disease A hereditary sphingolipidosis transmitted by an autosomal recessive gene. Enzyme deficiency leads to an accumulation of sphingomyelin. Symptoms include enlargement of the spleen and liver and neurological degeneration.

Nondisjunction The failure of replicated chromosomes to separate normally in meiosis or mitosis.

Nucleotide The fundamental unit of an RNA or DNA molecule. Each nucleotide contains a purine or pyrimidine base, a sugar, and a phosphate.

One gene/one enzyme hypothesis The genetic principle that states that a single gene functions by directing the synthesis, or formation, of a single enzymatic protein.

Ornithine An amino acid. It is found in the urine in abnormal amount among individuals with cystinuria.

Orotic aciduria An autosomal recessive disorder. There is accumulation of orotic acid, a pyrimidine precursor.

Osteogenesis imperfecta An autosomal dominant disorder producing bones that are fragile and fracture easily.

Ovum The female gamete which contains a haploid number of chromosomes.

Pancytopenia A deficiency in all of the elements of normal blood and bone marrow.

Penetrance The frequency with which a dominant allele is expressed in the phenotype of a heterozygote.

Penicillamine A part of the penicillin molecule that absorbs copper and eliminates it from the body. It is useful in the treatment of the Wilson disease.

Phage A viral particle that hybridizes with the DNA of a host cell.

Phagocytosis Process by which certain cells can surround, digest, and absorb foreign molecules. Certain kinds of white blood cells are phagocytic.

Pharmacogenetics The study of the relationship between drugs and genetics. In cases of drug sensitivity, involved individuals may have a genetically determined dysfunction.

Phenotype An observable characteristic expressed by a gene or genes in combination.

Phenylacetic acid A metabolite of phenylalanine observed in patients with phenylketonuria (PKU).

Phenylalanine hydroxylase The enzyme that ordinarily metabolizes, or converts, phenylalanine into tyrosine. In phenylketonuria this enzyme is lacking and high concentrations of phenylalanine build up in the body tissue, producing severe mental retardation.

Phenylketonuria (PKU) An autosomal recessive genetic disease. In the homozygous condition, two recessive genes fail to produce an active liver enzyme, phenylalanine hydroxylase, which ordinarily metabolizes phenylalanine into tyrosine. Absence of enzyme activity results in high levels of phenylalanine, and produces severe mental retardation.

Phenyllactic acid A metabolite of phenylalanine observed in patients with phenylketonuria (PKU).

Phenylpyruvic acid A metabolite of phenylalanine observed in patients with phenylketonuria (PKU).

Phenylthiocarbamide (PTC) A molecule that can be tasted by some individuals and not by others. This ability to taste is genetically determined.

Philadelphia chromosome A chromosome associated with certain forms of leukemia.

Phocomelia A condition of inherited malformation in which arms and legs fail to develop properly. They resemble seal-like flippers. Phocomelia was the most prominent feature of the thalidomide babies.

Pinocytosis A process by which foreign, or exogenous, DNA might be introduced into defective cells without a digestive breakdown of these large molecules.

Pituitary dwarfism A dwarfing condition that results because of insufficient supplies of pituitary growth hormone.

Plasmids Circular, self-replicating fragments of DNA found in certain microorganisms. They may be used for multiplying the effects of specific DNA molecules in a cell generation.

Platelet A disk-like blood cell that helps in the process of blood clotting.

Pneumococcus A bacterium that causes pneumonia.

Polygenic disease A genetic disease whose expression requires interaction of two or more genes.

Polypeptide chain A molecule, smaller than a protein, composed entirely of amino acids.

Pompe syndrome An autosomal recessive disease in which heart failure follows storage of glycogen in heart muscle.

Primaquine sensitivity A genetically determined deficiency of G6PD which leads to susceptibility to drugs such as the antimalarial drug primaquine. The result is a hemolytic anemia. This disorder affects approximately 10 percent of the American Negro population.

Probenecid (Benemid) A drug that promotes the kidney's excretion of organic molecules including uric acid. It is effective therapy for some forms of gout.

Protein A major component of all living things. Proteins are composed of amino acids linked together in large molecules. In a cell, proteins function both as structural supports and as enzymes.

Pseudocholinesterase An enzyme that breaks down esters like acetylcholine and succinylcholine into smaller molecules. Abnormality in the enzyme results from an autosomal recessive gene. Affected individuals are susceptible to prolonged effects from succinylcholine, a muscle relaxant frequently used by anesthesiologists.

Purines A class of nitrogen bases involved in the formation of DNA and RNA. Adenine and guanine are purines.

Pyloric stenosis A multifactorial condition characterized by enlargement of the muscle around the pylorus, the area leading from the stomach into the small intestine. When this enlarged muscle contracts, virtually nothing can pass from the stomach into the small intestine.

Pyrimidines A class of nitrogen bases involved in the formation of DNA and RNA. Cytosine, thymine, and uracil are pyrimidines.

Quinacrine mustard A molecule with fluorescent properties used to produce banding patterns in chromosomes.

Random mating Selection of a mate without regard to genotype: mating patterns that result in a mingling of human genes.

Recessive gene Any gene whose phenotypic expression is submerged in the presence of a more powerful, or dominant gene.

Recombinant DNA Strands of DNA that may be bonded or annealed to other chains of DNA, usually through crossing over or the use of a ligase enzyme.

rem A unit for measuring ionizing radiation.

Renal pyelogram A technique employing a dye injected into the bloodstream to outline the kidney.

Restriction enzyme An enzyme that can chemically recognize specific nucleotide sequences in a DNA chain and sever the chain at that site.

Reticulocyte A young red blood cell that is actively synthesizing hemoglobin.

Retinoblastoma An inherited cancer of the eye transmitted by a dominant gene.

Reverse transcriptase An enzyme that stimulates the proper linkage of random DNA nucleotides according to the specific code of M-RNA molecules present in solution.

Ribonucleic acid (RNA) One kind of nucleic acid molecule composed of ribonucleic acid nucleotides in specific sequence. There are two kinds of RNA. Messenger RNA is synthesized in the nucleus according to the nucleotide sequence of the master DNA molecules. Transfer RNAs are small single-stranded molecules each with three unpaired nucleotides at one end. They bond specific amino acids and bring them to the ribosomes, where protein synthesis occurs.

Ribosome Small cellular structures where translation of M-RNA into polypeptides or protein molecules occurs.

Rubella virus The virus that produces German measles. It is a teratogen that results in abnormality in the fetus when a pregnant woman is infected.

Sandhoff disease An autosomal recessive disorder that leads to degeneration of the nervous system. Hexosaminidase A and B are defective.

Sclera The white of the eye. The same dominant gene which causes osteogenesis imperfecta, or fragile bones, causes a bluish color in the sclera.

Screening A technique used to survey an entire population or part of a population for individuals with a genetic disease, carriers of a disease gene, or individuals "at risk" for a particular disease.

Sex-linked inheritance Traits determined by a gene located on the X chromosome are said to be sex-linked.

Sickle cell anemia A genetic disease caused by a recessive gene common among black populations. Red blood cells containing the abnormal hemoglobin S become deformed into sickle shapes, causing blockages in blood vessels.

Sphingolipidoses Degenerative diseases caused by an accumulation of sphingolipids, fatty substances, in brain cells. In Tay-Sachs disease the accumulation of sphingolipid molecules results from the absence of an enzyme, hexosaminidase A.

Spina bifida A multifactorial condition in which there are defects in the development of the spine and underlying neural tissue resulting in an incomplete closure in the lower back.

Spondyloepiphyseal dysplasia A form of dwarfism caused by a dominant autosomal gene.

Striato-nigral degeneration Deterioration of nerve cells in highly specific areas of the brain. This may be caused by the inheritance of an autosomal dominant gene, as in the Joseph Family disease.

Substrate In biochemistry, any substance that is acted upon by an enzyme.

Succinylcholine A drug used by anesthesiologists as a muscle relaxant. It is rapidly broken down by the enzyme pseudocholinesterase.

SV_{40} *virus* A virus whose DNA can hybridize with the chromosomal DNA of some host cells.

Syndrome Any group of symptoms that occur in association with one another. A patient with a given syndrome may be expected to express a number of different, characteristic abnormalities, or symptoms.

Tay-Sachs disease A sphingolipidosis disease that causes a deterioration of brain cells. The disease is transmitted by an autosomal recessive gene common in Ashkenazim, that is, descendants of Jews from Eastern Europe.

Teratogen Any agent that induces birth defects during pregnancy.

Teratogenesis The production of defects in a fetus because of abnormal physical or chemical agents in the environment.

Thalassemia A chronic hemolytic anemia found with frequency among persons of Italian, Greek, or other Mediterranean descent. It is transmitted by an autosomal recessive gene. Sometimes called Cooley's anemia.

Thalidomide A sleeping pill that is teratogenic when taken during the first months of pregnancy.

Thrombocytopenia Decreased number of platelets in the blood; this leads to bleeding.

Thrombosis Clotting of blood.

Thymectomy Surgical removal of the thymus gland.

Thymidine A molecular component of DNA. It can be made to absorb radioactive hydrogen for use as a marker in autoradiography.

Thymine One of the pyrimidine nitrogen base molecules in DNA.

Toxoplasma gondii An infectious agent that produces a chronic infection and permanent damage in a developing fetus. This virus is found in raw meat and excreted by cats.

Transduction A process by which foreign, or exogenous, DNA, especially viral DNA, becomes incorporated into the genetic material of a host, or recipient, cell.

Transfer factor A blood extract whose molecules are capable of altering the immunological response. This molecular intervention may correct the Wiscott-Aldrich syndrome.

Translocation A chromosomal abnormality in which part or all of the chromosome becomes attached to another chromosome.

Triplet code The sequence of three nucleotides within the strands of DNA or RNA that code for a specific amino acid.

Trisomy A condition of triploidy in which an individual has an extra, or third, autosome in addition to the usual pair.

Trisomy 21 Presence of an extra, or third, autosome 21, which produces the Down syndrome.

Turner syndrome A syndrome caused by the presence of only one X chromosome. These individuals, who are females, are typically short and have underdeveloped ovaries.

Tyrosine One of the twenty-four basic kinds of amino acids. It is the normal product of phenylalanine metabolism.

Uracil One of the pyrimidine nitrogen base molecules in RNA.

Urate The salt of uric acid.

Uremia A condition of severe toxicity resulting from the accumulation of products in the blood normally excreted in the urine.

Uric acid A molecule used by the body to dispose of purines. An important feature of the Lesch-Nyhan syndrome is the presence of an abnormally high concentration of uric acid in the blood and urine.

Valine An amino acid. The substitution of valine for glutamic acid at a specific site in the hemoglobin molecule provides the sole difference between hemoglobin A and sickle cell hemoglobin S.

Virus The simplest form of life, consisting of a single strand of DNA or RNA surrounded by a coat of protein. These organisms are parasites which cannot live outside the cell of a host. They may either invade a cell, completely overpowering its DNA, or hybridize with the host DNA. In the former case, the whole of the host cell is converted into new viral particles. In the latter case, descendant cells will exhibit characteristics of both the parent cell and the virus.

Waardenberg syndrome A disorder caused by an autosomal dominant gene of variable expressivity, characterized by a white forelock and deafness.

Werdnig-Hoffman disease An autosomal recessive disorder that affects the nerves controlling the muscles. Symptoms of the disease include a lack of muscle tone, floppiness, and tremors of the tongue. Death ensues due to respiratory failure.

Wilson disease An autosomal recessive disorder reflected in abnormal handling of copper and a deficiency of ceruloplasmin. Patients have neurological deterioration, muscular rigidity, garbled speech, and a green ring in the cornea.

Wiscott-Aldrich syndrome An X-linked condition that involves platelets and immunologic development.

Xanthine A metabolite of hypoxanthine and guanine that is converted to uric acid.

Xanthine oxidase An enzyme that produces uric acid from xanthine. Its inhibition with drugs such as allopurinol provides relief from the symptoms of gout.

X chromosome The larger of the two sex chromosomes found in all female gametes, or eggs, and in one-half of the male gametes, or sperm. It carries genes for characteristics other than sex determination.

X-linked recessive disease A disease caused by an abnormal recessive allele on the X chromosome. It occurs in males who have no potentially compensating second X chromosome, as do females.

Y chromosome The smaller sex chromosome, evidently containing few linked genes. In man it confers maleness.

YY syndrome A chromosomal abnormality in which a male possesses two Y chromosomes instead of one. There is some evidence that this genotype is associated with abnormally aggressive behavior.

Zygote The fertilized egg cell that results from the fusion of a sperm and ovum in the creation of a new individual.

Selected Readings

Ethical Issues in Human Genetics (Genetic Counseling and the Use of Genetic Knowledge). Edited by Hilton, Bruce; Callahan, Daniel; Harris, Maureen; Condliffe, Peter; Berkley, Burton. New York and London: Plenum Press, 1973.

Fraser, F. Clarke and Nora, James. *Genetics of Man*. Philadelphia: Lea & Febiger, 1975.

Harris, Harry. *Garrod's Inborn Errors of Metabolism*. New York: Oxford University Press, 1963.

McKusick, V. A. *Human Genetics*. Englewood Cliffs, New Jersey: Prentice-Hall, 1969.

Roberts, J. A. Fraser. *An Introduction to Medical Genetics*. London: Oxford University Press, 1970.

Smith, D. W. and Wilson, A. C. *The Child with Down's Syndrome*. Philadelphia: W. B. Saunders, 1973.

Stern, C. *Principles of Human Genetics*. San Francisco: W. H. Freeman, 1973.

Index

(Boldface numbers refer to definitions; numbers in italics refer to illustrations.)